THE HISTORY OF THE
US NUCLEAR
ARSENAL

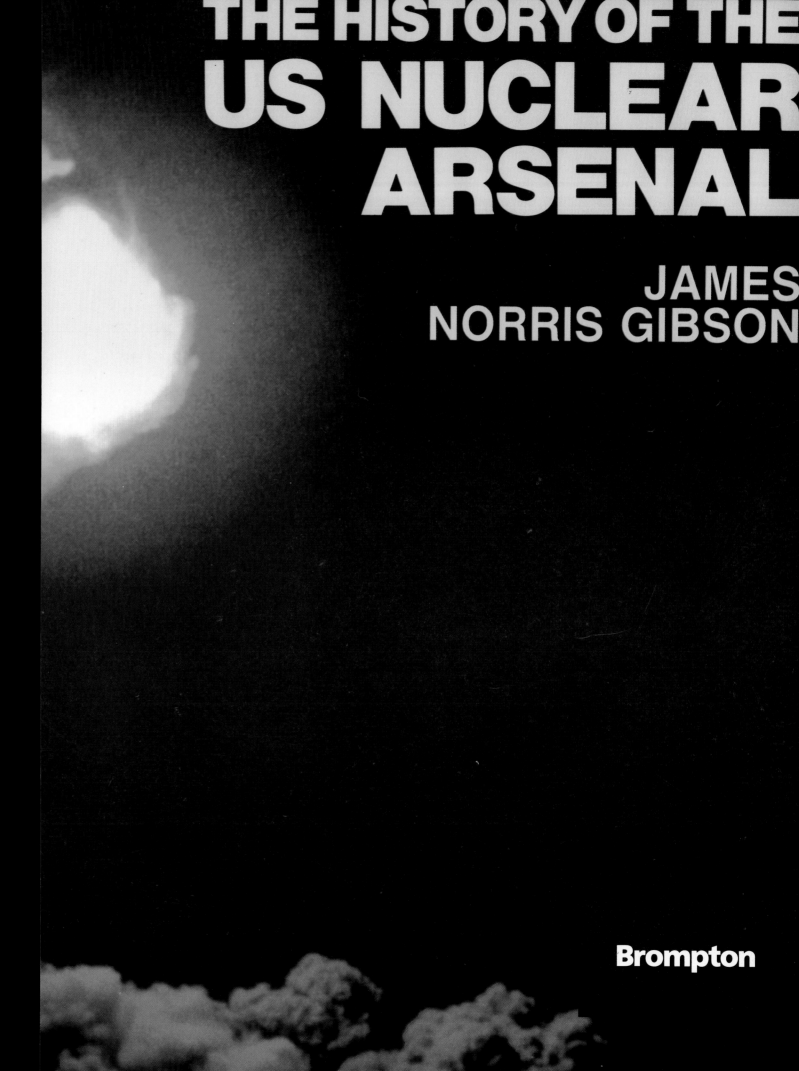

THE HISTORY OF THE US NUCLEAR ARSENAL

JAMES NORRIS GIBSON

Brompton

First published in 1989 by
Brompton Books Corp
15 Sherwood Place
Greenwich, CT 06830

ISBN 0 86124 564 4

Printed in Hong Kong

Designed by Tom Debolski
Edited by Timothy Jacobs

Picture Credits

Boeing: 67, 101, 108, 112, 113
General Dynamics: 13 (right), 155 (top),
    156 (all), 157 (all)
James Norris Gibson: 82, 90, 93 (middle
    and bottom), 94 (bottom), 187 (all)
Goodyear Aerospace: 181
Fairchild Hiller: 191
Hughes Aircraft Company: 79 (top)
Lockheed: 45 (all), 46, 47, 107 (top), 141
LTV: 76 (left), 152
Martin Marietta: 31 (bottom right), 65
McDonnell Douglas: 37, 38, 116 – 117
    (bottom), 129 (bottom), 133 (top and
    middle), 138 (all), 140
National Archives: 63 (top), 114, 115, 119,
    129 (top left), 130 (bottom right), 151,
    153
National Atomic Museum: 2 – 3, 80, 81, 83
    (all), 84, 85, 86 (left), 87, 88, 89 (all),
    91, 93 (top), 94 (top), 95, 96, 97 (all),
    178 (left), 183, 188, 192
Northrop Aircraft: 127 (top), 146 (bottom),
    147
Rocketdyne: 22, 23 (all)
Rockwell International: 55 (right), 106 –
    107 (bottom), 107 (middle), 124, 125,
    131, 132
Sandia National Laboratories: 86 (right), 99
    (top), 177 (bottom)
Smithsonian Institution: 103 (bottom)
US Air Force: 9, 10, 11, 12 – 13 (left), 14,
15 (all), 16 ,17, 18, 19, 20 – 21 (all), 25,
26 (all), 28 (all), 29, 30 – 31 (left and
top right), 35 (left), 36, 39, 57, 58 (all),
60, 61 (all), 64, 66 (all), 78 – 79
(bottom), 98 (top), 103 (top), 104 – 105,
109, 111 (all), 117 (top), 120 – 121, 122
(all), 123, 126 – 127 (bottom), 129 (top
right), 130 (left), 133 (bottom), 135 (top
and bottom), 136, 137 (middle and
bottom), 139, 145, 148, 149, 150 (all),
154, 161 (right), 166 (all), 190
US Army: 32, 34, 35 (right), 68, 69 (all),
70, 71 (all), 72, 73 (all), 74, 75 (all), 76
(right), 77 (all), 146 (top), 159, 160, 161
(left), 162, 163, 169, 170 (all), 171,
172, 177 (top left and top right), 178
(right), 179, 184 (all), 185, 186, 189
US Navy: 1, 41 (all), 42, 43 (all), 44, 48,
49 (all), 50, 51 (all), 52 (all), 53, 54, 55
(left), 98 (bottom), 99 (bottom), 117
(middle) 118, 137 (top), 155 (bottom),
167, 175 (all), 180, 182 (all)
White Sands Proving Ground: 6 – 7 (all), 63
(bottom), 158, 165, 168 (all), 173, 174
© Bill Yenne: 134

Page one: At 2:03 pm Eastern Standard
Time, on 18 January 1977, this scene — the
first launch of a Trident missile — took
place. *Pages 2 – 3*: A nighttime atomic test
in the American desert. The now-familiar
mushroom cloud is still the emblem of
intense international concern.

Contents

Introduction

On 16 July 1945, on an empty stretch of desert about 60 miles northwest of Alamogordo, New Mexico, an event occurred that would change the world forever. On that dark morning, at exactly 5:29 AM Mountain War Time (4:49 AM standard time), a giant explosion rocked the desert floor. So brilliant was this blast, that it could be seen for 200 miles around, and it was so powerful that it shook the earth for 30 miles. All this was caused by a circular device about six feet in diameter and weighing less than five tons. The bomb's name was 'Gadget,' of project 'Trinity,' and it was the world's first nuclear device. In a sense, with its detonation, the world as it was then known came to an end.

At that time, the United States was the only nation on Earth to possess a nuclear weapon. When it became increasingly apparent that the Soviet Union—an ally during World War II—was actually quite hostile to the US, this nuclear exclusivity took on an added importance. When the Soviets detonated their own nuclear device in August of 1949, the race for nuclear superiority between the two superpowers was in earnest. Despite the intensity of this superpower competition down through the years, the guiding philosophy behind the US nuclear arsenal has always been that of deterrence. With the progression of Strategic Arms Limitations Talks (SALT) thus far, nuclear proliferation on both sides is now more carefully modulated than ever before.

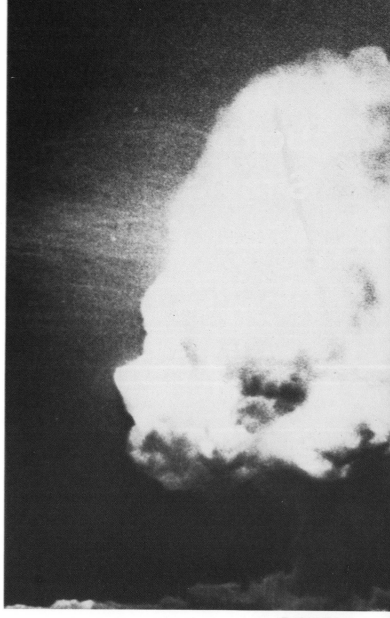

Project Trinity

Gadget nuclear device

The INF Treaty

The Treaty on the Elimination of Intermediate-Range and Shorter-Range Missiles (INF), which propounds the removal of intermediate and medium range missiles from Europe, is the first major nuclear arms agreement to be completed since the SALT II agreement of the late 1970s. Unlike the SALT agreements, which limited only the number of nuclear weapons each side could deploy, the INF treaty is the first agreement that calls for the *removal* without replacement of nuclear weapons already deployed. Not only will this mean a reduction of nuclear weapons instead of a controlled enlargement, it also brings forth the possibility that a similar agreement can be reached regarding other strategic nuclear weapons.

The INF agreement will, however, have little effect on the military situation in Europe. The reason for this is that the INF missiles are only a part of the total nuclear arsenal both sides have deployed in Europe and the surrounding territory. The long range nuclear forces of NATO and the Theater Nuclear Forces of the Soviet Union are composed like the larger arsenals of the Soviet Union and the United States with three types of weapons: ground launched missiles, sea launched missiles and manned bombers. To be more specific, along with its 1572 warheads on SS-20, SS-12 and SS-23 ground launched ballistic missiles, the Soviet Union also has over 6000 INF aircraft (medium bombers and fighter/bombers) and 18 SS-N-5 submarine ballistic missiles in addition to an undetermined number of warheads on missiles carried by older *Yankee* class submarines. As for NATO, with its force of 429 Pershing IIs and GLCMs, it has available armament of approximately 2000 nuclear capable aircraft, 400 US Poseidon or Trident I submarine warheads and 84 Polaris missiles on British submarines. This doesn't take into account the US FB-111 force, and Tomahawk SLCMs deployed on US Navy ships in the European theater, plus 256 warheads on French ballistic missile submarines. Thus, what the INF treaty does is to insure that if any long range nuclear weapons are used in Europe, they will not be fired by ground launched missiles.

The INF missiles are just a portion of the large number of nuclear weapons deployed in Europe by both sides. Though the withdrawal of the SS-20, SS-4, SS-12 and SS-23 missiles will mean a loss of 1572 warheads, the Soviet Union will still have a large stockpile of warheads for use by its remaining INF systems as well as a large number of nuclear projectiles for its artillery, and warheads for its 700 SRBMs — which are not banned by the agreement. In the same way, though the United States will lose 429 warheads by the INF treaty, and has since 1983 removed an additional 1400 warheads from Europe, the US still has over 400 warheads on ships and submarines, plus 3000 freefall bombs in stockpile, plus over a thousand nuclear artillery projectiles and about 200 warheads for the Lance SRBM.

It must also be understood that plans have already been made to improve these remaining nuclear forces. The Soviet Union is continuing to deploy the SU-24 Flanker Fighter/Bomber and is replacing its Frog rockets with the new SS-21 SRBM. Also in the immediate future, the USSR is expected to deploy large numbers of SS-N-21 cruise missiles on *Victor, Akula, Sierra* and converted *Yankee* class attack submarines and by the mid-1990s, the larger SS-NX-24 will equip *Yankee* subs for use against American, European and Asian targets.

As for the NATO alliance, several improvement programs are underway or being considered. Underway at this time is the replacement of older F-111s with F-15Es, the deployment of additional F-16 squadrons to Europe, the fielding of new 155mm nuclear artillery shells and the deployment of 700 nuclear tipped Tomahawk cruise missiles. In the near future, Great Britain is to add to this force by the deployment of four Trident submarines in place of their earlier Polaris subs. France is also expected to complete fielding the new M-4 MIRVed missiles on its remaining four ballistic missile subs, and plans as well to deploy a seventh sub. In addition to this is the consideration to develop a tactical air to surface missile system as a replacement for NATO's Lance missiles.

The INF treaty will result in only a minor reduction of the number of nuclear weapons in Europe, and of the capability of each side to destroy each other. Its primary virtue is that it is the first agreement that *actually removes* deployed nuclear weapons.

atomic test

Intercontinental Ballistic Missiles (ICBM)

Atlas (SM-65)

SPECIFICATIONS

	ATLAS (D)	ATLAS (E)	ATLAS (F)
Length:	75 ft	82 ft six in	82 ft six in
Diameter:	10 ft	10 ft	10 ft
Weight:	all models from 260,000 to 268,000 lb		

PERFORMANCE

Speed: 15,000 mph   Apogee: 500 mi

Range: 5500 to 9000 mi   CEP: 2000 ft approx

PROPULSION All deployed Atlas models propelled by one Rocketdyne sustainer and two Rocketdyne boosters. The fuel was alcohol (RP-1) and the oxidizer was liquid oxygen (LOX)

Max thrust Atlas (D): Sustainer – 60,000 lb, Boosters – 150,000 lb

Max thrust Atlas (E/F): Sustainer – 57,000 lb, Boosters – 165,000 lb

GUIDANCE Atlas (D) – Radio Command

Atlas (E/F) – Bosch Arma Inertial Guidance

WARHEAD Atlas (D) – First squadron: one 4 megaton W-49 warhead in a Mk-2 re-entry vehicle

Squadrons 2, 3 and 4: one 4 megaton W-49 warhead in a Mk-3 re-entry vehicle

Atlas (E/F) – all squadrons: one 4 megaton W-38 warhead in a Mk-4 re-entry vehicle

CONTRACTOR Convair (now General Dynamics)

NUMBER OF MISSILES DEPLOYED

129 (30 Ds, 27 Es and 72 Fs)

The Atlas was the first Intercontinental Ballistic Missile (ICBM) ever deployed by the United States. In the late 1950s, it was the symbol of US nuclear supremacy. To the military however, it was an extremely complicated weapon that would have been impossible to use.

Immediately following the cessation of hostilities in Europe, US scientists and technicians began extensive studies of captured V-2 documents and missiles. This research, plus information supplied by German scientists, quickly uncovered the plans and computations for what would have been Germany's ultimate weapon, the A-10/A-9, a missile capable to reaching New York city from Germany. Though many in the military found the idea of such a weapon hard to believe, its feasibility had to be investigated and, in 1946, the Army Air Service began a series of research programs into long range missiles. One of these programs was the Consolidated Vultee MX-774 project, begun on 19 April 1946.

Initially the MX-774 project involved the study of two different types of missiles as possible ICM's: a subsonic cruise missile, and a supersonic ballistic missile. The cruise missile had its advantages in that it could be developed using available construction techniques, but the ballistic missile could penetrate any form of defense then available. This fact led Consolidated Vultee to conclude that the ballistic missile had the most potential; as a result of which the majority of its research was directed towards the ballistic problem; later that year the Air Force cancelled the cruise missile part of the program in favor of the Northrop Snark MX-775.

Consolidated's research centered essentially on showing that by using lightweight materials and new construction techniques, a V-2 size missile could be produced that would travel significantly farther then a conventional V-2 (everything in that time was compared to the V-2). To do this, construction began on 10 research rockets which are known to us as the MX-774s.

The MX-774 rockets had some revolutionary concepts built into them. One was the integral fuel tank configuration, in which the missile's external skin is used to retain the fuel — making unnecessary the use of an internal fuel tank. Also, there was the gimballed rocket motor which, through the vectoring of the engine thrust, allowed changes to be made in the missile's flight path without the use of control fins and control rockets. The separable nose cone was a third innovation which made unnecessary the covering of the entire missile with a heat shield.

A fourth new design concept which was developed in the MX-774 program — and later used in the Atlas program — was pressure stabilized structure. In this concept, instead of a heavy internal bracing system, a greater than atmospheric pressure is created inside the missile to stiffen its skin (the principle is the same as inflating a football). By using this concept, the missile's external skin could be as thin as a dime, resulting in a significant reduction in weight. However, if even a small hole was made in the skin, the internal pressure would be lost and the missile would collapse under the strain of flight or the weight of its own payload. This problem would later arise in the Atlas program as a

Atlas A ICBM

pronounced vulnerability to conventional weapons projectiles such as bullets or shrapnel.

With the ending of the Second World War, funding for military programs began to be curtailed by Congress. By 1947, the Air Force found it impossible to fund all its missile and rocket programs. This led to the cancellation of programs that were deemed to be either duplicative or too highly speculative. Thus, since the entire concept of an intercontinental ballistic missile seemed impossible to some in government, the MX-774 program was cancelled in late June of 1947.

Nevertheless, Consolidated was given permission to use what remained of the original funding to complete and test three of its MX-774 rockets. The first was launched on 1 July 1948. This missile functioned perfectly for one minute until a malfunction occurred, causing the main engine to shutdown. The second flight, on 27 September was more successful, with the missile reaching an altitude of 40 miles before a malfunction caused it to destruct. The final launch, on 2 December also achieved a high altitude before an internal explosion destroyed the missile. (Though it may sound unbelievable, these three flights were actually quite successful considering the fact that many missiles of that period failed to leave the launch pad).

Consolidated Vultee became commonly known as 'Convair,' an abbreviation of the aircraft company's name. (This was officialized in 1954, when the company merged with General Dynamics and became 'Convair Division of General Dynamics.') For three years after the program cancellation, Convair continued limited studies into long range ballistic missiles at its own expense. This work, under the direction of Chief Engineer Karl J Bossart, bore fruit in May of 1949.

The new design which resulted was to become an Atlas missile trademark: the 'half stage' missile design. Similar to the much later Space Shuttle launch system, the half stage design was such that both the sustainer and the booster engines are ignited at liftoff.[1] Two minutes into the flight, the boosters and their aerodynamic shroud were jettisoned, leaving the sustainer motor to push the missile the rest of the way. The half stage design was actually a way of short cutting the problems inherent in getting the sustainer engine to ignite at altitude, which is required of sustainers on pure multistage missiles like the Titan and the Minuteman.

When the Soviets detonated their atomic bomb on 19 August 1949, it created impetus for renewed weapons funding, and the advent of the Korean War on 25 June 1950 'sealed the bargain.' The work done by Convair in the years previous had given the company a big lead in the field of ballistic missile design. Therefore, it was no surprise when Convair was awarded the government contract for the MX–1593 long range missile on 23 January 1951. By September of that same year, the program was officially known as the 'Atlas' missile program.

On 1 November 1952, the United States detonated the world's first megaton class thermonuclear device, which type of weapon became known as the 'H,' or hydrogen, bomb. This event, itself historically significant, was very important to the Atlas program. It meant that a bomb had now been developed that was powerful enough to make the Atlas effective against both military and civilian targets. At the same time, paradoxically, it almost killed the Atlas program because the bomb weighed in at a whopping 65 tons — a payload even such contemporary delivery systems as the Space Shuttle cannot carry.

Believing that a smaller bomb could be produced, Convair, in 1953, completed a preliminary design for the Atlas using payload data supplied by the AEC. The culmination of the previous eight years of work, this design featured dime thin, pressurized skin with, integral fuel supply; 'half stage' design; gimballed rocket motors; and vernier trim rockets. This was still not the design of the deployed Atlas, but of a missile 90 feet long by 12 feet wide, and with five main engines producing 600,000 lb of thrust. Such a missile would have been too cumbersome to deploy effectively.

On 10 February 1954, the Strategic Missile Evaluation committee announced that a possible breakthrough had been achieved in the design of the hydrogen bomb, making possible small high yield warheads. This possibility then became fact on 1 March 1954 with the successful detonation, in the Pacific, of one of these new small bombs during the Operation Castle test series. Code named Bravo, not only was this bomb successful, it exceeded its expected seven megaton yield with a 15 megaton blast!

Because it was more powerful than planned the Bravo bomb showed that the Atlas warhead could be even smaller than originally planned. As a result of this and an 8 February 1954 Rand corporation conclusion that a smaller missile would have a better chance of success, Convair's 1953 half stage missile design was reduced in size to that of the eventually operational Atlas. In December of 1954 the design was then frozen and, on 14 January 1955, the Air Force awarded Convair the contract for the development and testing of the Atlas missile.

The same year that the development contract was issued, it became known that the Soviets were also working on such a missile and were even then launching Intermediate Range Ballistic Missiles. With the concern that the Soviets might be ahead in the development of an ICBM, approval was given to accelerate the development of the Atlas through the flight testing of a pre-prototype missile known as the Atlas A. Having no sustainer motor and a dummy nose cone, this model was not intended for long range flight, but for use in finding any major flaws in the basic Atlas design before the first true intercontinental models could be

completed. Historically, the use of this 'dummy' missile cut a year off the Atlas development.

The first flight of an Atlas A occurred on 11 June 1957. After a successful liftoff, the missile functioned properly for approximately one minute before a malfunction occurred in a booster engine. For safety reasons ground control had to destroy the missile.

On 20 August, two months after the first Atlas launch, the Soviet Union announced that they had successfully launched and controlled an intercontinental ballistic missile. With no real evidence to back up this claim, the announcement was dismissed as propaganda and the second launch of an Atlas A occurred on 25 September 1957. Like the first flight, this missile was initially successful but had to be destroyed three minutes into its flight because of a malfunction. Nine days later, the Soviet Union launched Sputnik.

Sputnik did more to get the Atlas developed then any other event. Spurred on by its launch, the Secretary of Defense finally gave his approval on 5 October 1957 for the first US ICBM deployment program. This program called for four Atlas and four Titan squadrons to be operational by December of 1962. Following this, on 17 November USAF headquarters activated Vandenberg Air Force Base as the first ICBM and IRBM training site. On 12 December, it was further directed that the program be expanded so that a total of nine squadrons would be operational by 1962. The first successful Atlas launch occurred on 17 December 1957, and three-engined the third Atlas A completed a full 600 mile flight.

On 3 June 1958, the eighth Atlas A was launched completing the first phase of testing: half of the flights were successful. Testing of the three-engined Atlas B then began on 9 July 1958. The first successful flight of 2500 miles occurred on 2 August. Successively longer flights followed on 28 August and 14 September and, with the seventh launch on 28 November 1958, the first full range flight

Atlas D ICBM

Atlas E ICBM

of 6325 miles was achieved. Testing of the improved pre-production Atlas C then began on 23 December. All totaled, 25 Atlas missiles were launched before the first Atlas D was tested.

Atlas D

With the successes of the Atlas B and C, testing began on 29 July 1959 with the first Atlas production model — the Atlas D. Two months later, Vandenberg AFB became the first operational US ICBM base with the successful launch of an Atlas D at 11:49 pm PDT, on 9 September 1959. The first Atlas missile on active duty went on combat alert with a nuclear warhead on 31 October 1959, at launch site 576A-1.

The first Atlas D squadron, at Vandenberg, consisted of two satellite bases, each base having one launch control center and three open air launch pads. As early as 1957, however it had been realized that this form of basing was just too exposed for effective security, and a new type of launcher was indicated for follow-on bases. On 24 April 1958, the Atlas program was officially expanded to nine squadrons, with the last five to incorporate both inertial guidance and the new 25 PSI hardness 'coffin' launcher. Though these changes were intended for the later Atlas E squadrons, since they were issued *before* construction of the second Atlas D squadron at Warren AFB (in June of 1958), the second, third and fourth Atlas D squadrons were also equipped with 'coffins.'

Outwardly, a coffin launcher resembled a large concrete and steel warehouse with a large folding metal door at either end. Loading was easy: the Atlas missiles simply were rolled in horizontally through one of the big doors (the other door was then closed to form a blast deflector). Once inside, the Atlas would remain in this horizontal position until a launch order was given, following which the roof of the building would slide away and the missile would be rotated into firing position. Once vertical, fueling would commence and within 15 minutes the missile could be fired. The first successful Atlas D launch from a coffin launcher occurred on 22 April 1960. Following this, the first Atlas D complex at Warren Air Force Base was turned over to SAC on 8 August 1960.

The second Atlas D squadron, the 564th Strategic Missile Squadron (SMS) was declared operational on 2 September. This unit, similar in basic design to the first Atlas squadron consisted of two satellite bases, each base having one launch control center and three coffin launchers spread about 200 yards part. Soon after this, on 7 March 1961, the 565th SMS became operational at Warren Air Force Base and on 30 March deployment was completed with the 549th SMS at Offutt AFB. These last two squadrons differed from the first in that each had three satellite bases, and the launchers were both farther apart and had split roofs which separated at the center for launch.

Even with the new coffin launcher, the Atlas D was still highly limited by its use of radio command guidance. Besides being jammable, this system required the missiles to be based in tight little groups and restricted the rate at which the missiles could be launched from a satellite launcher to one every five minutes. Taking into consideration that it takes 15 minutes to fuel the missile, this means that it would have taken 30 minutes to launch a flight.

Atlas E

By the time the first Atlas sites were operational, a new missile was in development to meet the inertial guidance requirement specified in the 24 April 1958 order (see the Atlas D discussion). Called the Atlas 'E,' this model would be equipped with the Titan

I's Bosch Arma inertial guidance system, making it possible for an entire flight to be launched at once. This new model would also have the new, improved, MA-3 propulsion system and the larger, more accurate, Mk-4 re-entry vehicle. Testing of these components on the Atlas began on 8 March 1960 with the first launch of an Atlas D equipped with the Bosch Arma inertial guidance system. By October of that year, two such flights had been achieved, and the first Atlas E with the MA-3 power plant was launched on 11 October. Though unsuccessful, this launch did not delay development and, on 15 November a Mk-4 re-entry vehicle was successfully launched by an Atlas D. The first Atlas E missiles then arrived at Fairchild AFB on 3 December 1960, and the first successful flight of an Atlas E was achieved on 24 February 1961.

The first attempt to launch an Atlas E from a coffin — on 7 June 1961 — was a complete failure, as the missile exploded liftoff. As with the failure of the first Atlas E launch however, this did not delay the program and, on 28 September 1961, the 567th SMS at Fairchild AFB was declared operational (On November 11 this squadron was also declared Combat Ready). By the beginning of 2 November, the second Atlas E squadron at Forbes Air Force Base was completed and on 20 November the 566th SMS was completed at Warren. The first successful Atlas E launch then occurred on 28 February 1962.

Unlike the Atlas D, the Atlas E was deployed in what is called a 1X9 dispersal pattern. In this pattern, each squadron consisted of nine coffin launchers spread over a wide area, and each launcher had its own launch control center and facilities for the launcher crew. As a further improvement to its nuclear survivability, these launchers were either built into hillsides or were semi-buried such that only the roof and the two doors could be seen.

Atlas F

Even as the Atlas E program was getting underway the Air Force had become aware that the coffin launchers were not as hard — attack survivable — as the underground silo launcher being developed for the Titan Is. As a result, less than four months after construction began on the first Atlas E coffin at Vandenberg, on 4 November 1959, construction began at Vandenberg AFB on what was to be the first Atlas underground launcher silo. Following this, in April of 1960, the Air force again expanded the Atlas program to 12 squadrons. The last five of these squadrons were to have 12 missiles apiece, and the missiles were to be housed in an underground silo.[2] This was the beginning of the Atlas F program.

The Atlas F was essentially an Atlas E with minor changes to the fueling system to accommodate the new silo launcher. The first launch of this model occurred on 6 August 1961 and the first successful flight was achieved on 22 August. The first successful silo launch then occurred on 1 August 1962 and on 9 September the first squadron was declared operational at Schilling AFB. Over the next two months, Atlas Fs also became operational at Plattsburg, Walker, Lincoln, Altus and Dyess AFB, with the last Atlas F squadron (the 579th at Walker) being declared operational on 30 November 1962.

By deploying the Atlas in underground silo, the survivability of the missile reached its peak. Housed in these concrete structures, 175 feet deep and 52 feet in diameter, the missile was now completely protected from everything short of a direct hit by a nuclear warhead. Survivability during launch was also improved because the Atlas F could be fueled while still inside the silo reducing the time the missile was exposed to attack to the two minutes necessary to raise it to the surface. The silo also allowed what was called a quick fire mode in which, during periods of crisis, the missiles could be kept fully fueled inside their silos,

ready for launch within two to five minutes. This particular quick fire mode may have been implemented during the Cuban missile crisis when, in late October of 1962, all the Atlas Fs at Schilling, Dyess, Lincoln, Plattsburg and Altus AFB were put on alert.

Yet, while the Atlas F was the hardest of the Atlas models, it also had the most problems. By November of 1963, hydrocarbon spills at these sites had become such a serious concern that on the fourth, the Air Force initiated project HYCARB to correct the problems (later named Tiger Cat on 18 February 1964, the program was terminated on 1 December 1964 just prior to the start of Atlas F phaseout).[3] Following this, on 2 December 1963, the Air Force also began project Hot Bath to improve the pod air conditioning system for the Atlas F (this program was completed on 10 February 1964). An update program called project RED HEAT was then implemented on 26 December 1963. These problems, however, are nothing compared to the accidents that occurred with this model. On 1 June 1963 an Atlas F at Walker AFB, site 1, exploded during propellant loading destroying its silo. The next year, three more Atlas missiles would explode during the same operation: two at Walker — site 5 on 13 February and site 2 on 9 March and one at Altus on May 14. These explosions, the only ones in the Atlas program, established the Atlas F the most dangerous of the Atlas missiles.

Following the deployment of the last Atlas F, on 27 June 1963 the Air Force redesignated all the Atlas models as part of a joint Air Force, Army and Navy program to develop a unified designation system. Under this new system, the Atlas Ds at Vandenberg were redesignated from SM-65D to PGM-16D. In this case P stood for soft pad, G for surface to surface and M, of course, for missile. The Atlas Ds and Es in coffins became CGM-16D and CGM-16E (the C for coffin), and the Atlas Fs became HGM-16F (the H for stored in a silo).

Atlas E

Phaseout

Atlas D and E

With the completion of the first Minuteman squadron on 28 February 1963, the Air Force concluded that it was no longer militarily necessary, or economically practical, to continue to operate the older, less survivable, Atlas Ds and Es. As a result of this, on 24 May 1963, approval was given for the withdrawal of all the Atlas Ds by 1965 and all the Es by 1968. Phaseout then began at Vandenberg AFB on 1 May 1964 with the removal from combat alert of the Atlas Ds at launch complex 576B (the coffin unit). The first missiles were shipped out of Warren AFB on 26 May and the first squadron, the 564th SMS, was inactivated on 1 September. The Last series D was then removed from alert on 1 October — this was the 549th SMS at Offutt.

Even as phaseout of the Atlas Ds was beginning, on May 16,1964, Secretary of Defense McNamara ordered the phaseout of the Atlas Es to be accelerated with completion no later then the end of Fiscal Year 1965. Thus, the first missiles were taken off alert on 4 January 1965 (all three bases had missiles removed from alert). Three months later, on 31 March, the last Atlas E was removed from service at the 567th SMS, Fairchild AFB.

Atlas F

The Atlas F was not part of the original Atlas phaseout program; however the cost involved in modifying — and even repairing — the sites soon made the system too expensive to operate. The start of the Atlas F retirement program was on 22 June 1964, when instead of rebuilding the destroyed Atlas F sites, the Air Force permanently redesignated Walker AFB as a 1X9 dispersal site (the only Atlas F site so designated). On 19 November, Secretary of Defense

Atlas F ICBM

ICBM

McNamara then started project Added Effort to have the Atlas F withdrawn by June of 1965.

Though removal of the first missiles was originally to begin on 5 January 1965, the first Atlas F missile was withdrawn from alert at Dyess AFB on 1 December 1964. This missile, as well as one at Altus, was removed early to prevent the implementation of a planned, costly, maintenance operation. Phaseout was then completed on 12 April 1965, with the removal of the last Atlas F at Lincoln AFB.

The Atlas will forever be an important missile to the history of rocketry. Though crude and complex, as a weapon system it did show that the ICBM was a practical weapon, and it did lay down the basic requirements for all follow-on missiles. Also, in its role as a launcher for satellites and space probes, it opened up the heavens for telecommunications, weather monitoring, research and military intelligence. In the years following their retirement as weapons systems, these missiles have stacked up an impressive record for successful launches of space vehicles.[4]

[1] The Atlas boosters draw their fuel from the same fuel tank as the sustainer motor. In the shuttle system the boosters are independent, solid fuel, rockets.
[2] Development of the silo traced back to 26 December 1957, when SAC headquarters asked the Air Force Ballistic Missile Command to make a feasibility study of a super hard missile site.
[3] On 3 April 1964, it was discovered that the MEA wall panels in the Atlas F sites had become contaminated by hydrocarbons. Replacement was required.
[4] The missile used to launched John Glenn was not one of these Atlas ICBMs, but a specially constructed Atlas D equipped with an abort system and the more powerful MA-5 propulsion system.

Atlas F ICBM

Titan I (SM-68)

SPECIFICATIONS
  Length: 98 ft   Weight: 220,000 lb
  Diameter: First stage – 10 ft
              Second stage – 8 ft

PERFORMANCE
  Speed: 15,000 mph   Apogee: 500 mi
  Range: 5500 to 6300 mi   CEP: about a half mile

PROPULSION Liquid fuel rocket engines burning liquid
              oxygen and RP-1 (alcohol).
  First stage: Two Aerojet LR-87-AJ-1
    Max thrust: 300,000 lb
  Second stage: Single Aerojet LR-91-AJ-1
    Max thrust: 80,000 lb

GUIDANCE Radio Command guidance system developed by
              Bell Telephone Lab and Remington Rand
              UNIVAC

WARHEAD Either a single W-38, or a W-49 thermonuclear
              warhead of four megaton yield in a Mk-4 re-entry
              vehicle

CONTRACTOR Glen L Martin Company (Now Martin
              Marietta)

NUMBER OF MISSILES DEPLOYED 54 deployed; 163 constructed, 67 flown

The Titan I was the second ICBM to be deployed by the United States. The first US ICBM of the two stage design, it was the largest of the first generation US ICBMs.

Early in 1954, the Air Force began issuing contracts to various organizations for backup engine systems, re-entry vehicles, and guidance systems for the Atlas missile. Known as second sourcing, this was officially done to insure that if any one of the primary components of the Atlas was either delayed, or failed in development, the program could still be continued. At the same time, these contracts also laid the foundation for the later Titan I program.

For several years following the beginning of the Atlas program, a number of scientists and politicians challenged the reasoning behind the government's policy of only developing one ICBM design. For the politicians, the idea of two programs was better because it would stimulate competition which would, in turn, result in lower costs and higher quality. As for the scientists (including Werner Von Braun), the feeling was that the Atlas' thin-skin, inflated, structure would not be reliable enough for a weapon system. These arguments, plus the on-going work by the Soviets in both IRBMs and ICBMs, finally proved decisive, and on 27 October 1955 the Air Force issued the contract for the SM-68 Titan to the Martin company.

Using the backup Atlas contract as a starting point, Martin began development of a two stage missile with a semi-monocoque structure. In this design, (unlike the Atlas), internal structural stringers are run the length of the missile giving it enough strength to retain its shape without internal pressurization. This added strength also allowed a high takeoff speed. This design was, however, more complex compared to the Atlas and this complexity forced a longer development period. Thus, from the very start, the

Titan I was never a competitor to the Atlas.

For the first two years following its creation, the Titan program just ambled along. The construction of its development and manufacturing facility was the only significant event in this period. This was because the Air Force actually only planned to deploy Atlas (Titan would only be deployed if Atlas became extensively delayed). With the launch of Sputnik, on 4 October 1957, however the situation changed drastically, and on 5 October, the Secretary of Defense approved a revised deployment program calling for four Atlas and four Titan I squadrons to be operational by December of 1962. Besides being the first US ICBM deployment schedule to be approved at all levels, this plan was the first to call for the deployment of the Titan.

Even with its new deployment requirement, the Titan I was still to play second fiddle to the Atlas. Thus, when the Atlas E program needed an inertial guidance system, the Titan's Bosch Arma guidance unit was 'pirated,' leaving Martin to make do with the radio command guidance system developed by Remington Rand UNIVAC. This change in guidance had its compensation, however, for though the radio system was slower, and was susceptible to jamming, it was more accurate then the Bosch Arma inertial system.

With the delivery of the first missile on 17 June 1958, testing of the Titan I began and, on 20 December, the first attempt was made to launch a Titan (the first stage was live, the second stage was a dummy filled with water). This missile was designated as missile A-3. Three attempts later, on 6 February 1959, this same missile[1] successfully completed its planned flight of 300 miles. Two more successful flights then followed and, on 4 May, successful stage separation was achieved with missile A-6.

With the successful 4 May flight, testing then began on the full range missile. Problems with this model began almost immediately with the two static test vehicles, B-4 and B-3, which exploded on 15 May and 3 July, respectively. Following this, during the first attempted full power flight on 14 August 1959, missile B-5 exploded on the pad. Four months later, on 12 December a further delay occurred when, during the first flight with a live second stage, missile C-2 exploded just above the pad. As a result of these failures it wasn't until 27 January 1960 that a successful two stage flight of 2200 miles was completed with missile B-7A.

While the year 1959 had more then its share of failures, the year 1960 would be quite different. Two flights after the 27 January launch, on 24 February, a flight of 5000 miles was completed. This flight would then be repeated on 23 March, 21 April, 13 May and 27 May (two shots on 8 March and 8 April were moderately successful due to problems with the second stage). Though the first attempt to launch a operational J model Titan I, on 1 July 1960, was unsuccessful (the missile was destroyed just 300 feet off the pad), and the 28 July launch fell into the sea just 80 miles down range, on 10 August the pattern of 5000 mile flights began again and, on 24 October a flight of 6100 miles was achieved. The year ended with a Titan I exploding during its first silo lift launch attempt on 3 December: the elevator collapsed, causing the explosion.

Testing of the Titan I continued into 1961 and, on 23 September the first successful silo lift launch was achieved. The first all SAC launches of a Titan I then occurred on 20 January 1962, and on 29 January, the last Titan I test missile was launched.

While testing of the Titan I was underway on 19 May 1961, they began arriving at Lowry AFB. The first missiles were emplaced on 6 October and on 18 April 1962, the first Titan I squadron was declared operational: these missiles went on combat alert on 20 April. The second, third, fourth and fifth squadrons where than completed in the following order: Lowry, 4 May; Mt

Titan I ICBM

Titan I ICBM

Home, 16 August; Beale, 1 September; and Ellsworth, 26 September. The sixth and final squadron then became operational at Larson on 28 September and by 5 May 1963, all the units had been designated as Combat Ready.

The Titan I was deployed in what is called a 3X3 dispersal pattern. In this system, a squadron consisted of three missile complexes spread 10 to 12 miles apart, each complex having three silos and one Launch Control Center. The silos, 160 feet deep and having 232 ton doors, afforded the missiles complete protection from conventional weapons and a nuclear survivability up to 100 PSI^2 overpressure. As for the Launch Control Capsule, buried 50 feet down and connected to the silo by tunnels, it had all the equipment necessary to ready and fire the missiles, as well as living quarters for the maintenance personnel.

Though the Titan I was superior in design and firepower to the Atlas, it still suffered from its use of non-storable liquid fuels. Besides requiring a great deal more maintenance than the solid fuel Minuteman, the Titan's fuels created a safety hazard due to their volatility. On 24 May 1962, a Liquid Oxygen leak caused an explosion in a silo at Beale AFB (the silo was later rebuilt and became operational on 9 March 1963). Following this, on 10 August 1964 down loading of RP-1 almost resulted in an implosion of the missile (this incident was bad enough to be classified as a 'Dull Sword' or nuclear safety deficiency incident).[3] Thus, with the deployment of the Minuteman, and the Titan IIs, it became neither militarily necessary, or economically practical, to continue operating the Titan I. Phaseout was approved on 24 May 1963.

Initially, the Titan I was to be phased out of the arsenal in 1968. On 26 May 1964, however, Secretary of Defense McNamara ordered the program accelerated in order to retire the missiles by June of 1965. Five months later, phase out began on 9 October 1964 with the termination of Titan I Phase I Operational Readiness Training at Vandenberg AFB. The first missile was then withdrawn from alert on 4 January 1965, and on 15 April the last Titan I was shipped to Norton AFB for storage (the last missile had been removed from alert on 1 April).

Though its time in service was a short four years, the Titan I was a very important missile, in that it was the first big multi-stage missile. The technology learned in its development was later used in the development of the Titan II ICBM, the Titan III satellite launch vehicle and the Saturn 5 moon rocket.

[1] This missile was damaged during the 20 December 1958 attempt. Repairs took until January.
[2] 100 PSI was required when construction of first Titan sites was approved on 7 June 1958.
[3] One additional accident involving the Titan I occurred on 18 March 1963. On that day, at Larsen AFB, a separation rocket on a Titan ignited, causing a fire. The incident was a minor one.

Titan I ICBM

Minuteman (LGM-30)

SPECIFICATIONS

	Minuteman IA	—IB	—II	—III
Length:	53 ft 8 in	55 ft 11 in	57 ft 7 in	59 ft 9.5 in
Diameter:		Max all models 5 ft 6 in		
Weight:	65,000 lb		73,000 lb	78,000 lb

PERFORMANCE

Range:	6300 mi		7021 mi	8083 mi with Mk-12 RV
Speed:		all models – 15,000 mp		
Ceiling:		all models – 700 mi		
CEP:	approx 3000 ft	unspecified	1200 ft	with Mk-12: 900 ft Mk-12a: 700 ft

PROPULSION

First Stage: all models – Thiokol M-55E solid fuel motor
   Max Thrust: 210,000 lb
Second Stage: Minuteman I – Aerojet General solid fuel rocket rocket motor
   Max Thrust: 60,000 lb
Minuteman II & III – Aerojet General SR-19-AJ-1 solid fuel rocket motor
   Max Thrust: 60,300 lb
Third Stage: Minuteman I&II – Hercules solid fuel motor
   Max Thrust: 35,000 lb
Minuteman III – Thiokol solid fuel motor 73-AJ-1
   Max Thrust: 34,300 lb
Post Boost Stage: Minuteman III only — Rocketdyne RS-14 restartable liquid fuel motor burning a 1:1.6 ratio of monomethylhydrazine and nitrogen tetroxide. Max Thrust: 315 lb

GUIDANCE Inertial system by Autonetics division of Rockwell International

WARHEAD Minuteman IA – one Mk-5 re-entry vehicle carrying a W-59 warhead of 1 Mt yield
Minuteman IB&II – one Mk-11 re-entry vehicle carrying a W-56 warhead of 1-2 Mt yield
Minuteman III – either three Mk-12 re-entry vehicles, each carrying a 170 kt W-64 warhead, or three Mk-12a re-entry vehicles carrying 340 kt W-78 warheads. Seven small re-entry vehicles have been successfully launched by the Minuteman III but this configuration is not deployed

CONTRACTOR Boeing Aerospace

NUMBER OF MISSILES DEPLOYED

Min IA – 150 total deployed; none in service after 1969
Min IB – 650 total deployed; none in service after 1974
Min II – 500 total deployed; 450 in service as of 1986
Min III – 550 total deployed; 540 in service as of January 1987

Minuteman III ICBM

Minuteman IA ICBM

Minuteman IA ICBM

The world's first solid fuel ICBM, the Minuteman missile is one of the most powerful of all the United States' nuclear weapons. It now represents 95 percent of the US ICBM force, twenty-six years after it was first deployed.

Even as far back as the Second World War, there was a great interest in the possibility of a solid fuel ICBM. Because such a missile would be smaller in size, and easier to construct and maintain, *and* because it would be, above all, capable of instantaneous launch, it would be far superior as a weapon. In those early years however, solid fuel technology was still in its infancy, making only short range missiles possible. Thus, with funding for such weapons highly limited, and the long range liquid fuel missiles showing the greater potential for success, the idea of a solid fuel ICBM was put on the shelf for a later time.

In the years that followed, a number of advances were achieved in the design of solid fuel motors, making possible higher thrust and greater reliability. Thus, when — after the issuing of the Atlas contract, in January of 1955 — funding was made available for studies into alternative ICBM designs, members of the Air Force's Western Development Division (now the Ballistic Missile Office) began a study to again determine the feasibility of a solid fuel ICBM. This time the conclusion was positive, and by mid-summer 1957, development of the Minuteman was underway.

The Minuteman program, then called missile Q, was officially announced to the nation on 27 February 1958. Soon after this, the Air Force contacted 17 different corporations and invited them to submit bids on the project, or a portion thereof. By mid-summer, 14 of these companies had responded and, on 9 October 1958, Boeing Aircraft was selected as prime contractor for SM-80 Minuteman. Secretary of Defense Neil McElroy then approved of a one year acceleration of the program in April of 1959, and on 4 September 1959, the program was assigned the DX rating signifying Highest National Priority.

Following the issuing of the DX rating, on 15 September 1959, Boeing launched the first of 18 planned Minuteman Mockups (built of steel and with only enough fuel for three seconds of thrust and tethered to control its flight range) from a prototype launcher at Edwards AFB. So successful was this and subsequent launches that following the launch of the eighth missile of 6 May, the Air Force concluded that all foreseen problems with the launcher had either been solved or were insignificant, making it unnecessary to continue the series. Testing was therefore terminated, and the work was transferred to Cape Canaveral in preparation for the first, untethered, silo launch using a full range Minuteman.

While work was underway on the silo basing system the Air Force, on 12 October 1959, announced that a mobile basing system was also in development. This system, utilizing the public railway network, was intended to make the Minuteman invulnerable to attack by allowing them to move in an unpredictable pattern. As part of this program, on 20 June 1960, four trains left Hill AFB to test communications and other equipment necessary for the mobile operation of the Minuteman. Code named Operation Big Star, this testing program was successfully completed on 27 August; following this, on 1 December 1960, the Air Force officially activated the first mobile Minuteman wing at Hill. By the mid-1960s, this wing was to have three missile train squadrons; each squadron having 10 trains, and each train carrying three missiles.

With work on both the missile and the launching systems well under way, on 25 March 1960, the Department of Defense authorized a production commitment to achieve a 150 missile Minuteman force by mid-1963. Following this, on 13 December approval was given for the acquisition of the land for the fourth, fifth and sixth Minuteman squadrons; the construction of production facilities for the manufacture of the Minuteman at a rate of 30 per month; and for the hardening of the missile silos and Launch Control Capsules to withstand 700 and 1000 PSI overpressure, respectively. The first launch of an operational Minuteman missile then occurred, both successfully and on schedule, on 1 February 1961 and, on 16 March construction of the first fixed launch sites began at Malmstrom AFB.

Twelve days after construction began at Malmstrom, on 28 March, President John F Kennedy put before Congress a completely new nuclear weapon acquisition program. Under this new program the planned production capability for the Minuteman would be doubled and following the deferral of the mobile basing system three fixed base sites were added to the planned Minuteman force.

Why the Kennedy administration initially *deferred,* instead of *cancelled,* the Mobile Minuteman program has never been explained. It could have been because the Minuteman had yet to be launched full scale from a silo. It also could have been for the benefit of Congress — out of the feeling that other announced cancellations would not have been approved. Whatever the reason, the end result was that Kennedy spared himself some political hot water. This was because the first full scale silo launch, on 30 August 1961, resulted in one of the most spectacular explosions ever seen at Cape Canaveral.

On 17 November 1961 the second attempt to launch a Minuteman from a silo occurred successfully; the missile travelled 6000 miles. Fourteen days later, on 1 December the Department of Defense deleted the three mobile Minuteman squadrons from the military budget. As a result of this, the Air Force was forced to deactivate the 4062nd Mobile Missile Wing on 20 February 1962.

Minuteman IA

On 29 June 1962 the first Air Force crew launch of a Minuteman IA missile was successfully enacted. Following this on 23 July 1962, deployment of the Minuteman IA began with the arrival of the first IAs at Malmstrom AFB. By November, deployment was well underway with an Initial Operational Capability being achieved on 30 November with the completion of the first two launched missile flights. The first full squadron of 50 missiles

was then completed on 28 February 1963 and the first wing became operational on 3 July 1963.

In addition to being the smallest ICBM the US has ever deployed, the Minuteman IA was not a very effective missile. Designed more for the mobile basing system than anything else, it was extremely limited in both range and firepower compared to other ICBMs of the period. Also, since it only had enough memory in its guidance system for one target, it was both less flexible and less reliable then later Minuteman models. As a result of this, with the completion of the wing at Malmstrom, no more Minuteman IAs were deployed.

The Minuteman IA, like all other Minuteman models, was deployed in what is called a 5X10 squadron dispersal pattern. In this system, each squadron is divided into five flights, each flight consisting of ten silos and one LCC. The silos, 80 feet deep and 12 feet in diameter, afford the Minuteman complete protection from sabotage or conventional attack; as a further measure the silo has an internal cluster of lithium batteries which, if the primary power source fails, have enough energy to power the silo over an extended period of time. As for the LCC, buried 50 feet down and manned by two armed SAC officers, its job in peace time is to monitor the 10 silos in its flight for any signs of intrusion or malfunction. In time of war, it can not only launch all 10 of these missiles, but has the capability of launching every Minuteman in the squadron.

During the deployment of the Minuteman IA, on 27 June 1963, the Air Force redesignated it as part of a joint Air Force, Navy and Army program to develop a uniform designation system. As a result of this, the Minuteman went from SM-80 to LGM-30: L for silo launch, G for surface to surface and M for missile.

To insure against the unauthorized launching of a missile, the Minuteman system has several preventive systems known under the colloquial term 'Fail Safe.' One such system, designed to insure that two people are necessary to launch a missile, involves the placing of the two launch control keys approximately 12 feet apart in the LCC. Since both keys must be turned at the same time, two people are needed to launch a missile.[1] Another system, designed to prevent a launch by two unbalanced people, requires that two sets of launch codes, from two separate LCCs, be transmitted in order for a missile to be launched instantaneously. If only one set of

Minuteman IA ICBM

Minuteman II ICBM

codes is sent, an eight hour delay activates, giving the High Command enough time to either override the order or get the two people out of the LCC. It should be noted, that it may have been because of this system, that two Minuteman flights had to be completed before the first Minutemen were officially declared operational.

Minuteman IB

Following the deployment of the Minuteman IA, the first of the (improved) Minuteman IBs (LGM-30B) began arriving at Ellsworth AFB. This model, designed when the mobile basing system was still in development, was intended to improve the capability of the Minuteman force without greatly increasing the size of the missile.

By using the longer and more powerful Mk-11 re-entry vehicle,[2] and a new second stage with a Titanium (instead of stainless steel) motor casing, a major increase was achieved in both the range and the firepower of the missile. As a further improvement, a new guidance unit was added with two pre-stored targets. Thus, if for some reason the missile couldn't reach its primary target, it could retarget itself for a closer, secondary target (this is called 'engaging a target of opportunity').

The first Minuteman IB was emplaced in April of 1963 and was on alert in July. The first squadron was then declared operational on 30 September and the first wing on 23 October 1963. Wings were then completed at Whiteman and Minot in 1964, and in August gradual replacement of the Minuteman As with Minuteman Bs was begun at Malmstrom. Deployment of the Minuteman IB was then completed at EF Warren AFB on 15 June 1965.

The Minuteman IB is the only model of the Minuteman to have been involved in a serious accident. On 5 December 1964, during an inner zone security system inspection, a separation rocket fired,

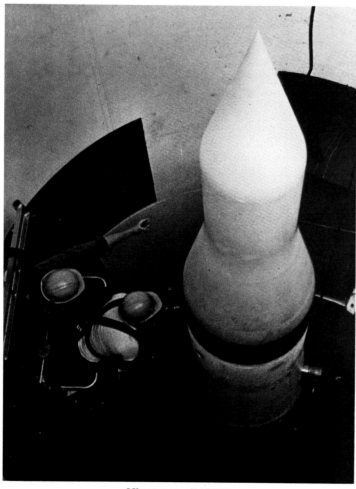

Minuteman II ICBM

Minuteman II

blowing the warhead off the missile and causing it to drop 75 feet to the base of the silo. Thankfully, all safety systems worked properly, and there was no concussion detonation of the warhead's conventional explosives.

As previously stated, the Minuteman IB was an attempt to improve the capabilities of the basic Minuteman without causing a major increase in its size (this, because of the need for it to be mobile). With the cancellation of the Mobile basing system, however, the only restriction on the missile's size was the interior dimensions of the fixed silo. As a result of this, it was now possible to greatly improve the performance of the Minuteman through the enlarging of a stage or two. Thus, with the issuing of Annex A to the Minuteman System Operational Requirement SOR-171 on 2 October 1963, development officially began on what came to be called the Minuteman II (LGM-30F). This version has become the second most important Minuteman model.

Minuteman II

Because it has an enlarged second stage, the Minuteman II can reach targets way out of range of the both models of the Minuteman I. Furthermore, due to its improved guidance system, it is not only more accurate, but is capable of having from six to eight targets stored in its computer memory. The first launch of this model occurred successfully on 24 September 1964, and the first silo launch was achieved on 18 August 1965.

Deployment of the Minuteman II was in two parts. Part one involved the deployment of the missile in new, never before occupied, silos at Grand Forks and Malmstrom AFB. The first missile arrived at Grand Forks on 5 August 1965 and was emplaced in its silo two days later. The entire flight became operational on 31 October 1965, the first squadron on 25 April 1966; and the first

ICBM

wing on 7 December — all at Grand Forks. Phase one deployment of the Minuteman II was completed on 21 April 1967, with the completion of the 1000th Minuteman silo at Malmstrom AFB.

Part two of the Minuteman II deployment program — also called Minuteman force modernization — consisted of the deployment of the LGM-30F in place of Minuteman IAs at Malmstrom and Minuteman IBs at Whiteman. This was an operation requiring the complete retrofitting of each Minuteman silo and Launch Control center. The program began at Whiteman AFB on 7 May 1966. Following the completion of the wing on 3 October 1967, work began at Malmstrom with the first squadron there being completed on 12 December 1967. Retrofitting was then completed on 2 July 1969 with the rearming of the last Malmstrom squadron.

On 10 October 1967, the first Minuteman IIs mounting Emergency Rocket Communication Satellites (ERCS) became operational with the 351st SMW at Whiteman AFB. Basically a UHF transmitter with a prerecorded message, the ERCS allows the military to transmit important commands to all units within the line of sight of the rocket. Following the first test launch of this system on 31 May 1962, the system became operational on 11 July 1963, at Blue Scout Jr missile sites at Wisner, West Point and Tekamah Nebraska. Even before the system was operational, however, a requirement was issued on 7 June 1963 for a replacement system using the Minuteman. As a result of this, on 13 December 1966 a Minuteman II was launched with ERCS. Testing was then completed on 17 April 1967 prior to operational deployment at Whiteman.

Minuteman III

On 15 July 1965, even before the first Minuteman II had been deployed, on 15 July 1965 Boeing Aerospace was issued the R&D contract for an advanced version of the Minuteman. Called the Minuteman III, it was the result of the political wrangling, and technological developments, that occurred during the late 1950s and early 1960s.

During the early 1960s, the Soviet Union began constructing an anti-ballistic missile system for the defense of its military forces. To counter this system, the United States began equipping its ICBMs with decoys (inflatable spheres and chaff) which were to cover the approach of the real warheads by creating a large number of false images on Soviet radar screens. These initial decoys were not a perfect solution, for they would either bounce off the upper atmosphere, or burn up on re-entry, leaving the real warheads unprotected in their final approach to the target. To rectify this, work was begun to develop heavier decoys that could follow the real warheads all the way down to their target. Some writers believe that these heavier decoys eventually became *additional warheads*, thus resulting in the development of a Multi-warhead or Multiple Independently-targetable Re-entry Vehicle (MIRV) missile.

Where some writers thus believe the work on decoys marked the beginning of the Minuteman III program, other writers cite the Navy's Polaris A-3 program. Because of a late 1950s ban on nuclear weapons tests, the Navy could not test the warhead it had originally planned for this missile (it was intended that the Polaris A-3 would be the Navy's first megaton class SLBM). Unwilling to give up this capability, the Navy opted instead to simulate the destructive power of a single large warhead by bracketing the target with three smaller warheads. In solving this problem, the Navy thus became the first service to deploy a Multi-warhead strategic missile.

Regardless of what a majority of other writers have stated on this subject, a major flaw exists regarding either of these programs as the beginnings for the Minuteman III program. In both of these two programs, attention is only given to the carrying and dispersion of more than one warhead against a single target. To go from this to MIRV, where each warhead is targeted against *separate* targets, is not possible without the development and use of some form of course correcting booster system. It is in this point that this author differs with previous writers.

At the same time that these two programs were underway, the Air Force and NASA were doing work to improve the economics of our nation's space boosters. The best example of this work was the 1965 test launch of a Titan III missile carrying four satellites. In this and subsequent flights, each satellite, through the use of a restartable transtage, was successfully delivered to its separate, independent, orbit. The technology involved in this is essential for the development of the MIRVed ICBM.

The concept of a MIRVed ICBM found great support among members of the US government. To some, it meant an effective counter to the Soviet Union's planned ABM system; to others, it was a low cost means of matching Soviet nuclear increases. There were even a few who saw it as a means by which the US bomber force could be deactivated without causing a major decrease in the number of US strategic nuclear warheads. Given this milieu, situation development of the Minuteman III was assured.[3]

In essence, the Minuteman III is a Minuteman II with an enlarged third stage, a post boost motor for the speed and attitude changes necessary for multiple targeting, a new guidance unit to control and implement these changes, and an enlarged payload area; everything else about the Minuteman III is the same as the Minuteman II. By developing the Minuteman III in this way, it was possible to construct it using already existing Minuteman II manufacturing facilities, as well as deploy it in available silos (later on, it was discovered that this design also allowed the upgrading of Minuteman IIs to the Minuteman III configuration). Another beauty of this design was that development could be done rather quickly, with the first flight being achieved on 16 August 1968. The first silo launch occurred on 11 April 1969.

The first Minuteman III arrived at Minot AFB on 14 April 1970: it was emplaced three days later. The first operational flight was completed on 15 June 1970 and, on 29 December the first squadron was operational. Following the completion of the Minot Wing on 19 December 1971, rearming than began at Grand Forks, with the first Minuteman III there being emplaced on 24 December (It appears that the Minuteman IIs at Grand Forks were transferred to Ellsworth, where they completely replaced the Minuteman IBs there on 13 March 1973). Deployment at EF Warren Air Force Base then began in November of 1972, and on 27 September 1974, the last Minuteman IB was removed from its silo. Deployment of the Minuteman III then ended on 11 July 1976, with the deployment of the 550th LGM-30G at Malmstrom AFB.

Minuteman IV

On 2 November 1971, even before the first Minuteman III wing was completed, the Air Force released a report stating that in the near future, even further improvements would have to be made in the ICBM force's accuracy, range, payload and target flexibility. To meet these new requirements for the long term the Air Force, in December of 1971, began development of the Peacekeeper ICBM. As an interim measure, work was also begun on improving the Minuteman III, creating what some have called the Minuteman IV.

To improve the missile's target flexibility, the Air Force has installed into the launch controls of all its Minuteman III sites a Command Data Buffer which allows the LCC to electronically retarget any Minuteman III in 25 minutes, or the entire Minuteman

Minuteman III ICBM

III force within ten hours.[4] The program was completed at Malmstrom on 15 August 1977. Along with the Command Data Buffer, the Air Force has also installed the new NS-20 software into the Minuteman III's guidance system, improving its accuracy from 1000 feet CEP to 912 (the program was completed on 29 September 1978). Following this, the final improvement program began in 1979 when the Carter administration, to give the Minuteman III an interim hard target kill capability, ordered the rearming of 300 of these missiles with the Mk-12A warhead. With these new warheads the accuracy of the Minuteman III was now up to a CEP of 700 feet and the yield was doubled to 340 kilotons per warhead. At the same time, because these warheads are heavier, the range of these 300 missiles has been reduced, making it impossible for them to engage all possible hard targets in the Soviet Union. This program was completed in 1983.

While these improvements in the Minuteman III were being implemented, other programs involving all the Minuteman models were underway. Ranging from silo improvements to the incorporation of an Airborne Launch Control System, these modifications have helped to keep the Minuteman force survivable even with the increased accuracy of Soviet ICBMs.

At this point, the author would like to make note of a Minuteman test program of the mid to late 1970s which, though not well known, is of historical interest. This program involved a series of launches, probably in 1975, in which the Minuteman III missile carried seven warheads instead of the standard three. As part of a program to see if such bulk loading was practical, these launches did not result in any changes to the Minuteman force. Instead, it resulted in the Minuteman III being listed as carrying seven warheads for the purposes of SALT II counting.

Even with all these changes and improvements, there are still some lingering doubts about the ability of the Minuteman missiles to respond to a launch order. During the late 1960s, a program was initiated to prove that the Minuteman could be successfully launched from operational silos. Called project Long Life, it began quite well on 1 March 1965, with the successful launch of a Minuteman IB from an operational silo at Ellsworth AFB.[5] The next year, similar launches of Minuteman IIs on 19 October 1966,

and 28 October were unsuccessful; a third attempt on 14 August 1968, under the new program title Giant Boost, was also unsuccessful. These failures prompted the Air Force to initiate a test program in the 1970s, in which eight Minuteman missiles would be launched full scale from an operational SAC base. The program was not implemented, because Senators and Congressmen, representing the states over which the missiles would fly, would not give their approval.

Another problem with Minuteman missiles is their solid fuel motors. The termination of Minuteman production came on 14 January 1977. In the year following, cracks were found in the solid fuel of Minuteman II second stages, a problem that makes the engines in useable. To rectify this, the Air Force began an extensive refurbishment program in July of 1978, in which the motors would be bored clean and then repoured. Since this program was begun, cracks have also been found in Minuteman II third stage motors, prompting the development of a new third stage. As of last report, both of these programs are still in progress.

At the present time, the plan is to progressively replace the Minuteman missiles with the Peacekeeper and the SICBM, or Small Intercontinental Ballistic Missile. Rearming of the first Minuteman squadron began in September of 1986 with the first flight of 10 missiles being completely replaced with Peacekeepers on 22 December 1986. By 1988, the whole squadron was to have been rearmed. With the deployment of the SICBM in 1992, the remaining Minuteman missiles will be withdrawn. This, however, means that the Minuteman will still be operational into the mid 1990s.

[1] According to some writers, the two Air Force officers are armed so that one could shoot the other if he fails to obey a launch order to turn his key. In truth, the two men are armed to insure that one doesn't force the other to turn his key.
[2] The first Mk-11 launch from a Minuteman was on 7 December 1962.
[3] A small minority of Senators and Congressmen were against development in 1968, on the grounds that MIRVed missiles could make arms control verification impossible, and that they could be used in a first strike. Surprisingly, this opposition was led by Republicans.
[4] In the old system to retarget the missile required the physical installation of a new targeting tape into the missile's guidance computer.
[5] Only the first stage was live; the second and third stages were dummies and the missile was tied to a long elastic cord.

Minuteman III ICBM

Minuteman III ICBM

Titan II (LGM-25C)

SPECIFICATIONS
Length: 103 ft   Weight: 330,000 lb
Diameter: 10 ft

PERFORMANCE
Speed: 15,000 mph   Apogee: 600 mi
Range: 13,000 mi   CEP: 4264 ft

PROPULSION Storable liquid fuel rocket engines, burning a fuel mixture of 50% by weight hydrazine and unsymmetrical dimenthylhydrazine. The oxidizer was nitrogen tetroxide.
First Stage: Two Aerojet General LR-87s
Max thrust: 430,000 lb
Second Stage: One Aerojet General LR-91
Max thrust: 100,000 lb

GUIDANCE Inertial system

WARHEAD One W-53 Thermonuclear warhead, of nine megaton yield, inside of an Mk-6 re-entry vehicle

CONTRACTOR Martin Marietta

NUMBER OF MISSILES DEPLOYED 135 known constructed: 54 deployed, 81 launched in testing and training

The Titan II is the largest and most powerful ICBM ever deployed by the US Air Force. The last totally liquid fueled ICBM to be developed by the US, for 20 years it gave the Air Force the ability to destroy the largest cities, or the hardest military sites, anywhere in the world.

In 1959 the Martin Company submitted a proposal to the Air Force for an improved version of the Titan I, which would be capable of instantaneous launch through the use of an inertial guidance system and storable liquid fuels. Though such a missile was already in development (the Minuteman), the payload capabilities of this new missile were to be so great that the Air Force couldn't pass it up and, in October, approved the project. The Martin company was issued a formal development contract on 20 June 1960 for Titan II.

Similarities between the Titan II and the earlier Titan I made development of the basic missile extremely fast. By 1961, construction of the first test missiles was underway and, on 16 March 1962, the first launch occurred successfully. The first launch with decoys (penetration aids) took place on 12 September 1962, and the first all SAC-launch on 6 February 1963.

While development of the basic missile was underway, work was also in progress on the Titan II's silo launcher. Unlike the Titan I, where the missile is first raised out of the silo for launching, the Titan II was to be launched from within its silo, improving its launch survivability. An initial test of this concept occurred on 3 May 1961, when a Titan I was successfully launched from within its silo. Soon after this, on 23 September, another Titan I was launched from the first operationally configured Titan II silo. Two more launches occurred the following year, and on 28 April 1963, the first Titan II was successfully launched from within its silo.

Even before the first silo launch occured on 27 November 1962, deployment of the Titan II began with the arrival of the first missiles at Davis Monthan Air Force Base. The first missile was emplaced on 8 December 1962, and in April of 1963 the first Titan II was on combat alert. The first squadron was declared operational at Davis-Monthan on 8 June 1963, and the wing was completed in November. Deployment at Little Rock and McConnell AFBs was already underway by this time, and on 31 December 1963, the last Wing was declared operational at Little Rock.[1]

The Titan II was deployed in what is called a 1X9 dispersal pattern. In this pattern, a squadron consisted of nine missile complexes, each complex having one missile silo and one underground Launch Control Center[2] which were connected by an underground tunnel. For protection against nuclear attack, these complexes were spaced over 10 miles apart and were hardened to withstand 300 PSI blast overpressure. In other words, these sites could withstand a 500 kiloton blast (the average yield of a Soviet warhead) occurring 1750 feet away.

On 27 June 1963, the Air Force, as part of a joint services program to create a uniform designation system, redesignated the Titan II from SM-68B to LGM-25C. In this new system, L stands for silo launched, G for surface to surface, and M for missile.

For the period in which it was developed, and for the capabilities it was to have, the Titan II was a very well designed weapon with an 80 percent reliability record in test and training launches.[3] Few modifications were ever made to the missile, and most of these were actually meant to replace equipment that had become too expensive to maintain or repair.

However, one modification that *was* made to the Titan II was the installation of the Universal Space Guidance System. Proven in several Titan IIIC launches, this unit was first tested on a Titan II on 27 June 1976. The first unit then became operational at Little Rock, Complex 373-6, in February of 1978. Later that same year Davis-Monthan was also completed, and in December of 1979 the last McConnell site completed conversion.

Though more effective as a weapon then its predecessor the Titan I, the Titan II still required a great deal of maintenance compared to the Minuteman. Because it used liquid fuels it had a mechanical engine system which had to be checked regularly for proper function. Also, because the fuels used were acidic in nature, the fuel tanks had to be drained and purged regularly in order to maintain their integrity. These fuels were also highly toxic and hypergolic, meaning that they ignite when mixed, and any work involving them was dangerous. Accidents involving these fuels have occurred throughout the missile's deployment. A fuel truck overturned in May of 1963, and on 19 September 1980 exploded a Titan II, killing one Air Force technician, injuring 21 others and throwing the warhead 200 yards into a nearby field. This particular accident was presented by the Reagan administration as one of the reasons for the retirement of these missiles. The worst accident of the Titan II program had nothing to do with the missile's fuel. On 9 August 1965, 53 civilian workers were killed when an electrical fire broke out in the silo they were working in. All casualties were caused by suffocation.

Though the Titan II was in many ways more troublesome to operate then the Minuteman missiles, the Air Force in the late 1970s could not just retire them from service. Liquid fuel missiles may require a greater amount of year round maintenance than solids, but because of the 5–7 year life span of solid fuels, 5–7 years, liquid fuel missiles do not require complete replacement as often. In 1970 the Titan IIs represented only 19 percent of the total megatonage in the US ICBM stores. Following the total replace-

Titan II ICBM

ment of the megaton class Minuteman Is with the kiloton class, MIRVed Minuteman IIIs, that percentage was 29 percent by 1976. To retire these missiles without some offsetting improvements would result in almost a one-third reduction in the megatonage of the ICBM force.

In 1979 the Carter administration began a program to retrofit 300 Minuteman III missiles with the new higher yield (340 kt) Mk-12a warhead. Though primarily intended to give the Minuteman a hard target kill capability, this retrofit program would also reduce the percentage of US ICBM force megatonage carried by the Titan II. Furthermore, the planned deployment of the Peacekeeper missiles would also affect this percentage, bringing it down to the point where the retirement of the Titan IIs would affect only 3.5 percent of the 1976 megatonage total. Thus, with the controversy caused by the 1980 explosion as additional incentive, in October 1981 President Ronald Reagan announced that the Titans would be withdrawn from service by 1987. Phaseout began at Davis-Monthan on 1 October 1982, and on 31 July 1984 the first squadron was deactivated.

The Titan II is the first US ICBM to be retired under the withdrawal procedures laid down in the SALT agreements. As per these procedures, following the removal of the Titan II missiles and equipment from the site, the upper 25 to 30 feet of the silo will be blown off using high explosives. After this the silo will be left undisturbed for six months to allow Soviet intelligence satellites enough time to view the silo and confirm its destruction. After that the silo will be filled in and covered with earth; the surrounding land will be reclaimed for other uses.

The last Titan II was withdrawn from service in the fall of 1987. At the present time these missiles are in storage at Norton Air Force Base in preparation for their use as satellite launch vehicles.

[1] Originally there were to be four wings and bases, but John F Kennedy vetoed the fourth base on 28 March 1961.
[2] The Titan II had four-man LCC crews.
[3] This high reliability was one of the primary reasons for the selection of this missile for the Gemini program.

Titan II ICBM

Titan II ICBM

Peacekeeper (LGM-118A)

SPECIFICATIONS
Length: 70 ft   Weight: 192,300 lb
Diameter: 7 ft 8 in

PERFORMANCE
Speed: 15,000 mph   Apogee: 500 mi
Range: over 6780 mi   CEP: approx 400 ft

PROPULSION The first three stages are solid fuel rocket engines with the fourth utilizing storable liquids
The first stage is manufactured by Thiokol
Max thrust: 500,000 lb
The second stage is manufactured by Aerojet, the third by Hercules, and the fourth by Rocketdyne

GUIDANCE Inertial Reference Sphere by Northrop

WARHEAD Ten W-87 warheads of 300 kt yield, each mounted in a Mk-21 re-entry vehicle

CONTRACTOR Martin Marietta

NUMBER OF MISSILES DEPLOYED
At least ten in service, 223 planned for construction, 108 for testing, 15 for age monitoring, and 100 for deployment

The Peacekeeper, or MX, is the newest ICBM in the US Strategic arsenal. It is intended to partially replace the Minuteman missile force.

Even before development of the Minuteman III had begun on 23 October 1963, Headquarters SAC issued a Qualitative Operational Requirement for a large payload ICBM. Two years later a second QOR was issued on 13 July 1965 for a mobile ICBM, and in April of 1966 development began on an advanced ICBM (Weapon System 120A) using either hardened silos or a mobile basing system. Development of the missile was then blocked on 4 October 1967 by Secretary of Defense McNamara in favor of a hard rock basing system for the Minuteman III.

Work on a new ICBM did not begin again until, on 2 November 1971, the Air Force submitted a report stating that, in order to offset future Soviet ICBM capabilities, a new ICBM would have to be developed to improve the survivability, accuracy, range, payload, and target flexibility of the US ICBM force. Known as Required Operational Capability 16-71, the approval of this report in February of 1972 initiated development of the Peacekeeper. Two months later, on 4 April, the Air Force would then designate the new ICBM Missile-X or MX.

Development of the Peacekeeper, or MX, was initially to emphasize air and ground mobile basing systems — U.S. Air Force directive 22 December 1972. Regardless, studies were conducted concerning all possible types of missiles (big, small, MIRVed, single warhead, fixed, and mobile). Concept definition then began in May of 1974 with Full Scale Engineering Development planned to begin four years later and an Initial Operational Capability by

1983; on 21 November, Secretary of Defense Schlesinger put the IOC back to 1985 in order to lower defense spending.

As part of the work to determine the direction the Peacekeeper program would go, on 14 August 1974, it was ordered that the feasibility of extracting an ICBM from an airborne C-5A be demonstrated (part of the work to determine an effective basing mode). In September, dropping of inert shapes began, followed by the first successful air launch of a Minuteman on 24 October. Seven months later all work on the airmobile basing system was terminated, and it was directed that the program be oriented towards the development of a large missile for use initially by vertical silos (Minuteman) and later by a ground mobile basing system. On 20 January 1976, preparation of the prototype began.

With the decision to work towards a large missile, the Peacekeeper program began. On 20 January 1976 the program began a transition from conceptual design to the fabrication of test components (transition was completed on 9 March 1976). After this, in 1977, the final size and general configuration of the missile was established: large, four stage, capable of being launched from a minuteman silo. As per ROC 16-71 it was to have greater resistance to nuclear effects than the Minuteman, greater target flexibility and a higher accuracy, making it effective against the hardest of Soviet military targets.

To give the Peacekeeper all these capabilities, several concepts in missile technology were used for the first time in the design of an ICBM. The first of these new concepts is the extendable exit cones used by the second and third stage engines. In this concept, following staging, the exit cone of the solid fuel motor telescopes outward changing from a short inefficient nozzle into a long efficient one. By utilizing this concept the Peacekeeper could have the range and payload of a longer missile while still being short enough to fit inside of a Minuteman silo.

Another new technology used in the Peacekeeper is Kevlar Fibers. By using this new material, instead of aluminum, for the construction of the motor casings a large reduction was achieved in the missile's bulk weight. Such a reduction not only increased the range of the Peacekeeper, but also made the missile light enough and strong enough for some form of mobile basing system (it still not as easy to move as a Minuteman).

The final new concept used in the Peacekeeper design is the Cold Launch method used for years by the Navy's Ballistic Missile submarines. Unlike the hot launch method used by the Minuteman, where the first stage is ignited inside the silo and the exhaust vented between the missile and the silo wall, this form of launch features a steam generator at the base of the shipping canister, which produces a jet of gas that pushes the missile out of the silo like a cork coming out of a champagne bottle. After this, when the missile is 100 feet above the silo, the first stage ignites and the missile heads for its target.

By using the cold launch method the Peacekeeper also has a rapid reload capability compared to the earlier Minuteman. Because this system causes minimum damage to the silo, two or three men with an automated missile loader can have a silo rearmed within a few days. In the Minuteman system, however, two teams of ten men each, each team working opposite 12 hour shifts, would take 17 days to rearm one Minuteman silo[1] (it should be noted that the Soviet SS-18 and SS-17 missiles use this cold launch system).

The plan to initially deploy the Peacekeeper in Minuteman silos did not sit well with Congress. Thus, in April of 1977, it was announced that Full Scale Development of the Peacekeeper (still known as the MX) would be delayed one year to give additional time for the selection of a mobile basing system. Nevertheless, contracts for the development of major components were issued: the first two, in April of 1978, to Martin Marietta for missile assembly and Rockwell's Rocketdyne Division for the development of the fourth stage. One month later contracts were also issued to Thiokol, Aerojet, and Hercules for the development of the first, second and third stages respectively.

On 7 September 1979, Full Scale Engineering Development of the Peacekeeper finally began with the approval of a new basing plan called Multiple Protective Shelters (MPS). In this new plan 200 Peacekeeper missiles were to be shuttled back and forth between 4600 soft shelters spread over the Northeastern and Southwestern quarters of the states of Nevada and Utah. The idea behind this concept was that since the Soviet Union could not tell which shelters contained a real missile (dummy missiles would be placed in empty shelters) they would have to destroy every shelter to destroy all the Peacekeepers. This of course would use over half their available warheads, too many if they then planned to engage all the remaining military and, in particular, Minuteman sites.

Initially the development of the Peacekeeper was very fast. The first static firing of a Peacekeeper first stage occurred in February of 1981; by the end of the year all four stages had been tested. Following this, in January of 1982, a full scale dummy Peacekeeper was launched 100 feet into the air using the planned cold launch system.

Though the Peacekeeper missile had begun development of the Multiple Protective Shelter basing system, it didn't go anywhere. From the day it was proposed the MPS system continually drew political criticism because of its large land use and high cost (quoted at $37,171,000,000). Eventually it became an election year issue with presidential candidate Ronald Reagan stating that he would cancel the system if elected. Thus, following his election in 1980, in October of 1981, president Reagan cancelled the MPS basing system in favor of a two phase deployment program in which the Peacekeeper would first be deployed in Minuteman silos and then, later, deployed in a new more survivable basing system.

The idea of basing the Peacekeeper in Minuteman silos, however, had as much appeal to Congress in 1981 as it had in 1976, the idea was immediately rejected. As a result of this the Administration went back to the drawing board and on 22 November 1982 placed before Congress a new proposal called Dense Pack in which 100 missiles would be placed exactly 1800 feet apart in super hard silos, (Peacekeeper was also officially named on 22 November). The idea behind this system was that because the silos were so close together, the detonation of an enemy's first wave of warheads would predetonate the next wave, creating a chain reaction that would protect the missiles (fratricide). This concept for defending the missiles, however, didn't fare any better with Congress; it withheld funding for procurement of the first missiles, and flight testing was forbidden until a basing mode had been approved.

To get the Peacekeeper program going again, in January of 1983, the Reagan administration formed a special bipartisan committee to determine just how to base this missile. Known as the Scowcroft Committee, it issued a report to the President in April, calling for the prompt deployment of the Peacekeeper in modified Minuteman silos followed by the development and later deployment of a small ICBM in a mobile basing system. The President endorsed this report on 19 April and on 26 May Congress also gave its approval. Flight testing began. On 18 June 1983 the first Peacekeeper was launched from its shipping canister.

With flight testing successfully underway, in September of 1983, $4.8 billion was allocated for the production of the first 21 operational Peacekeeper missiles. Following this support system, design review occurred in October and preliminary design review of the basing system occurred in November. Construction of support facilities then began at EF Warren (AFB) in mid 1984.

Peacekeeper ICBM

Peacekeeper ICBM

Before Peacekeeper can be deployed a number of changes would have to be made to the Minuteman silo. First, the silo's guidance and cooling system would have to be replaced with a new system capable of handling such a large missile. Following this a new 96 Volt DC power supply would be installed, as well as an AC/DC converter and new lead acid batteries for emergency power if the primary system failed. To allow the missile to be controlled from an Airborne Launch Control Center (ALCC) a UHF transmitter/receiver would also be added as well as a Demodulator/decoder for encrypting. Finally a new shock isolation system would be installed and six feet of the launch control tube liner removed to facilitate loading and unloading of the silo with the transporter/emplacer.

During this time a major change took place in the Peacekeeper design. Back in 1982 the DOD decided to replace the Peacekeepers originally planned Mk-12a re-entry vehicle with the new more accurate and cheaper Mk-21. Because this warhead is heavier then the Mk-12a the maximum range of the Peacekeeper was reduced. Furthermore, because this change increased the payload of the Peacekeeper beyond the Salt II limit, fuel had to be removed from the fourth stage, reducing range even further. As a result of all this it is now impossible for the Peacekeeper to engage all possible Soviet targets from launch sites as far south and west as the original Southern Utah and Northern Nevada MPS sites.

The first Peacekeeper to launch the new Mk-21 warhead was the fourth in the testing series, launched in 1984. Following this the first Peacekeeper was fired from a Minuteman silo at 9:40 AM PDT, 23 August 1985. The first 10-warhead flight occurred on 21 June 1986 and, on 23 August, the first multiple target Peacekeeper warheads struck two separate targets, 70 miles apart.

The first four Peacekeeper missiles were delivered to the Strategic Air Command in September of 1986, and on 22 December an Initial Operational Capability of ten missiles was achieved, at E F Warren. Though there have been problems with the guidance systems in these first missiles, over 20 were operational by January 1988. Full deployment was scheduled for

completion in December. In Fiscal Year 1989 the first missiles will be requested for use by the new Rail Garrison basing system, selected by President Ronald Reagan on 19 December 1986 as the primary Peacekeeper basing method. At the present time Initial Operational Capability for this system is to be achieved in December of 1991 at EF Warren AFB. The following ten bases are also possible sites for these missile trains: Barksdale AFB, Louisiana; Blytheville AFB, Arkansas; Dyess AFB, Texas; Fairchild AFB, Washington; Grand Forks AFB, North Dakota; Little Rock AFB, Arkansas; Malmstrom AFB, Montana; Minot AFB, North Dakota; Whiteman AFB, Montana; and Wurtsmith AFB, Michigan.

Rail Garrison

In the Rail Garrison basing system a total of 50 Peacekeeper missiles will be deployed on 25 specially designed trains in a manner similar to a concept tested for the earlier Minuteman IA (see Minuteman section of this text). During peacetime these trains, consisting of two locomotives, two Missile Launcher Cars (MLC), two security cars and one Launch Control Car (LCC), will be kept within the secure confines of their selected military bases inside of hardened shelters. During times of high international tension, however, the trains would leave the bases and disperse throughout the nation's rail network. When off the base, Special Security teams will accompany these missiles to protect them from sabotage and conventional attack.

On 18 May 1988 it was announced that a $106,001,407 contract had been issued to Westinghouse Electric's Marine Division for the development and testing of the MLC. On that same day it was also announced that Rockwell International's Autonetics Division had been awarded a $161,741,359 contract for the design, development and testing of the Launch Control System (LCS), the LCC and the Security Car.

[1] The reported record for rearming a Minuteman silo at Vandenberg.

Peacekeeper ICBM mockup

SICBM

SPECIFICATIONS
  Length: 53 ft   Weight: 37,000 lb
  Diameter: 3 ft 10 in

PERFORMANCE
  Speed: approx 15,000 mph   CEP: approx 500 ft
  Range: approx 6000 mi

PROPULSION Solid fuel rocket engines. Stage one is from
          Thiokol, stage two from Aerojet, and stage three
          from Hercules

GUIDANCE Initially Inertial Reference Sphere (IRS). Later
          possibly ring laser gyros or stellar inertial

WARHEAD One W-87 warhead of 500 kt yield mounted in a
          Mk – 21 re-entry vehicle

CONTRACTOR As of this writing the prime contractor has yet
          to be determined. Information has it however
          that Martin Marietta is in charge of assembly

NUMBER OF MISSILES DEPLOYED 1000 SICBMs are
  planned to be deployed

The Small Intercontinental Ballistic Missile (SICBM), or 'Midgetman' as it is unofficially called, is the first single warhead ICBM to be deployed by the United States since the Minuteman II. The smallest ICBM ever conceived by any nation, this missile is intended to give the US the mobile ICBM system it originally was to have in the late 1960s.

The concept of a mobile ICBM system is not new to the United States Air Force. Development of the first such missile system in fact began in the late 1950s with the advent starting of the mobile Minuteman program. Announced on 12 October 1959, this system was intended to use the Nation's railway network to move the missiles about in a random and untrackable manner. The final test of the system, code name Operation Big Star, occurred from 20 June 1960 to 26 August. Following this, on 1 December 1960 the first, and only, Mobile Minuteman wing was activated — the 4062nd at Hill AFB.

At about the same time that the Mobile Minuteman system was announced, the Air Force also began a study into an even smaller, third generation, missile to replace the Minuteman IA. Known as (System Study Requirement) SSR-7790-19782, this study was to ascertain the requirements for an ICBM capable of being deployed in mobile, possibly armored, trucks by the year 1967. By 1961, a preliminary set of requirements had been settled on calling for a missile utilizing either solid or storable liquid fuels, a combination of inertial and terminal guidance, and a maximum weight of 30,000 lb. That same year the program was given the official name of Midgetman.[1]

With the election of John F Kennedy, major changes occurred in US strategic policy. Believing in the superiority of the ICBM, Kennedy began redirecting military funding from bomber modernization to ICBM and SLBM procurement in 1961. At the same time, feeling there was no need for a mobile ICBM system, funding for the procurement of the first three mobile Minuteman squadrons was deferred on 1 March 1961. Nine months later, on 1 December all funding for such a mobile missile system was deleted from the military budget.

With funding cut off, the mobile Minuteman system and the Midgetman program quickly ceased to exist. On 20 February 1962, the 4062nd SMW at Hill AFB was deactivated marking the official end of both programs.

For the next 20 years, various things worked together to keep the concept of a mobile ICBM unappealing to the Federal government. In the late 1960s, the development of the MIRVed ICBM made the SICBM an overly expensive way of matching Soviet nuclear forces. In the 1970s, the era of detente, the idea of a small, mobile ICBM was seen as incompatible with the philosophy of the SALT agreements and arms monitoring. All things change with time however, and with the fall from grace of the MIRVed ICBM in the late 1970s, the SICBM found new life.

On 6 April 1983, the bipartisan Scowcroft commission recommended that the United States should develop a small (15 ton), single warhead ICBM on the grounds that such a weapon could easily use any kind of mobile basing system, and at the same time it would be a less valuable target compared to the Peacekeeper. This recommendation was approved by President Ronald Reagan on 9 April and by Congress on 26 May. As a result of this, in September, development of what is now called the SICBM began.

To make the SICBM a reality will require the use of certain new developments in missile technology. To meet the weight requirement, work is underway to develop graphite composite materials for use in place of Kevlar in the construction of motor casings and extendable exit cones. Laser fiber optics are also being developed as a lightweight substitute for the heavy ordnance transmission systems used on current missiles. To meet propulsion requirements, work is underway to tailor advanced high energy solid propellants for the small ICBM concept. Finally, to meet the requirement for

SICBM HML

an accurate guidance system, the Inertial Reference Sphere — developed for the Peacekeeper — is being stripped down into a less complex unit (because only one warhead is carried, the new IRS will not need a heat transfer system or a long lasting power source); work is also underway on ring laser gyroscopes and stellar inertial guidance systems as possible alternatives to the IRS.

Like its bigger brother, the Peacekeeper, the SICBM will also use the cold launch method for launch. The first test of this system occurred at Vandenberg AFB at 9 AM PDT on 22 October 1987. Please see the 'Peacekeeper' portion of this text for further information, on the cold launch method.

While work is underway to develop the SICBM, the Air Force is also developing the special mobile launcher that will carry it. Known as a Hard Mobile Launcher, or HML (an additional name is Armadillo), this armored vehicle will be just over 100 feet long, 5.5 feet high, 14 feet wide and weight approximately 200,000 lb (gross). In peacetime, these vehicles will move about the confines of large military reserves in the southwestern United States. During times of crisis however these vehicles will move off the reserves making them even harder to target for attack. Road speed for these vehicles will be 55 mph with a cross country speed of 15. These vehicles will also be capable of withstanding 30 PSI overpressure when emplaced, and 10 PSI when in motion.

The biggest problem in the development of the HML is not the making of a vehicle that can withstand 30 PSI overpressure, but the designing of one that can create a near perfect seal with the ground. If such a seal is not achieved the shockwave from a nuclear explosion can get under the vehicle and flip it over onto its back like a turtle. To solve this, many concepts have been tried — from fold down flaps to block and channel, the shockwave, to the vehicle having an adjustable suspension system so that it can lower itself to the ground.

SICBM

Prototype

SICBM mockup

Jupiter IRBM

While the development of the HML is underway, two other basing systems are also being studied for the SICBM. The first of these studies is a look into the feasibility of creating a silo that can withstand over 25,000 PSI overpressure: a super hard missile silo. The other study concerns the feasibility of basing the missile over 2000 feet beneath the earth: deep basing. If either of these methods were to prove economically feasible, it could later be used by either the Midgetman or Peacekeeper missiles.

Concept definition and pre-full scale development of the SICBM was completed in 1985. Following this, on 19 December 1986, the decision was made to begin full scale development. On 23 December, Boeing was then issued a $283.6 million contract for full scale development of the HML.

At the present a total of 22 SICBM test flights are planned in the program, with the first to occur in 1989; the first five flights are to be from a test pad, the remaining to use the HML. Initial Operational Capability is to have been achieved at Malmstrom by December of 1992.

[1] Because this program was called Midgetman the Air Force doesn't call the new SICBM by that name. The two programs are only related in that both were to develop a small mobile ICBM.

Jupiter (SM-78)

SPECIFICATIONS
Length: 60 feet
Diameter: 8 ft 9 in

Weight: 110,000 lb

PERFORMANCE
Speed: 10,000 mph
Range: 350 to 1850 mi

Apogee: 380 mi

PROPULSION One Rocketdyne S-3D liquid fuel, gimballed, rocket engine burning a 2.24/1 mixture of liquid oxygen and kerosene
Max thrust: 150,000 lb

STAGES 1

GUIDANCE Inertial by Ford instrument company

WARHEAD Single four megaton W-49 Thermonuclear warhead mounted in a Goodyear re-entry vehicle

CONTRACTOR Chrysler

NUMBER OF MISSILES DEPLOYED 45; 30 in Italy, 15 in Turkey

The Jupiter IRBM is one of the least known, and shortest lived, of the early US nuclear missiles. At the same time its program was also one of the most important in the history of US rocketry.

The Jupiter missile program had its beginnings in the year 1954 when, following the development of the Redstone missile, the Army's missile research group at Redstone arsenal began initial studies and design work, on a missile capable of either delivering nuclear payloads over a distance of 1000 miles or placing a satellite into orbit. Early the next year, on 14 February 1955, the Science Advisory Committee issued the Killian report, urging the concurrent development of an Intermediate Range Ballistic Missile, or IABM with the ICBM. This conclusion, plus the fact that the Soviet Union was already known to be testing IRBMs, prompted Secretary of Defense Charles E Wilson, to approve development of the THOR IRBM on 8 November 1955. That same day, Secretary Wilson also approved of development of the Jupiter as a sea-launched IRBM with only a secondary role as an alternative to the Thor IRBM.

Initially, the collaboration with the Navy would prove quite beneficial to the Jupiter program. To meet the Navy's deployment requirements, the planned length of the Jupiter was reduced, and instead of fins, a gimballed rocket engine was used to control the missile in flight. In the end, the Jupiter's liquid fuel engine system would prove completely unsuitable and, with engine tests underway by November of 1955, the Army was not willing to change it. As a result of this impasse, on 16 February 1956, the Navy began development of its own version of the Jupiter using solid fuel, the missile was called the Jupiter S.

Though the Navy had dropped out of the liquid fuel program, it was still involved in the Jupiter missile program. This fact kept the program going and, on 14 March 1956, flight testing of components began on a modified version of the Redstone, called 'Jupiter A.' Three months later, on 11 June the Army awarded the Jupiter's production contract to Chrysler corporation; that same month, the first test engines were delivered to Cape Canaveral for flight testing. The big event occurred on 20 September 1956, when a Jupiter C, which was a Jupiter A with a special payload section, reached an altitude of 650 miles and traveled a distance of 3400 miles down the Atlantic test range. This flight gave the Jupiter program the free world ballistic missile record for altitude as well as range.

The Jupiter C launch, though important for both the Army and the nation's prestige, was, however, to become the last straw in an ongoing rivalry between the Army and the Air Force. The Air Force, which was in charge of the development of the nation's two ICBMs — Atlas and Titan, as well as, the Jupiter's rival, the Thor IRBM — felt that the Army's research was infringing on its unofficial monopoly on long range missile systems. Since this disagreement involved jurisdiction, it could only be settled by the Secretary of Defense. Thus, on 28 November 1956, Secretary Wilson settled the dispute by issuing a 'Roles and Mission' directive, giving the US Air Force sole control of all missiles with a range greater than 200 miles. As a result of this order, the Jupiter IRBM was now an Air Force weapon.[1]

Though the Jupiter was now officially an Air Force missile, all the development was still being done at the Army's Redstone arsenal (a formal agreement, signed on 8 November 1958, would make the Army responsible for the missile's development and production, and its costs through 1958). Thus, when the first missile was launched from Cape Canaveral in March of 1957, it was an Army, not an Air Force, team that operated it. Though this particular launch was unsuccessful, two months later, on 31 May a completely successful flight of 1500 miles was achieved. Since this was four months before the first successful Thor flight, Jupiter had won the race to be the first successful US IRBM.

Though the Jupiter had beaten the Thor to the 1500 mile mark, the program was badly behind its competitor. Whereas, in the Jupiter program, flight testing was being done with engineering development missiles, in the Thor program production line missiles were being used — the first Thor missile had been delivered on 22 October 1956. Additionally, where development of the Thor's launch and support equipment was done concurrently with the missile, development of the Jupiter's launch and support equipment did not begin until the fall of 1957. This particular delay was then compounded by the fact that when work began it was directed towards modifying the Thor's support equipment for use by the Jupiter which was an impossible task.

With the appointment of Neil H McElroy as Secretary of Defense on 9 October 1957 a new attitude appeared in the DOD towards the Jupiter. On November 27 following the 22 October 1957 launch of the first prototype Jupiter, on November 27, the DOD announced that both the Thor and the Jupiter would be produced, with the first units to be ready by December of 1958. On 2 January 1958, the DOD then approved of the use of Army-designed launch support equipment (equipment similar to that of the Redstone/Jupiter, and not the Thor) and, on 4 January Chrysler was issued a $51.8 million contract for production of the Jupiter. The first Jupiter squadron, the 864th SMS, was then activated on 15 January; training began in February, and the second and third squadrons, the 865th and the 866th, were activated on 1 June and 1 September respectively. The first production model Jupiter was then delivered in August, with the first all-Air Force launch occurring on 15 October 1958. By this time, the first Thors had been delivered to Great Britain.

Even as they were deploying their own development, the Thor IRBM, in England, the Air Force had come to realize that the Jupiter was a far more effective IRBM. Because it was mobile, it was impossible for any potential enemy to pretarget the weapon for a preemptive nuclear missile strike. Additionally, since the missile was built stronger for ground movement, it had a higher resistance to conventional weapons, further enhancing its survivability. Finally, since the Army had developed the Jupiter to use an ablative re-entry vehicle instead of the Thor's blunt Mk-II RV, the missile was significantly more accurate, making it more effective against hardened military targets (all later Air Force ICBMs would use the ablative method pioneered by the Jupiter). These facts would push the Air Force to make the Jupiter operational.

Though deployment of the Jupiter was now officially approved by both the Air Force and the DOD, it would still be some time before the missile could be deployed. Because the negotiations for launching sites did not begin until after the decision was made to deploy the Jupiter, it would not be until 16 March 1959 that Italy and the US would sign an agreement allowing the missiles to be deployed on Italian soil. Since development of the launching equipment was also delayed, it would not be until 6 May 1959, that the first Jupiter squadron could be declared operational. Even with all these political delays, on 11 July 1960, the first Jupiter missile was emplaced in Italy.[2] Following the first launch from a tactical launcher on 20 October 1960, the first squadron was then declared operational in June of 1961. The first launcher in Turkey, NATO II squadron, then began operating on 7 November 1961.

Though each squadron had 15 missiles, because of its mobile basing system only one third of all the Jupiter missiles were ready to launch at a moment's notice: the remaining two-thirds were either being set up or were in transit to a new launch site.

Setting up a Jupiter was a tedious task requiring a large number of men, a minimum of twenty vehicles including the missile transporters, a 6000 gallon fuel semi-trailer and a 4000 gallon LOX liquid oxygen trailer. The surveying of the launch site was done to ascertain its exact location for the missile's guidance system. Then the launch pedestal was emplaced and the missile's base hinged to it. After this, using a combination of an A and an H frame, the missile was pulled vertical, the fuel lines attached and the flower petal shelter emplaced around it (the shelter was to protect personnel from conventional weapons during maintenance on the missile: it opens up like a flower for the launching). All in all, very time consuming.

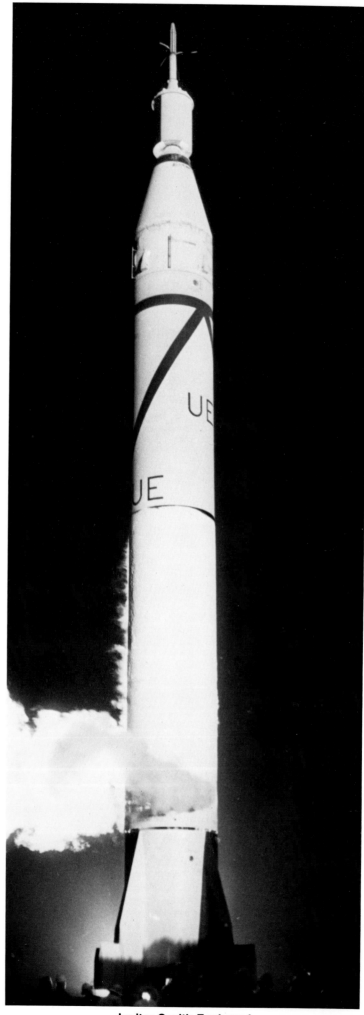

Jupiter C with Explorer I

When all three Jupiters were ready for launch, control was then turned over to the flight's three-man launch crew (one officer and two enlisted men), and the site's mobile maintenance crew. Located far from the launch site in the LCT, the launch crew's job was to monitor the missiles for any kind of malfunction and implement any changes in targeting. Three LCT crews were used per day, with a spare crew on call to replace any primary crew member that was ill, injured or on leave. This spare crew also made it possible to allow one crew a weekend off. If a malfunction occurred the maintenance crew would then be called in. If the malfunction was too big for this team, two other maintenance crews — a 'graveyard' and a swing shift — were also available at the main base, to support the on site unit.

Though the Jupiter was now deployed, problems still remained. Because training of Italian and Turkish crews did not begin until mid 1959, the first Jupiter field units had to be operated by American squadrons. The first all-Italian unit would not begin operating until late 1961, following the first Italian launch of a Jupiter on 27 April 1961. The first Turkish unit took control of its missiles on 25 May 1962, one month after the first Turkish launch on 18 April. The same day the Turkish unit took custody, the last American Jupiter Squadron the (866th), was officially inactivated, ending US operation of the Jupiter. However, though the missiles were no longer controlled by the US, the warheads were still in the custody of a SAC officer working with the Italian and Turkish units.

Even as the last Jupiter was being turned over to allied troops, plans were being made to deactivate the sites. Since production of the missile had ended in December of 1960, there was a continually

decreasing number of missiles for both training and operational deployment. Furthermore, following the deployment of the Polaris, the Jupiters had become unnecessarily cumbersome to operate. Thus on 17 January 1963, the US announced the planned phaseout of the Jupiter's in Italy. Six days later, the Turkish government also announced the phaseout of its single squadron. By 1964, the last missile had been withdrawn.

It should be noted that, since the Jupiters were still operational on 27 June 1963, they were redesignated under the new unified Army, Navy and Air Force designation system. In this new system, they became 'PGM-19As,' the P standing for soft pad, the G for surface to surface and the M for missile.

Though its use was extensively delayed by politics, and its time in service was short, the Jupiter was still an important missile. For the military, it was the first mobile strategic ballistic missile ever deployed and the first missile to use the superior ablative re-entry vehicle system. As for the space program, the Jupiter led to the development of the Jupiter C — which would later be used to launch the first US satellite. Also, in its Juno configuration, the Jupiter would be used to launch the monkeys Able and Baker into space on 28 May 1959, as well as the deep space probe Pioneer III, the earth science satellite Explorer VII and the first US satellite to orbit the Sun, Pioneer IV.

[1] On 8 December 1956 Secretary of Defense Wilson ordered the Navy to stop work on the Jupiter S and to begin development of the Polaris. This not only let the Navy bow out of the Jupiter program, it gave that service a more effective missile.
[2] One Jupiter base in Italy was Gioia Del Colle. The other base has not been specified.

Jupiter IRBM

Jupiter IRBM

Thor IRBM

Thor (SM-75)

SPECIFICATIONS

Length: 65 ft

Diameter: 8 ft

Span: 14 ft

Weight: 110,000 lb

PERFORMANCE

Speed: 10,000 mph

Range: 1500 mi

Ceiling: 300 mi

CEP: over a 1000 ft

PROPULSION Main engine – a single Rocketdyne MB-3 liquid
fuel rocket engine burning a 2.24:1 mixture of
liquid oxygen and kerosene
Max thrust: 160,000 lb
Twin vernier motors — to provide added thrust at
liftoff and for roll and altitude control during,
and after, main engine operation
Max thrust: 1011 lb

GUIDANCE Inertial by AC Spark Plug

WARHEAD One W-49 thermonuclear warhead of 4 megaton
yield in a Mk-2 re-entry vehicle[1]

CONTRACTOR Ramo-Wooldridge, manufactured by
McDonnell Douglas

NUMBER OF MISSILES 60 missiles deployed

The Thor was the first Intermediate Range Ballistic Missile to be deployed by the United States. Intended as a stopgap until the deployment of the Atlas ICBM, it would later become one of the major workhorses of our nation's space program.

The beginnings of the Thor program can be found in a mid-1954 Air Force study to determine the feasibility of a 1000 mile Tactical Ballistic Missile to replace the earlier Matador Ground Launched Cruise Missile. By the fall of that year, this study concluded that such a missile, with a range of at least 1500 miles, could be used against strategic targets in the Soviet Union, and could thus serve to supplement the planned Atlas ICBM force. As a result of this, on 2 December 1954, the Air Force issued 'General Operation Requirement 50' for an Intermediate Range Ballistic Missile.

Two months after the issuing of GOR-50, on 14 February 1955, the Technological Capabilities Panel of the Defense Department's Science Advisory Committee issued the Killian report, which urged the President and the National Security Council to give the Air Force ballistic missile effort the highest national priority, and to approve the concurrent development of an IRBM. This conclusion, plus recent intelligence reports regarding Soviet missile developments,[2] would prompt the NSC in mid-1955 to request that the Air Force actively determine the best method to develop an IRBM. This was the beginning of the Thor program.

By late August, the Ballistic Missile Division (BMD) of the Air Force had come a long way in determining the Thor's final configuration. First, the propulsion system was to be a derivative of the S-3 motor which was being developed by Rocketdyne for the Jupiter IRBM. Guidance was then to be provided by the inertial unit being developed for the Atlas by AC Spark Plug, and the re-entry vehicle was to be the Mk-II which was also being developed for the Atlas by General Electric. With this information, plus the range requirement, and the given internal dimensions of the C-124 Globemaster cargo aircraft — which would be the missile's main transportation to its various launch sites — the BMD could declare that for a range of 1750 miles, the Thor would be 65 feet long, eight feet in diameter, and would weigh 55 tons.

With the specifications set by the BMD, all the Air Force needed now was permission to build the Thor. This permission would be long in coming, however, as the nation's political system prevented the necessary paperwork from reaching the NSC until mid-September. Then, on 13 September President Eisenhower approved the development of both land- and sea-launched IRBMs.[3] The bureaucracy again delayed things, keeping Secretary Wilson from getting the official written order until the end of the month. Then Wilson and the DOD kept things in limbo for another month until, on 8 November the Secretary of Defense added the Thor IRBM to the Air Force Ballistic Missile program.[4] Red tape again delayed the delivery of the official orders until 28 November.

Since it had already been decided who would make the rocket motor, guidance system and re-entry vehicle; with the issuing of the orders the Air Force could now begin its search for a contractor to make the airframe and integrate the system. As a result of this, on 30 November, representatives of three pre-selected companies met with officers of the BMD to be given the missile specifications and the timetable for its development, so that they could prepare a proposal. The timetable, however, was intensive, as the Thor was to begin flight testing in July of 1957, and was to be in the field by January of 1960. This fact didn't dissuade any of the companies, and, on 8 December, all three submitted their development proposals. On 23 December 1955, Douglas Aircraft was issued the Thor contract. That same month, contracts were issued to Rocketdyne for the propulsion system, AC Spark Plug for the inertial guidance unit and General Electric for the Mk-II re-entry vehicle.

To meet the Air Force timetable, Douglas had to completely develop the Thor on paper: there wasn't time for the development of a prototype. The design work was finished in eight months, and

in August of 1956, production began at the Douglas facility in Santa Monica, California. The first production round was then delivered to the Air Force on 26 October with the first flight planned for 20 December.

The speed at which the Thor was developed would not be matched by its testing program. The first attempt to launch a Thor on 20 December 1956 was a complete failure, with the missile's main engine failing to ignite. When a second attempt was made with this first missile on 25 January 1957 it toppled back on to its pad, destroying it. Testing began again on 19 April, but a malfunction in the range radar system caused the destruct order to be issued after 30 seconds of flight. Additional flights in May and August would also end in failure. On 20 September the first successful flight of 1100 miles was achieved.[5] Two weeks later, on 4 October 1957, the Soviet Union successfully orbited Sputnik, the world's first satellite.

The launch of Sputnik would cause the Thor program to be accelerated even further. On 27 November 1957, Secretary of Defense McElroy ordered the Air Force to put the Thor in full production. Ten days later, Phase II testing with the AC inertial guidance system began. The first successful flight occurring on 19 December 1957.[6] The agreement to deploy the missiles in Great Britain was signed on 1 February 1958, followed by the 20 February activation of the 705th Strategic Missile Wing at Lakenheath RAF station in England. The first operational missile was then delivered on 31 May, and the first successful flight from the prototype tactical launcher was achieved on 4 June 1958. The first Thors were then delivered to the 77th SMS at Feltwell RAF station on 19 September and on 26 November the first operational missile was successfully launched.

Initially, the Thors based in England were operated by American, not English, crews. The first launch by a RAF crew would not even occur until 6 April 1959. This fact had little effect

Thor IRBM

on the deployment schedule, with SAC transferring control of the first operational squadron (the 77th RAF SMS) to the Royal Air Force on 22 June; the US maintained control of the warheads. The first RAF combat training launch of a Thor occurred on 6 October 1959, with the first wing being declared operational on 11 December 1959. The last base was completed on 22 April 1960, and on 3 June, the first warhead was mated to a Thor at Feltwell, making the system a nuclear-armed one.

The Thor was deployed at four Royal Air Force bases: Feltwell, Hemswell, Driffield and North Luffenham. Each base had a total of five missile complexes, or 'satellites,' with each complex having three missile launchers.[7] For protection against both conventional weapons and the elements, each missile was kept in a horizontal position inside a metal shelter; for defense against a nuclear strike, the complexes were spaced 12 miles apart. Following the issuing of a launch order, these shelters would be rolled away, and the missiles were raised to their vertical firing position. Fueling of the necessary 10,000 gallons of fuel then took only eight minutes — following which, the weapon could be fired.

Two years after the last missile was deployed in England, the AEC selected the Thor for use in a new series of high altitude nuclear explosions. Like the Redstone before it (please see 'Redstone' portion of this text), the Thor was to deliver a nuclear device to an altitude of 200 miles, where it would be detonated to determine what effects such an explosion would have on radio and radar systems.

The Thor would prove less reliable than the (earlier) Redstone. The first such ventures, code named 'STARFISH' and 'BLUE-GILL,' were unsuccessful. On 9 July 1962, the first successful test detonation — STARFISH Prime — was achieved. The bomb, detonated at an altitude of 280 miles, turned night into day for six minutes in Hawaii. Soon after this flight, on 25 July, the BLUEGILL Prime missile exploded on liftoff, destroying the launch pad and contaminating the area. Testing would not resume until October, following which BLUEGILL Triple Prime was successfully launched on 25 October and KINGFISH succeeded on 1 November. The detonation altitude of the BLUEGILL and KINGFISH shots were less than 62 miles, and in fact, no further high altitude tests have ever been done.

While the Thor was being used for the AEC tests, plans were in progress to replace the Thors with either the Polaris SLBM, or the Skybolt air-launched missile. During this same period, on 1 May 1962, Secretary of Defense McNamara informed the British Minister of Defence that after 31 October 1964, the US would no longer provide logistical support for the Thors based in Great Britain. Three months later, on 1 August 1962, the British Minister of Defence, Peter Thorneycroft, announced in Parliament that the Thors would be phased out of Britain by 31 December 1963. The first missiles were then removed from alert on 29 November 1962, and on 15 August 1963, the last Thor was drawn down and then airlifted back to the US on 27 September. On 20 December 1963, SAC officially ended its responsibility for the Thors in England.

The removal of the Thor IRBMs from Great Britain did not mean an end to the use of the Thor as a nuclear weapon system. On 9 February 1962, prior to the 1962 high altitude tests, the Air Force began a program (titled Project 437) to turn the Thor into a direct ascent anti-satellite weapon. The idea was to launch a large nuclear warhead into space using the Thor, and then detonate the warhead near an enemy reconaissance or hunter/killer satellite. Testing of unarmed Thors began at Johnson Isle on 15 February 1964 and, on 29 May the project entered the realm of military reality, when the 10th Aerospace Defense Squadron of the Air Defense Command TAC was declared operational. President Lyndon B Johnson officially announced that the system was operational on 17

September 1964. The last SAC Thor was then turned over to the ADC on 31 March 1967.

For a total of eight years on 24 hour alert, the Air Defense Command operated the two Thor ASAT (anti-satellite weapon) launchers at Johnson Isle and two at Vandenberg AFB (the Vandenberg site was a training unit). During this time, the system became less and less reliable, due to a shortage of spare parts and a limited amount of training shots. As a result of this, and the heavy damage incurred on Johnson Isle from Hurricane Celeste on 19 August 1972, the Thor ASAT system was withdrawn to reserve status on 8 December 1972. This reserve status lasted an additional three years until, in 1975, the remaining Mk-49 Thor warheads were dismantled.[8]

In retrospect, the Thor was not a very effective weapon system. In both its IRBM and ASAT forms, it was slow to respond, vulnerable to nuclear attack and was not very reliable: the Thor IRBM in testing had a 23 percent failure rate. On the other hand, and to touch on a subject not covered by this history, the Thor has become very important as a launch vehicle for satellites and other space payloads. Even today — in the era of the Space shuttle — Delta rockets, the great grandsons of the original Thor, are still being used to place both military and civilian satellites into orbit.

[1] The yield of the STARFISH warhead was 1.4 megatons. Whether the warhead was a W-49 is unknown to author.
[2] In 1955, the Soviet Union deployed the 750-mile range SS-3 missile. Though not a true IRBM, it had three times the range of anything the US then had.
[3] That year's Geneva summit may have added to delay.
[4] President Eisenhower suffered a heart attack on 28 September 1955. He did not resume his duties in the White House until November of that year
[5] By this time, Jupiter had already had a successful flight of 1500 miles.
[6] On 24 October 1957 a stripped down Thor traveled 1645 miles.
[7] The Thor had 18-man launch crews.
[8] Following the reorganising of the ADC, the remaining Thor IRBM boosters were returned to the Strategic Air Command on 1 November 1979.

Thor IRBM

Thor IRBM

Submarine-Launched Ballistic Missiles (SLBM)

Polaris (UGM-27)

SPECIFICATIONS

	POLARIS A1	POLARIS A2	POLARIS A3
Length:	28 ft 6 in	31 ft	32 ft 4 in
Diameter:	Max all models — 4 ft 6 in		
Weight:	28,800 lb	32,500 lb	35,700 lb

PERFORMANCE

Range:	1380 mi	1700 mi	2880 mi
Speed:	all models — 8000 mph		
Ceiling:	400 mi	500 mi	500 mi
CEP:	approx 3000 ft	3000 ft	2000 ft

PROPULSION

Polaris A-1: First and second stages by Aerojet General

Polaris A-2: First and second stages by Aerojet General

Polaris A-3: First stage by Aerojet General, second by Hercules Inc

GUIDANCE Inertial system developed by MIT and manufactured by General Electric and Hughes

WARHEAD Polaris A-1 & A-2: one W-47 thermonuclear warhead of 500 kt yield
Polaris A-3: three W-58 thermonuclear warheads, of 200 kt yield, mounted in Mk-2 re-entry vehicles

CONTRACTOR Lockheed Missile and Space Co

NUMBER OF MISSILES DEPLOYED
80 Polaris A-1s deployed, 163 produced
192 Polaris A-2s deployed, 346 produced
644 Polaris A-3s deployed, 644 produced

The Polaris Submarine Launched Ballistic Missile (SLBM) is the first nuclear-armed, strategic, ballistic missile ever deployed on US Navy submarines. It is by far the most important missile system the US Navy has ever deployed.

The concept of launching strategic ballistic missiles from submarines was first studied by the German Navy as a possible means of attacking American coastal facilities during the Second World War. After the war, the documentation pertaining to this research was turned over to the US Navy, which then initiated its own research to determine the feasibility of launching such weapons from American Navy surface ships. Initially, this research was quite promising[1] but following Operation Pushover, a 1948 test to determine what damage would be caused if a V-2 type missile were to topple over during a nautical launch, the Navy was forced to concluded that it was too dangerous to deploy liquid fuel missiles on ships. Since solid fuel technology was still in its infancy, this decision effectively shelved the idea of a sea launched ballistic missile for some years.

However, in the first two years following Operation Pushover, several important advances occurred in the design of large solid fuel rocket motors. These developments would prompt the Navy, in late 1950, to begin development of a large, two stage, solid fuel missile called the 'Big Stoop,' to determine if it was now feasible to use a solid fuel missile to deliver a nuclear payload. Though the available solid fuels still limited this 51 foot tall missile to a range of 20 miles, its three successful flights in 1951 were enough to convince anyone that the basic idea was sound. Two years later the four successful flights of the Thiokol 5000 lb solid fuel motor, which was the first motor to incorporate the aforementioned new design developments, would confirm this analysis, and prompted the Navy to propose to the Department of Defense, in 1955, a program to develop a sea launched solid fuel IRBM.

President Eisenhower would approve the ideas on 13 September 1955. Though the idea of putting long range ballistic missiles on Navy ships would catch the attention of the President and the DOD, many in the administration felt that the Navy was being too optimistic as to how long it would take to develop the high energy solid fuels necessary to achieve the required range of 1500 miles. Thus, on 8 November 1955, Secretary of Defense Wilson directed the Navy to work with the Army on developing the liquid fuel Jupiter IRBM as a sea launched ballistic missile.

Since the Jupiter was a liquid fuel weapon, the Navy knew it

Polaris A-1 SLBM

Polaris A-2 SLBM

was impossible to deploy it on ships without posing a major risk to the crews.[2] As a result of this, on 16 February 1956, the Navy dropped halfway out of the Jupiter program by beginning development of a solid fuel version of the Jupiter called the Jupiter S. The Office of the Secretary of Defense Ballistic Missile Committee then approved of this solid fuel research on 20 March following which, on 11 April, contracts were issued to Lockheed and Aerojet for development of both the Jupiter S *and* a new, smaller, solid fuel missile designed to make maximum use of rumored developments in small, high-kiloton yield, thermonuclear warheads.[3] When, in September, this breakthrough was confirmed by the AEC this smaller missile, with its lower overall costs as compared to the Jupiter S, very quickly became the favorite design of Secretary of Defense Wilson who, on 8 December 1956,[4] gave his permission for the Navy to drop out of the Jupiter program and develop the small solid fuel IRBM. With this action, the Polaris program officially began.

Polaris A-1

When the Polaris program was begun in early 1957, the plan was for the deployment of a 1700 mile range missile by the year 1963. The range was set to match that of the Jupiter and the Thor IRBMs. Following the launch of Sputnik 1, on 4 October 1957, the Navy began to investigate the possibility of accelerating the program and, in November, a revised plan was put forward calling for the deployment of a 1380 mile range missile by the year 1960. With the approval of this new plan development of the Polaris A-1 began on 9 December 1957.

With the reduction in required range, testing of the Polaris began immediately, with the first pad launch of a component test vehicle occurring at Point Mugu on 11 January 1958. Two months later, on 23 March, the underwater launching system was successfully tested, with the successful launch of a full scale dummy Polaris off San Clemente Isle. The first launch of a AX model Polaris (essentially a Polaris A-1) was be attempted on 24 September, with the first successful flight occurring during the fifth launch on 20 April 1959. By the end of the year, successful flights of up to 700 miles would be completed as well as launches from the ship *Observation Island*. The first Polaris A-1 tactical round was also launched on 21 September 1959.

With the launching of the first Tactical round, phase II testing of Polaris had begun. The launch of the first inertially guided Polaris was successfully completed on 7 January 1960, with the first limited burn flight from the underwater San Clemente Isle launcher occurring on 14 April. Three months later, 20 July 1960, the first Polaris A-1 missile would be launched from the USS *George Washington*. The *George Washington* would then go on its first war patrol on 15 November 1960 following which, on 17 November testing of the Polaris A-1 was completed. The Polaris A-1 program was completed on 7 December 1961 with the delivery of the last missile.

On 6 May 1962, as part of Joint Task Force 8, a Polaris A-1, with a live warhead was launched successfully from the USS *Ethan Allen*. The Polaris system's ultimate test, the missile performed perfectly, detonating above Bikini Atoll. This was the first live flight of a US strategic missile.

Polaris A-2

While development of the A-1 was underway, work was also continued on the 1700 mile range missile. This work would eventually result in the development of the Polaris A-2.

The Polaris A-2 was not just an upgraded version of the Polaris

A-1, but a more sophisticated missile. Not only was its first stage longer than its predecessor, the second stage of the A-2 would use a lightweight fiberglass casing instead of the A-1's thin-gauge steel. Testing began in 1960, with the first flight on 10 November resulting in a successful flight of 1600 miles. The first submerged launch from the submarine *Ethan Allen* then occurred on 23 October 1961 and on 26 June 1962, the first A-2 missiles went to sea.

The last submarine to be deployed with A-2 was the USS *John Adams* on 3 November 1964.

Polaris A-3

During the development of the Polaris A-1, many important design improvements were generated. Because of the urgency of the program, there wasn't time to incorporate these changes in the Polaris A-2. Thus, in September of 1960, approval was given for the development of the Polaris A-3 missile.

The Polaris A-3 was to give the Navy an IRBM capability beyond that of the Air Force Thor and Jupiter missiles. By using fiberglass casings for both stages, and by using a guidance package one-third the size of the A-2, enough weight would be cut to give the missile a range of 2880 miles — almost twice that of Thor. Furthermore, by deploying three warheads on the Polaris A-3 missile for bracketing the target, the destructive equivalent of a Thor megaton class warhead could be achieved.[5] This multiwarhead capability would also make the Polaris A-3 harder to intercept by any anti-ballistic missile system, because the warheads were deployed far enough apart that a single nuclear armed ABM could only intercept one of the warheads. It was because of these improved capabilities that, in 1961, President John F Kennedy ordered the development of the A-3 accelerated in order to make it available one year sooner. This action would also reduce the number of Polaris A-2 missiles procured.

The first test launch of a Polaris A-3 on 7 August 1962, was to be partially successful. In February of the following year, two successful flights were run and, on 26 October 1963, the first launch from a submerged submarine, the USS *Andrew Jackson,* was successfully completed. The first submerged launch of a production A-3P missile was completed form submarine USS *Daniel Webster* on 25 May 1964, and on 28 September 1964, the *Webster* went on the first A-3 patrol. Rearming of the earlier *George Washington* class began on 1 January 1965 and on 7 July 1965 the last A-1 missile was withdrawn from service.

While deployment of the Polaris A-3P was underway, on 17 November 1966, flight testing began on an improved A-3 missile. Called the A-3T, testing of this missile lasted two years with the first underwater shot being completed 29 August 1968. The next year this missile began rearming all Polaris A-2 and A-3 submarines deployed with the Atlantic fleet. Conversion of the Atlantic Fleet was completed on 17 July 1970 with the Pacific fleet being completely rearmed on 1 April 1972. Before deployment of the A-3T was completed, on 31 March 1971, the USS *James Madison* took to sea armed with the new MIRVed Poseidon C-3 missile.

With the transfer of the USS *Robert E Lee* to the Pacific on 10 August 1973, the Poseidon C-3 missile completely replaced the Polaris A-3T in the Atlantic. Conversion of the remaining *Lafayette* subs to Poseidon was then completed on 21 February 1978 (the USS *Daniel Webster*) leaving only the earlier *George Washington* and *Ethan Allen* class subs armed with Polaris — these submarines would never be rearmed. The fact that the Polaris A-3 was being phased out did not stop work on improving the weapon system and on 28 June 1978, an improved Polaris A-3TA was launched from the USS *Patrick Henry*. By April of 1979 at least six of the ten

Polaris subs had been rearmed with this model. Two years later the Polaris A-3 patrol was completed by the USS *Robert E Lee* on 1 October 1981.

Even as testing of the Polaris A-3 was underway, work was in progress to develop an even more formidable weapon called the Poseidon. As a result of this and government cut backs, production of the Polaris A-3 was ended in June of 1968. Three years later, the Poseidon began replacing the A-3 and, by 1977, only the earlier *George Washington* and *Ethan Allen* class subs were armed with Polaris. These submarines would never be rearmed. The last Polaris A-3 patrol was completed by the USS *Robert E Lee* on 1 October 1981, prior to that submarine's conversion into an attack/training sub.

Even though the US stopped operating the Polaris A-3 in 1981, the missile is still in service on the four ballistic missile submarines operated by Great Britain. These missiles should remain operational until their operating submarines are replaced in the early 1990s by submarines carrying the enormous Trident II missile.

[1] On 6 September 1947, a V-2 missile was successfully launched from the USS *Midway,* proving that it was possible to fire a large missile from a rolling and pitching, ship in forward motion.
[2] On 4 February 1972 an improved A-3T with a SPALT on the first stage motor to eliminate separation anomalies was launched from the USS *George Washington.*
[3] Though a megaton yield warhead was officially required for both IRBMs and ICBMs, the accuracy of an IRBM was so much better that a high kiloton warhead would be just as effective against a military target.
[4] On 26 November 1956, Secretary Wilson restricted the Army to weapons having a range of 200 miles, making the Jupiter an Air Force program.
[5] An agreement ending nuclear tests between the Soviet Union, Great Britain and the United States in 1985 made it impossible for a single megaton class warhead to be tested for Polaris.

Polaris A-3 SLBM

Poseidon C-3 SLBM

Poseidon C-3 (UGM-73A)

SPECIFICATIONS
Length: 34 ft 1.2 in   Weight: 64,400 lb
Diameter: 8 ft

PERFORMANCE
Speed: supersonic   CEP: 2000 ft
Range: approx 2880 mi

PROPULSION
First stage – Solid fuel rocket motor developed by
              Hercules & Thiokol
Second stage – Solid fuel rocket motor developed by Hercules

GUIDANCE Inertial system by developed by MIT, manufac-
         tured by General Electric and Raytheon

WARHEAD Ten 50 kt W-68 thermonuclear warheads mounted
        in Mk-3 re-entry vehicles; 14 warheads carried in
        tests, but the range was significantly reduced

CONTRACTOR: Lockheed Missiles and Space Co

NUMBER OF MISSILES: 496 missiles deployed during the
                    1970s; 288 operational 1988, 619
                    produced

The Poseidon was the first MIRVed SLBM ever deployed.
At the present time it makes up approximately 40 percent of
the SLBM force.

During the development of the Polaris A-3, independent studies
of the design of this missile indicated that further improvements in
accuracy and range were possible using state of the art technology.
Furthermore, in a study of the *Lafayette* class submarines, it was
concluded that by removing the missile tube liners an even larger
missile could be deployed, giving the Fleet Ballistic Missile force
a striking range of over 4030 miles. As a result of this, in
November 1963, the Navy authorized the development of a
follow-on missile to the Polaris A-3 called the B-3.

The original purpose of the B-3 program was to develop an
improved range missile. In November of 1964, however, the
concept of Multiple Independently-targetable Re-entry Vehicles, or
MIRVs, was added to the design to improve the missile's ability to
penetrate enemy anti-ballistic missile systems. Two months later,
on 18 January 1965, presidential approval was given for development. The missile was to be called the Poseidon C-3. Project
definition terminated in April and, in October of 1965, development began; the Poseidon was designed to have twice the payload
of the Polaris A-3 and a range of 4030 miles. The following year,
project development accelerated, but between this event and the
first launch the Poseidon's range was reduced to that of the Polaris
A-3.

The first Poseidon test missile was launched from a flat surface
pad at Cape Canaveral on 16 August 1968. Ten months later, on 29
June 1970, the 20th and last flight was launched from this pad,
completing phase one of the testing program: 14 flights had been
successful. The first launch from a submerged submarine occurred
on 3 August 1970: the vessel involved was the SLBM converted

Poseidon C-3 SLBM

submarine USS *James Madison*. By March 1971, seven more submerged launches were completed, and on 31 March, the *James Madison* set sail on its first Poseidon patrol. SLBM conversion of the remaining *Lafayette* class submarines subsequently took place during each ship's regularly scheduled reactor refueling.

In 1972, even as deployment was getting underway, Operational Tests (OT) of the Poseidon were ending in a failure of one kind or another. Subsequent analyses of these flights showed that the production Poseidon system had quality control problems in its small electronic parts, poor gimbal assembles, a faulty firing unit and flaws in the submarine/missile connecting flexible cables. To rectify this, in March of 1973, OT activities were suspended, and a modification program was begun to improve the missiles still in production. Deployment of these improved missiles began with the 21st *Lafayette* submarine conversion in 1974 and continued until, in February 1978, the last *Lafayette*[1] class subs had been rearmed: this included all of the previous 20 subs, which were rearmed from the earlier Poseidon to the improved model.

OT run throughs of the improved Poseidon began in 1974. Four years and over 40 flights later, no percentage reliability had been determined for this missile by the Department of Defense.

As previously noted, the range of the Poseidon never reached the planned 4030 miles. This fact would greatly concern the Navy in the late 1960s, for without this additional range the Poseidon subs were potentially vulnerable to enemy anti-submarine operations. As a result of this, in 1969, development began on a longer-range missile, which could be deployed in the same missile tubes. Originally called the Extended Range Poseidon, this missile would eventually become known as the 4600 mile Trident I, which in October 1979 began replacing the Poseidon missiles deployed on 12 *Lafayette* class submarines.

As a result of the Trident I retrofit, the total number of Poseidon missiles deployed has been reduced from 496 to 304. Furthermore, because of the continued deployment of the Trident-armed *Ohio* class submarines and the need to keep within the SALT 2 limits, in 1987 the submarine *Sam Rayburn* had its Poseidon missiles removed, reducing the number deployed to 288.[2] Further reductions in the Poseidon force will occur in the coming years, as the older *Lafayette* class submarines are withdrawn from service due to age. By the mid-1990s there will be no Poseidon missiles in service.

---

[1] The ten *Ethan Allen* and *George Washington* class submarines were exempt from this because their tubes were not of the same design as the *Lafayette* subs.
[2] Jane's lists 256 Poseidon missiles in service.

Poseidon C-3 SLBM

Trident I C-4 (UGM-96A)

SPECIFICATIONS
Length: 34 ft 1.2 in   Weight: 65,000 lb
Diameter: 6 ft 2 in

PERFORMANCE
Speed: classified   CEP: 1250 ft
Range: 4600 miles

PROPULSION
First stage solid fuel rocket motor manufactured by Thiokol.
Second stage solid fuel rocket motor manufactured by Hercules.
Third stage solid fuel rocket motor manufactured by United Technologies Corp

GUIDANCE Stellar inertial system

WARHEAD Eight 100 kiloton W-76 warheads mounted in Mk-4 re-entry vehicles; 14 warheads possible but at a reduced range

CONTRACTOR Lockheed Missiles and Space Co, Inc

NUMBER OF MISSILES 384 deployed as of 1987, 570 manufactured

The Trident I is the newest Submarine Launched Ballistic Missile to be deployed by the US Navy. It was developed and deployed to meet the military and political needs of the late 1970s.

When development of the Poseidon began in the mid-1960s, the plan was to improve the survivability of launching submarines by allowing them to standoff an additional 1000 nautical miles from their targets. Before the first missile had been launched, it had become apparent that the Poseidon would not have this increased range, and quite possibly would not even match the range of the earlier Polaris A-3.[1] To rectify this the Navy began a research program called the Extended Range Poseidon (EXPO), to determine whether it would be possible to develop a longer range missile that could still be fitted in the missile tubes of the operational *Lafayette* class submarines. By 1971 this program had been absorbed by the Navy's Undersea Long-range Missile System (ULMS), where it was called ULMS-1 and, on 14 September, Secretary of Defense Melvin R Laird approved development of this improved missile. The development contract was issued in December. President Nixon issued his approval in January of 1972, and in May the program was accelerated under the new title Trident I.

To give the Trident I a range greater than the Poseidon without increasing its dimensions or reducing its payload was a challenge the engineers at Lockheed handled admirably. First, by rearranging the payload section, they added a third stage to give the missile a greater fuel capacity. To improve range, they used a new high energy, high density solid fuel developed in the Patriot missile program; this allowed the missile a greater thrust per cubic volume of fuel expended. Constructing the motor casings with new lightweight Kevlar improved the range, and the installment of a drag reducing, telescoping aerospike produced a maximum range of 4600 miles.

Because all this new technology took time to integrate properly, the first test launch did not take place until 18 January 1977. A nearly perfect test program followed, however: 10 out of the first 12 flights succeeded (the two failures were due to guidance problems and a failure of the second stage insulator/case). The last flat pad launch, the 18th, was completed on 23 January 1979. Then testing shifted to the submarine USS *Francis Scott Key* which had finished its Trident conversion on 4 December 1978. The first submerged Trident I launch was completed on 10 April 1979, and by 31 July seven PEMS (Performance Evaluation Missiles) had been launched from the *Francis Scott Key*. DASO (Demonstration and Shakedown Operation) began on 28 August, and on 20 October 1979 the *Francis Scott Key* ventured on its first Trident I patrol.

The *Francis Scott Key* was just the first of 12 subs to undergo the Poseidon/Trident conversion. Twelve subs would be converted, half during their regularly scheduled 6 year refit, half during unscheduled layovers. While this was underway, on 13 March 1982, the *Ohio* launched its first Trident I missile. By the time the *Lafayette* conversion was completed, the *Ohio* had already returned from its first deterrent patrol.

Though the Fleet Ballistic Missile force was greatly improved, the primary reason for the deployment of the Trident I on twelve *Lafayette* class submarines, as well as the development of the missile, was to allow the United States to meet its commitment to Spain and to end by 1979 its FBM operations at the Spanish port of Rota. By placing the longer range Trident I on the subs based at Rota, 12 in all, it was possible to withdraw them to Kings Bay in Georgia without having a reduction in the on station time of these subs. To use the Poseidon missile for this would have required the subs to sail east for two additional days before they would be within striking range of their targets in the Soviet Union.

At the present time both production and deployment of the Trident I has been completed; 12 *Lafayette* and eight *Ohio* class submarines have been equipped with this missile. By the mid-1990s, however, all these *Lafayettes* are scheduled to be withdrawn from service, and the Trident Is deployed on the first eight *Ohio* subs to be replaced by the larger Trident II (D-5).

[1] The Poseidon was never deployed in the Pacific in place of the Polaris A-3.

Trident I C-4 SLBM

Trident I C-4 SLBM

Trident II D-5 and Trident I C-4 SLBMs

Trident II (D-5)

SPECIFICATIONS

Length: 44 ft 6.6 in   Weight: 130,000 lb
Diameter: 6 ft 11 in

PERFORMANCE

Speed: over 20,000 ft/sec   CEP: 300 ft
Range: 4606+ mi

PROPULSION Three stage solid fuel rocket motors: first and
second stages by Hercules and Morton-Thiokol;
third stage by United Technologies Corp

GUIDANCE Inertial system

WARHEAD 8 to 14 W-87 thermonuclear warheads of 300 Kt
yield mounted in Mk-5 re-entry vehicles. Mk-5 is
the Navy designation for the Mk-21 re-entry vehicle.

CONTRACTOR Lockheed Missile and Space Co

NUMBER OF MISSILES Not yet fully specified 82 test
missiles planned

The Trident II, or D-5, missile is the largest Submarine
Launched Ballistic Missile the US has attempted since the
solid-fueled Jupiter IRBM in 1956. With the deployment of
this missile, both US and British submarines will be able to attack
targets in the Soviet Union from any point on the compass.

Development of the D-5 initially began in the year 1966, when
the US Navy began a program titled the Undersea Long-range
Missile System (ULMS). The purpose of this program was to
ascertain the performance requirements for the next generation of
SLBMs and their launching submarines. This was in preparation for
the retirement of the Polaris/Poseidon subs in the late 1970s/early
1980s. In 1967, because the Poseidon was not reaching its 3500
mile planned range, work was redirected towards the development
of a long range missile that could be deployed in the Poseidon
submarine tubes. This was the start of the Trident I program.

In 1975, while development of the Trident I was underway, the
US Navy began a program to determine methods for improving the
accuracy of its SLBM force. This program would soon reveal that,
not only could accuracy be improved, but, with a warhead of
sufficient yield, an SLBM could be used effectively against such
hardened targets such as ICBM silos. A warhead of this size could
not be deployed on the Trident I without incurring either a loss of
range or a reduction in carried warheads. Thus, in 1978, Lockheed
began advanced design work on a new SLBM that would make
maximum use of the new *Ohio* class submarines' launching tubes.
This was the start of the Trident program.

Even before the design of the D-5 had been set, the performance
possibilities of this new missile were so great that, in March of
1982, Great Britain decided to acquire the Trident II, instead of the
Trident I, as the replacement for its Polaris missile system. Now,
with Great Britain also involved in the program, on 21 October
1983 the Navy issued a letter contract to Lockheed to start
operational systems development and production. The official
$5.765 billion contract was signed on 12 March 1984, putting the
Trident II in full scale development with an Initial Operational

Capability planned for 1989; this initial deployment will be on the
ninth *Ohio* class submarine, the USS *Tennessee* (SSBN-734).

The D-5 is a product of major advances in solid fuel propellants,
electronics, aerodynamics and construction materials. Though the
third stage still uses filament-wound Kevlar motor casings that were
pioneered in the Trident I, the first and second stage motors are
encased in Graphite epoxy to produce a lighter, stronger casing; the
casings, which surround new high energy propellants, give the
missile greater range. For improved aerodynamics, a telescoping
aerospike is used to create a more streamlined shape for atmospheric flight. Finally, for greater electronic flexibility, the missile
subsystems make extensive use of configurable gate arrays in the
primary logic functions.

The Trident II will do more than just allow the Navy to strike
hardened targets. Its longer range will allow the Navy to increase
the amount of ocean its submarines can sail in, greatly complicating
enemy anti-submarine operations. It will also increase the missile's
flight time, allowing any potential enemy a greater warning time
and lessening the danger of a launch on warning. Furthermore,
because of the Trident II's longer range, it would no longer be
necessary for the Navy to base its SLBM force overseas. The
Navy, by terminating operations of these submarines from Holy
Loch, Scotland, could lessen the internal political problems Great
Britain has been facing.

Flight testing of the Trident II missile began on 15 January
1987, with the successful 10:25 am (EST) launch of Trident D5X-1
from Pad 46A at Cape Canaveral.

Originally, the plan was to launch from 25 to 30 missiles during
the D-5 testing program, about 20 of which would be from flat
pads. The planned start of submerged testing in the summer of
1989 may be delayed, pending the results of the post-flight analysis
of the 19 January 1988 flight; in the progress of this flight, the test
vehicle had to be destroyed two minutes and 45 seconds after
lift-off.

Trident II D-5 SLBM

Nuclear Missile Submarines
(SSN) (SSBN)

Los Angeles Class

DIMENSIONS

Length: 360 ft   Width: 33 ft

Height: 32.3 ft   Weight: 6900 tons surfaced

                                     7880 tons submerged

ARMAMENT 12 vertical launch tubes for Tomahawk; four mid-ship 21 inch torpedo tubes for the launch of Tomahawk, SUBROC and Mk-48 torpedoes

SPEED 30 knots submerged

POWERPLANT Single S6G pressurized water nuclear reactor

CREW COMPLEMENT 12 officers, 115 enlisted

NAMES OF SUBMARINES

(688) *Los Angeles*, (689) *Baton Rouge*, (690) *Philadelphia*, (691) *Memphis*, (692) *Omaha*, (693) *Cincinnati*, (694) *Groton*, (695) *Birmingham*, (696) *New York City*, (697) *Indianapolis*, (698) *Bremerton*, (699) *Jacksonville*, (700) *Dallas*, (701) *La Jolla*, (702) *Phoenix*, (703) *Boston*, (704) *Baltimore*, (705) *City of Corpus Christi*, (706) *Albuquerque*, (707) *Portsmouth*, (708) *Minneapolis-St Paul*, (709) *Hyman G Rickover*, (710) *Augusta*, (711) *San Francisco*, (712) *Atlanta*, (713) *Houston*, (714) *Norfolk*, (715) *Buffalo*, (716) *Salt Lake City*, (717) *Olympia*, (718) *Honolulu*, (719) *Providence*, (720) *Pittsburgh*, (721) *Chicago*, (722) *Key West*, (723) *Oklahoma City*, (724) *Louisville*, (725) *Helena*, (750) *Newport News*, (751) *San Juan*, (752) *Pasadena*

Though this section is titled the *Los Angeles* class, it is also about the Navy's fleet of attack submarines and how the deployment of the Tomahawk has affected them.

Attack submarines like the *Los Angeles* class have been capable of launching nuclear weapons for over 30 years: during the 1950s and early 1960s it was the Regulus strategic cruise missiles; during the late 1960s and 1970s it was the ASTOR torpedo and the SUBROC. The Tomahawk land attack cruise missile, deployed in 1984 on *Sturgeon* and *Los Angeles* class subs, is not the first nuclear weapon these ships have carried. It has returned the Navy attack subs' ability to engage strategic targets that was lost with the retirement of the Regulus I in the mid-1960s.

By placing nuclear tipped Tomahawk cruise missiles on the 37 *Sturgeon* and 44 *Los Angeles* class attack submarines (in the future the new Seawolf class), the US Navy has created a second submarine missile force in addition to the Poseidon Trident force. Mounted on these high speed, high maneuverability attack subs, this missile force is less vulnerable to anti-submarine weapons in comparison to the Fleet Ballistic Missile force and is more effectively dispersed because each sub only carries a few missiles. Furthermore, since the Tomahawk is a terrain hugging cruise missile, this force cannot be easily neutralized by surface to air or, by anti-ballistic missile systems, as could the ballistic missiles. These factors, plus the high accuracy of the Tomahawk, give the Navy attack sub force a unique strategic strike ability.

Though the Tomahawk gives all the attack subs strategic nuclear capability, massive capability will be achieved with the *Los Angeles* class subs. This is because back in 1985 it was ordered that all newly constructed *Los Angeles* class subs were to be equipped with 12 Tomahawk vertical launch tubes in their bow tanks. With the addition of these tubes, a single *Los Angeles* class sub will now be able to launch a total of 16 Tomahawk missiles (12 from the vertical tubes, four from the standard torpedo tubes) in just a few minutes. Though not all of these missiles will be armed with

Los Angeles **Class USS** *Birmingham*

Los Angeles **Class USS** *City of Corpus Christi*

nuclear warheads by being able to deploy Tomahawks in such massive groups the missiles' ability to penetrate strong defense systems is increased.[1] The first of these new subs is expected to be in operation in 1989.

Though it will not happen if the *Los Angeles* class submarines are armed with only nuclear tipped Tomahawks, the strategic strike capability of these ships will be equal to that of the earlier *George Washington* class Fleet Ballistic Missile subs.

[1] The missiles would overwhelm the defenses by numbers. Additionally the conventionally armed Tomahawks could be programmed to destroy the defenses clearing a safe route for the nuclear tipped missiles.

Lafayette Class

DIMENSIONS
  Length: 425 ft
  Height: 31.5 ft
  Width: 33 ft
  Weight:
    (616 class) 7310 tons surfaced   8260 tons submerged
    (627 class) 7320 tons surfaced   8240 tons submerged
    (640 class) 7350 tons surfaced   8250 tons submerged

ARMAMENT 16 steam ejection launch tubes for Polaris,
              Poseidon & Trident missiles;
              four 21 inch torpedo tubes

SPEED 20 knots surface, 30 knots submerged

POWERPLANT Single S5W pressurized water nuclear reactor

CREW COMPLEMENT
  (616) 14 officers, 130 enlisted
  (627) 14 officers, 132 enlisted
  (640) 14 officers, 126 enlisted

NAMES OF SUBMARINES
  (616) *Lafayette*, (617) *Alexander Hamilton*, (619) *Andrew Jackson*, (620) *John Adams*, (622) *James Monroe*, (623) *Nathan Hale*, (624) *Woodrow Wilson*, (625) *Henry Clay*, (626) *Daniel Webster*, (627) *James Madison*, (628) *Tecumseh*, (629) *Daniel Boone*, (630) *John C. Calhoun*, (631) *Ulysses S Grant*, (632) *Von Steuben*, (633) *Casimir Pulaski*, (634) *Stonewall Jackson*, (635) *Sam Rayburn*, (636) *Nathanael Greene*, (640) *Benjamin Franklin*, (641) *Simon Bolivar*, (642) *Kamahameha*, (643) *George Bancroft*, (644) *Lewis and Clark*, (645) *James K Polk*, (654) *George C Marshall*, (655) *Henry L Stimson*, (656) *George Washington Carver*, (657) *Francis Scott Key*, (658) *Mariano G Vallejo*, (659) *Will Rogers*

Lafayette **Class USS** *Francis Scott Key*

The *Lafayette* class of Fleet Ballistic Missile submarines are the major operational class of FBM in the US fleet. Produced in greater number than any other class of US Ballistic Missile submarines, both past and present, these ships still make up over 75 percent of the FBM force.

Though they are all technically *Lafayette* class submarines these ships are officially grouped under the following sub-classes: the *Lafayette* class (SSBN-616 to 626), the *James Madison* class (SSBN-627 to 636), and the *Benjamin Franklin* class (SSBN-640 to 659).

Lafayette Class (616-626)

With construction of the *Ethan Allen* class well underway on 15 July 1960, President Eisenhower authorized the construction of the next five Fleet Ballistic Missile subs. Though one of these subs, the *Thomas Jefferson* (SSBN-618), was of the *Ethan Allen* class the remaining four were to be of an improved design with quieter machinery and steam ejection for the missile tubes. Seven months later, on 17 June 1961, construction began on the first of these improved submarines, the USS *Lafayette*.

Twelve days after construction of the *Lafayette* began, newly elected President John F Kennedy accelerated procurement of this submarine class by authorizing the next five subs one year ahead of schedule, by the end of the year construction was underway on nine subs.

Construction of the USS *Lafayette* was completed in May of 1962, it was christened on 8 May. Sea trials began soon afterward and on 26 June 1962 it launched its first Polaris A-2 missile. The submarine was then commissioned on 23 April 1963 and 4 January 4 the *Lafayette* went on its first deterrent patrol carrying 16 Polaris A-2 missiles. Four months later, on 25 May 1964, the *Lafayette* entered the harbor at Rota Spain, effectively opening this new advanced FBM facility there. Four months later the last *Lafayette* class submarine, the *Daniel Webster*, went on its first patrol on 28 September 1964 ending the deployment of this submarine class. Deployment of this last sub also inaugurated the deployment of the Polaris A-3P missile with the US fleet.

Since their deployment in the early 1960s, the *Lafayette* submarines have operated on an almost continuous basis with the Atlantic fleet. Over the years several improvements have been done to keep these subs effective starting with the first overhaul, from November of 1968 to August 1970, during which all the subs were rearmed with the Polaris A-3P missile with the exception of the *Lafayette*, the *Alexander Hamilton*, and the *Andrew Jackson*.

During their second overhaul period, June 1975 to September 1978, all nine subs were then armed with the Poseidon C-3 missile system.

Prior to 11 February 1988, the *Nathan Hale* was decommissioned. This leaves only eight *Lafayette* class submarines in service.

James Madison Class (627-636)

Six months after President Kennedy accelerated the *Lafayette* program, on 19 July 1961 he authorized the construction of 10 improved *Lafayette* subs designated *James Madison* class. Construction of the first sub, the *Daniel Boone*, began on 6 February 1962 and it was christened on 22 June 1963.[1] The sub was commissioned on 23 April 1964 and on 25 May the *Daniel Boone* became the first US FBM submarine to visit Hawaii. Three months later the *Daniel Boone* was permanently assigned to the Pacific and on 25 December it left Apra Harbor, Guam on its first deterrent patrol.

Four of the *James Madison* class subs (*Daniel Boone*, *Tecumseh*, *Ulysses S Grant*, and *Stonewall Jackson*) were initially deployed to the Pacific while the rest were based in the Atlantic. With the deployment of the Poseidon missiles in March of 1971 the situation changed, the *Lafayette* subs deployed to the Pacific were transferred to the Atlantic fleet prior to their conversion. Poseidon deployment with this class was completed in April of 1972.

Eight years after the Poseidon conversion was completed on 6 September 1980 the USS *Daniel Boone* became the first *Madison* class submarine to go to sea armed with the Trident I missile. It was followed two months later by the *Stonewall Jackson*, on 15 November, and then by the *John C Calhoun* on 24 November. After this the *James Madison*, the *Von Steuben*, and the *Casimir Pulaski* were also rearmed during their second overhauls. Trident deployment to this class was completed 3 June 1983. Following

Lafayette **Class USS** *Woodrow Wilson*

Trident conversion these subs were re-based to King Bay Georgia (previously these subs were at Rota Spain).

As of March 1 1987 the submarines *Sam Rayburn* (SSBN-635) and the *Nathanael Greene* (SSBN-636) have been decommissioned.

Benjamin Franklin Class (640 – 659)

Sometime after he authorized the *James Madison* class, President Kennedy authorized the construction of six more subs, with additional authorization to procure, for six additional subs, those items which would require a long lead-time for delivery. Called the *Benjamin Franklin* class, these subs were the most quiet of all *Lafayette* types as well as the heaviest.

Construction of the first *Benjamin Franklin* class submarine, the

Benjamin Franklin Class USS Francis Scott Key

Simon Bolivar, began on 17 April 1963. It was launched a year later on 22 August 1964 but was not commissioned until 29 October 1965, seven days after the *Benjamin Franklin*. The *Simon Bolivar* then went on its first deterrent patrol in the Atlantic on 27 April 1966 while on 7 May the *Benjamin Franklin* joined the Pacific fleet. Deployment of this class was completed on 3 October 1967 when the USS *Will Rogers* departed Charleston, South Carolina for its first War patrol.

The first missile the *Franklin* class subs were deployed with was the Polaris A-3 missile. Deployment of the Poseidon with these subs then began in November of 1972 and was completed in September of 1974. Five years later, on 20 October 1979, the Trident I missile became operational on the *Franklin* class sub the USS *Francis Scott Key*. Deployment of this missile was completed on 20 July 1982 after the rearming of the *Francis Scott Key*, the *Henry L Stimson*, the *Mariano G Vallejo*, the *Benjamin Franklin*, the *Simon Bolivar* and the *George Bancroft*.

As of 1988, all of the *Benjamin Franklin* class of submarines are still in service with the Atlantic fleet.

Phaseout

As presently planned, the remaining 28 *Lafayette* class submarines are to be gradually replaced by the new *Ohio* class until the year 1990 when block withdrawal will begin. Removal of the submarines following 1990 is necessary since the subs were not designed to operate for more than 30 years (originally they were designed for 20 to 25 year life spans but studies done in the late 1970s indicated that the lifespan could be extended to 30). Beyond this point the reliability of these submarines would be questionable.

[1] For some unexplained reason the *James Madison* was christened on 15 March 1963, prior to the *Daniel Boone*, but was not commissioned until 28 June 1964 after both the *Daniel Boone* and the *Tecumseh*.

USS Lafayette

Ohio Class

DIMENSIONS

Length: 560 ft   Width: 42 ft
Height: 35.5 ft   Weight: 16,600 tons surfaced
                                         18,750 tons submerged

ARMAMENT 24 launch tubes for Trident missiles;
                four 21 inch torpedo tubes

SPEED Classified

POWERPLANT Single S8G pressurized water nuclear reactor

CREW COMPLEMENT 16 officers, 139 enlisted

CONTRACTOR General Dynamics Electric Boat Division

NAMES OF SUBMARINES
(726) *Ohio*, (727) *Michigan*, (728) *Florida*, (729) *Georgia*,
(730) *Henry M Jackson*,[1] (713) *Alabama*, (732) *Alaska*, (733)
Nevada, (734) *Tennessee*. Four additional subs have been
authorized

The *Ohio* class, more commonly called the Trident
submarines, are the largest ballistic missile submarines ever
deployed by the United States. This class of submarines will
be the main type of FBM in the US Navy by the year 2000.

Following the launch of the last *Lafayette* type submarine, on 1
November 1966, Secretary of Defense Robert S McNamara began
a comprehensive study to determine what capabilities the next
generation of Fleet Ballistic Missile submarines would need. This
study was concluded in August of 1967 following which, on 1
February 1968 advanced development began on an Undersea Long
Range Missile System to replace the planned Poseidon system of
subs and missiles in the late 1970s to early 1980s. Three years later
the Electric Boat Division of General Dynamics was issued the
contract to design the next generation of US ballistic missile
submarine.

The year after Electric Boat won the design contract, on 16 May
1972, the entire ULMS program was renamed Trident. Funding for
the first of these Trident subs was authorized on 15 November 1973
and on 25 July 1974 the Navy awarded the General Electric boat
yards the contract for construction of the USS *Ohio*. Construction
began that same year but an exact date is unknown because this
class of submarine is made using a large number of prefabricated
components which are assembled at the General Electric boat yard.

USS *Ohio*

Ohio* Class USS *Michigan

Regardless of this, on 21 April 1978, the *Ohio* was rolled out of the assembly building for final construction and launch.

Following rollout in December of 1978 it was discovered that the *Ohio's* nuclear reactor turbines were defective. The submarine's launching was therefore delayed until 11 April 1979 to allow for replacement of these units. Sea trials began soon afterward and after two years of testing on 28 October 1981 the submarine was delivered to the US Navy. The *Ohio* was then commissioned on 11 November 1981.

With the *Ohio* now commissioned final demonstration and shakedown could begin, and on 13 March 1982, the submarine's Gold crew launched its first Trident I missile. After five months, on 25 August, the *Ohio* sailed into Puget Sound in the state of Washington. Several days later it completed strategic outload at Bangor and entered deployed status. Initial Operational Capability was achieved on 1 October when the *Ohio* went on its first deterrent patrol.

With the deployment of the *Ohio*, a major improvement occurred in the capability and reliability of the Navy's Fleet Ballistic Missile force. Because of the submarine's greater speed, maneuverability, and lower submerged noise levels it is significantly less vulnerable to anti-submarine weapons compared to the earlier *Lafayette*. Also, with a 9 year life span on each reactor fuel core, and easier maintenance, the submarines spend less time in the yard, increasing the amount of time they are at sea (note the earlier subs had spent up to two years in dock undergoing overhaul). Longer patrol periods were also achieved because of more extensive internal crew facilities (the ship has two libraries and music headphones for every bunk).

In addition to these performance improvements, the *Ohio* subs are, in many ways, more cost effective than the earlier subs. Because each *Ohio* class sub carries 24 missiles compared to the earlier submarine's 16 missiles the Navy can replace all 31 *Lafayette* subs with with just 20 new *Ohios*. This reduction in the number of subs also means a reduction in the number of spare parts

procured to keep the subs operational over their planned 30 year service life. An additional savings will come from the fact that with the new longer range Trident missiles these subs can be based in the United States making the operation of the overseas bases unnecessary. Shutting down the overseas bases is also a good security and a good political move.

As of 11 February 1988, a total of eight *Ohio* class submarines are in service with the ninth in construction. When this ninth submarine, the USS *Tennessee*, is deployed in late 1989 it will be the first sub to carry the new Trident II D-5 missile system. This submarine will also be the first *Ohio* class submarine to be based on the east coast of the United States at the new Trident bases at Kings Bay, Georgia (all previous subs are based at Bangor, Puget Sound, Washington.) All follow on *Ohio* class subs will be armed with this new missile as will be the previous subs armed with the Trident I.

[1] Originally this submarine was named *Rhode Island* but following the death of Senator Henry M Jackson, the sub was renamed after him on 27 September 1983.

Ethan Allen Class

DIMENSIONS
Length: 410 ft   Width: 33 ft
Height: 32 ft   Weight: 6900 tons surfaced
                                          7880 tons submerged

ARMAMENT 16 air ejection tubes for Polaris missiles; four 21 inch torpedo tubes

SPEED 20 knots on the surface, 30 knots submerged

POWERPLANT Single S5W pressurized water nuclear reactor

CREW COMPLEMENT 15 officers, 130 enlisted

NAMES OF SUBMARINES
(608) *Ethan Allen*, (609) *Sam Houston*, (610) *Thomas A Edison*, (611) *John Marshall*, (618) *Thomas Jefferson*

The *Ethan Allen* class were the first US submarines designed, from the keel up, to launch ballistic missiles. Though not as well designed as the later *Lafayettes* these subs were the first deep diving US Feet Ballistic Missile Subs.

When development of the Polaris missile system began in December of 1957 the plan was to construct five specially designed subs to carry and launch the planned 1800 mile range missile. Because the program was accelerated, on 9 December 1957 these special subs would have to take a back seat to the five quick construction *George Washington* class subs begun in January of 1958 (later in the year funding for the first four of these specially designed subs was actually withheld on 22 August 1958.) At the end of the year, on 23 December 1958. President Eisenhower changed his mind and authorized the first true USS FBM submarine, the USS *Ethan Allen*.

Construction of the *Ethan Allen* began soon after authorization was given and on 22 November 1960 it was launched from the General Electric Boat yards. Following initial sea trials on 23

Ohio Class USS *Nevada*

October 1961, it launched its first 1800 mile range Polaris A-2 missile (the missile it was originally designed to carry). Seven months later, the *Ethan Allen* was at the Pacific nuclear testing range, as part of Joint Task Force 8, to launch the first Polaris missile with a live nuclear warhead. As a result of this test, on 6 May 1962, not only was the *Ethan Allen* the only US FBM ever to launch a nuclear armed missile, it would become the only member of the *Ethan Allen* class to both carry and launch the Polaris A-1 missile. Following this test the *Ethan Allen* returned to the East Coast where after being rearmed with the Polaris A-2, on 26 June 1962, it went on its first operational patrol.

Unlike the earlier *George Washington* class the *Ethan Allen* subs were much larger and better designed internally. They were also quieter when submerged, and because of their modified Permit submarine design they could dive to much greater depths making them less vulnerable to anti-submarine systems.

Within six months of the *Ethan Allen's* (SSBN-608) initial deployment, a total of four *Ethan Allen* class subs were at sea in the North Atlantic. The following year, on 14 April 1963, the USS *Sam Houston* (SSBN-609) sailed into Izmir, Turkey as the first Polaris submarine assigned to the Mediterranean (three *Ethan Allen* class subs were deployed to the Mediterranean.) The last *Ethan Allen* class submarine, the *Thomas Jefferson*, went to sea on 28 October, ending construction of this class.

The *Ethan Allen* class subs would operate in the Atlantic and Mediterranean for the remainder of the 1960s. With the coming of the 1970s, and the deployment of the Poseidon missile, they were progressively transferred to the Pacific fleet based at Guam (Polaris phased out of Atlantic 10 August 1973). During this same period, in October of 1972, the *Ethan Allen* began its second overhaul during which it was rearmed with the Polaris A-3T missile. The first patrol with this missile began on 29 August 1974 (Polaris A-2 retired on 9 June 1974 with the return of the *John Marshall* (SSBN-611).

For several years after the Polaris A-3 refit, the *Ethan Allen* class made deterrent patrols in the North Pacific. By 1980, however, these subs were reaching their maximum life span on both their structure and their nuclear reactors. Thus in 1981 all five of these subs were removed from duty as FBMs. They had their missile tubes decommissioned, and were then converted into attack subs. Two years later on 1 December 1963, the *Thomas A Edison* was decommissioned leaving only four of these subs in service. By early 1987 the *Ethan Allen* was also reported to have been decommissioned leaving only three of these subs operational.

George Washington Class

DIMENSIONS
 Length: 381.7 ft   Width: 33 ft
 Height: 29 ft   Weight: 6000 tons surfaced
                                             6700 tons submerged

ARMAMENT 16 steam ejection tubes for Polaris missiles;
             six 21 inch torpedo tubes

SPEED 20 knots on the surface, 30 knots submerged

POWERPLANT Single S5W pressurized water nuclear reactor

CREW COMPLEMENT 12 officers, 127 enlisted

NAMES OF SUBMARINES
 (598) *George Washington*, (599) *Patrick Henry*,
 (600) *Theodore Roosevelt*, (601) *Robert E Lee*,
 (602) *Abraham Lincoln*

USS *Ethan Allen*

The *George Washington* class were the United States first ballistic missile submarines. The prototypes for today's Fleet Ballistic Missile subs, they were crudely constructed and are no longer in service.

On 22 October 1957, one year after development of the Polaris missile system began, the Secretary of the Navy proposed an acceleration of the Fleet Ballistic Missile program to achieve a 1300 mile range missile system by December of 1959. Though such an acceleration was desirable, it required not only the development of the shorter range Polaris A-1 missile but also the quick construction of a ballistic missile submarine using components slated for other subs. The proposal was accepted by the Secretary of Defense on 9 December 1957, and on 31 December, the Navy ordered that the attack sub, *Scorpion*, be completed as a ballistic missile submarine. The following month the *Scorpion* was cut in half and a 130 foot launch tube section was inserted, construction was completed the next year. Following the 9 June 1959 launch of the submarine, on 30 December 1959, the submarine was commissioned as the USS *George Washington*.

All the *George Washington* class of subs were built using components originally planned for a *Skipjack* class attack submarine (none however as far along as the *Scorpion*). Though this method of construction did allow these subs to be operational at least one year before the originally planned *Ethan Allen* class, it also left them depth limited and thus more vulnerable to Soviet anti-submarine systems.

Following commission, the *George Washington* launched its first Polaris A-1 missile on 20 July 1960. Four months later it left Charleston, SC on 15 November on the nation's first war patrol. Sixty-seven days later she returned to New London, Connecticut, on 21 January 1961, for a change of crew that involved the submarine tender, the *Proteus*. Two months later the *Proteus* would do the same thing for the submarine *Patrick Henry* but this time at the recently opened base at Holy Loch, Scotland. At this new base the *George Washington* class subs could now do general refurbishment and crew changes without having to leave their launching zones in the North sea for an extended period of time. As a result of this, after the last sub went to sea in August of 1961, the Navy had a force of 80 Polaris missiles on continuous alert.

The *George Washington* class subs operated out of Holy Loch with Polaris A-1 for a total of four years. Then, on 2 June 1964, the USS *George Washington* (SSBN-598) returned to the General Electric boat yards for its first scheduled overhaul (once every five years). During this overhaul the SSBN-598 would also be rearmed with the new Polaris A-3 missile, giving this sub the ability to attack targets over a distance of 2800 miles. While this overhaul was underway the last *George Washington* class subs also went in for overhaul/conversion. With the return of the USS *Abraham Lincoln* to the states on 14 October 1965, the Polaris A-1 was retired from the fleet. Four months later on 2 February 1966, the USS *George Washington* completed its overhaul and began its first Polaris A-3 patrol on 30 June.

By November of 1967, all five of the *George Washington* class subs had completed their Polaris A-3 rearming and had returned to the Atlantic fleet. These subs remained there until after their second overhaul from June of 1972 to August 1974, when they were again rearmed with the improved Polaris A-3T missiles. When these submarines were returned to service they were deployed with the Pacific Fleet Ballistic Missile force out of Guam (replacement of the Polaris A-3 with the Poseidon in the Atlantic was completed on 10 August 1973, when the USS *Robert E Lee* was transferred to the Pacific). They remained until late 1980 when the Navy began retiring the whole class from service.

Withdrawal of the *George Washington* class officially began on 28 February 1981 with the decommissioning of the *Theodore Roosevelt* and the *Abraham Lincoln*. Later in the year, the other three submarines of the class were converted into attack submarines following the removal of their missiles. Two years later on 1 December 1983, the *Robert E Lee* was decommissioned, leaving only the *George Washington* and the *Patrick Henry* in service. In the next few years these two subs will also be decommissioned.

In closing, it is necessary to note that the *George Washington* class of submarines' use of equipment originally intended for *Skipjack* class attack subs, may have a bearing on future FBM designs. Because of the high cost of the new *Ohio* class submarines, the slow rate at which they are deployed, as well as Congressional pressure for a force of smaller size ballistic missile subs, in the future the Navy may return to this method of construction for its next generation of Fleet Ballistic Missile Submarines.

USS *George Washington*

George Washington* Class USS *Robert E Lee

Air-Launched Cruise Missiles

Hound Dog (AGM-28)

SPECIFICATIONS

Length: 42 ft 6 in	Span: 12 ft
Diameter: 28 in	Weight: 10,000 lb

PERFORMANCE

Speed: Mach 2+	Ceiling: 55,000 ft
Range: 700 mi	

POWERPLANT One Pratt & Whitney J-52 turbojet
       Max Thrust: 7500 lb

GUIDANCE Inertial system developed by North American
       Aviation Autonetics Division

WARHEAD Single W-28 thermonuclear warhead (information
       on yield has varied from 4 megatons to 500 kilo-
       tons)

CONTRACTOR North American Aviation

NUMBER OF MISSILES 722 known constructed
                            600 known to have been deployed

The Hound Dog was the first cruise type weapon ever deployed on a US bomber. Originally intended as an interim weapon with a three year life span, this missile would eventually serve for 15 years as the US Air Force primary strategic bomber weapon.

Even before the first B-52s were delivered, the Air Force realized in early 1956 that recent developments in supersonic fighters and surface to air missiles would soon make this new bomber ineffective as a strategic weapon. To remedy this situation, on 15 March 1956, USAF headquarters issued General Operational Requirement (GOR) 148 for an air-to-surface missile to be carried by the B-52. By early 1957, the project was known as 'Weapon System 131' and, following an intense design competition, on 21 August 1957, the Missile Development Division of North American

Aviation was awarded the development contract for GAM-77 Hound Dog.

One of the major reasons that the North American proposal was accepted, was that the Hound Dog did not require the development of any new equipment or technology. The missile's airframe and guidance system came directly from North American's earlier Navaho intercontinental cruise missile program. Its powerplant was also already proven, having been developed by Pratt & Whitney for use in a manned fighter.

Development of the Hound Dog was one of the fastest such projects in recent history. Immediately following the issuing of the production contract in November of 1958, drop testing of dummy Hound Dog missiles began. Five months later, on 23 April 1959, the first powered flight occurred over the Atlantic Missile Range. The first guided flight then occurred in October and, in formal ceremonies, on 21 December 1959, the Air Force accepted the first production missile. The first SAC launch occurred three months later on 1 March 1960 and on 12 April, the first full scale demonstration occurred, when a B-52G successfully launched a Hound Dog after completing a 13 hour non stop flight over the North Pole. A total of three years had elapsed from initial contract to deployment.

The deployment of the Hound Dog, or GAM-77 as it was then designated, marked a major improvement in the penetration capability of the B-52 bomber. With this missile, the B-52 could attack heavily defended strategic targets while remaining outside of the targets, terminal air defense system. The B-52 could also use the Hound Dog to disrupt enemy defenses by using it to destroy enemy radar and SAM sites along the bombers penetration route, or by launching it against a secondary target in order to divert enemy fighters. It was nuclear-armed, so that fighters had to to stop it before it reached its target. These particular improvements were limited in that the B-52 could only carry two Hound Dogs.

Along with the penetration improvements, the Hound Dog also improved the B-52's guidance system. From the moment the B-52 takes off, the inertial guidance systems in the two Hound Dogs (and the two Kollsman star trackers mounted in the wing pylons), are actively following the bomber's course. Thus, if at any time in the flight the navigator wishes to check position information supplied by the bomber's navigational unit, he could interrogate the missiles for comparison data. It should also be noted that, if the bomber's navigational system were to fail in flight, the B-52 could still continue to its target, using the Hound Dog's guidance system.

The final improvement to come to the B-52 from the Hound Dog was that, during takeoffs and emergencies, the pilot of the

B-52 could add thrust to the aircraft by turning on the Hound Dogs' engines. Since the Hound Dog was directly linked to the B-52's fuel tanks by its mount, and since both missile and bomber used the same fuel, following their use, the missile's fuel tank could be replenished by simply transferring fuel from the bomber. This particular improvement was rarely used for takeoffs, since the Hound Dog was slung so low on the B-52 that its engine was highly susceptible to ingesting any debris lying on the runway, and thus could be damaged.

The Hound Dog was an extremely sophisticated weapon for its time, capable of penetrating the strongest air defenses. It could follow a number of possible flight patterns, making it very hard to track and destroy. It also could be programmed to deceive enemy defenses by heading for a false target before abruptly making a turn, or dog leg, and speeding toward its real target.

During operational testing, some deficiencies showed up in the Hound Dog's guidance. To overcome these problems, development began on an improved model incorporating a radar altimeter and the improved Kollsman KS-140 star tracker in place of the original KS-120. Called the GAM-77A, this new model was first tested on 20 June 1961, and the first production missile was delivered to Beale AFB on 25 August 1961. Initial operational capability was then achieved on 2 September 1961 and the first combat evaluation launch occurred on 9 January 1962.

Originally, the plan was for the Hound Dog to serve as an interim weapon pending the deployment of the Skybolt air-launched ballistic missile. On 31 December 1962, the Department of Defense cancelled the Skybolt, forcing the service life of the Hound Dog to be extended almost indefinitely. The Skybolt cancellation also meant the B-52H would now be equipped with Hound Dogs, bringing the number of B-52s so armed up from 193 to 295. This action resulted in more missiles on ready alert, and an increased number of training flights, creating a strain on the stockpile of spare parts.

Production of the Hound Dog was completed on 28 March 1963 with the delivery of the 722nd missile. Two months later, the last Hound Dog unit became combat ready on 24 May 1963.

On 27 June 1963, the Hound Dog was redesignated as part of a joint Air Force, Army and Navy program to develop a unified designation system. As a result of this, the GAM-77 and GAM-77A became the AGM-28A and the AGM-28B respectively.

As the years passed, the Hound Dog was put through various tests and studies to ascertain its limitations. One of these studies was Operation Net Profit, in which the 320th Bomber Wing, on 1 September 1963, began testing the feasibility of permanently mating the Hound Dog to the B-52. Another of these tests was operation Big Litter, in which crews from the 5th Bomber Wing at Travis AFB tested the missile under prolonged flight conditions by flying non-stop for 31 hours, from 19–20 February 1963. In 1971, the Hound Dog was also tested with a TERCOM guidance system and, in 1973, under the title Hound Dog II, a special anti-radiation seeker head was tested. None of these tests result in any changes to the missile.

With the deployment of the SRAMs in 1972, the Air Force began progressively withdrawing the Hound Dog from service. Officially, however the reason given for this withdrawal was that the mounting of the Hound Dog on the B-52, increased aerodynamic drag by such an extent that the range of the aircraft was significantly reduced. The logic of this statement disappears when it is noted that the SRAMs were also mounted externally on the B-52 producing just as much drag. The last Hound Dog operational launch occurred on 24 July 1973, and on 30 June 1975, the last missile was removed from combat alert.

Though they had been withdrawn from combat alert, for two years, 250 Hound Dogs were kept in the SAC inventory as a reserve force. In early 1978, this retention was discontinued, and on 15 June 1978, the last Hound Dog was demilitarized and removed from the stockpile.

Hound Dog air-to-surface missile

B-52 Stratofortress with two Hound Dog missiles

Hound Dog missile launch from B-52

ALCM (AGM-86B)

SPECIFICATIONS
Length: 20 ft 9 in   Span: 12 ft
Diameter: 2 ft .5in   Height: 4 ft
Weight: 2825 lb

PERFORMANCE
Speed: 500 mph   Flight alt: 100 to 50 ft
Range: 1550 mi   CEP: 300 ft

POWERPLANT Single Williams Int. F-107-WR-100 turbofan
          engine Max Thrust: 600 lb

GUIDANCE Inertial with Terrain Contour Matching system,
          TERCOM, by McDonnell Douglas

WARHEAD Single W-80-1 thermonuclear warhead of 200
         kiloton yield

CONTRACTOR Boeing Aerospace Company

NUMBER OF MISSILES 1739 as of 1984

The ALCM is the newest weapon to be carried by the B-52 bomber. With this weapon, the B-52 should remain effective as a strategic aircraft until the early 1990s.

Development of the Air Launched Cruise Missile or ALCM began on 19 January 1968, when the Strategic Air Command submitted a Required Operational Capability to US Air Force Headquarters for an improved decoy missile to replace the earlier Quail. Called the Subsonic Cruise Aircraft Decoy, or SCAD,[1] it was intended to electronically simulate the radar signature of either a B-52, or the then planned B-1A, and divert enemy fighters or surface-to-air missiles away from the aircraft. Initial research funding for the missile was approved by Congress in 1969 and, on 15 July 1970, full scale development was approved by Deputy Secretary of Defense David Packard.

Though full scale development of the SCAD had been approved by the DOD, it had not been approved by Congress. Thus, on 12–14 December 1970 the funding request to start full scale development in Fiscal Year 1971 was refused. Two years later, Congress changed its mind, and allowed the Air Force, in February of 1972, to begin issuing requests for proposals to major contractors. Five months later, Boeing Aircraft was issued the $66.5 million development contract for the SCAD.

Following the start of engineering work, the cost of the SCAD's electronic systems — the devices that created the B-52 simulation — rose extensively. As a result of this, in early 1973 Congress withheld almost half of that year's funding request for use in a study of possible low cost alternatives. This study, plus the Navy's own submarine-launched cruise missile program, would soon reveal that by giving the SCAD nuclear armament, it wasn't necessary for the missile to have expensive electronic systems to attract enemy fighters or SAMs. Nuclear armed, the SCAD would in fact become more important than its launching bomber. As a result of this, on 30 June, Deputy Secretary of Defense William P Clements terminated engineering development of the SCAD and reoriented

the program towards a technology program. At the same time, he directed the Navy to continue development of its two prototype cruise missiles with some air-launched capability.

Though the SCAD had been cancelled, on 20 July 1973, the head of the DOD's Defense Research and Engineering Agency directed the Air Force to begin development of a long range Air Launched Cruise Missile based on the earlier SCAD vehicle design. In response to this, the Air Force again issued RFPs for the new missile and, in September of 1974, Boeing was awarded the contract for Advanced Development of the AGM-86 Air Launched Cruise Missile (ALCM).

The first model of the ALCM to be developed was the AGM-86A. Though essentially a SCAD stripped of all its electronics and equipped with a nuclear warhead, this 14 foot long missile had over seven times the range of the operational Short Range Attack Missile, and three times the accuracy. Also, because it was the same size as the SRAM, it could be carried on the same pylon mounts, as well as the rotary launcher, allowing a single B-52 to carry 20 of them plus four Mk-28 free-fall bombs. A B-1A could carry up to 38 AGM-86As. Drop testing of dummy AGM-86As from the SRAM rotary launcher began on 25 June 1975 and, on 7 November the first flight test vehicle (FTM-1) was rolled out. The first of six powered flights was then completed on 5 March 1976, with the first fully guided flight occurring on 9 September.[2] By November of 1976, testing of this missile had been completed and, on 14 January the Deputy Secretary of Defense directed the Air Force to begin full scale production of the ALCM AGM-86A.

During development of the AGM-86A the Air Force issued a new longer range requirement. To meet this new requirement, Boeing studied two different methods: a low drag external fuel tank that could be mounted to the underbelly of the AGM-86A, and a new lengthened missile called the Extended Range Vehicle (ERV). The external fuel tank approach had its advantages in that it gave the AGM-86A a range of 1100 miles, while allowing it to be carried on the standard external SRAM mounts used by the B-52 and B-1; it did, however, make the AGM-86A too wide to fit on the SRAM rotary launcher. The ALCM ERV, though it met the 1500 mile range requirement, made the weapon too long to fit on the external SRAM mounts as well as the rotary launcher (it was so long it couldn't even fit in the B-1A bomb bays). As a result of this, the Air Force planned to initially deploy the AGM-86A and then later, as the need required, deploy the external fuel tank and or the ERV: Jimmy Carter however would change this.

Carter came to the presidency stating that too much money was being wasted by the military. Thus, in January of 1977, he created the Joint Cruise Missiles Project in order to 'realize the cost savings inherent in common component development and testing, resource sharing and quantity manufacturing in the development of the Tomahawk and ALCM missiles.' Now, both Tomahawk and ALCM had been designed from the beginning to have interchangeable guidance and propulsions systems, just in case one service failed in development, but now only Air Force propulsion systems and the Navy TERCOM guidance system would be completed. Furthermore, to achieve maximum commonalty in performance, on 15 May 1977, Secretary of Defense Harold Brown informed the Senate Appropriations Committee that 'because of a significant advantage in cost to deliver weapons against suitable targets'[3] in the 1980s, the Air Force had been directed to develop the Extended Range Vehicle, or AGM-85B, before the AGM-86A. This set the stage for the 30 September announcement that the AGM-86B and the General Dynamics Tomahawk sea-launched cruise missile would take part in a competitive 'fly-off' to determine which missile would be produced for the Air Force. As a result of all this, now not only had production of the ALCM been delayed until

1980, it was no longer assured that the AGM-86 would be produced.

The first AGM-86B extended range missile was rolled out of the Boeing Development Center on 26 February 1979. The competitive fly-off then began on 1 July, with the first flight of the AGM-86B occurring on 3 August. A total of 10 flights were completed (six successful, one partial and three failures) and, on 22 January 1980, the Boeing segment of the fly-off was completed. Two months later, on 25 March, the Secretary of the Air Force announced that the AGM-86B had won the competition.

On 18 April 1980, Boeing broke ground on a new facility totally dedicated to the construction of the ALCM. The production contract was then awarded on 1 May and on 12 June a new flight testing program began to fully evaluate the AGM-86B. The first two training missiles were then delivered to Griffiss AFB on 11 January 1981 and, on 23 April SAC received its first operational ALCM. The first launch from a B-52 equipped with the Offensive Avionic System (OAS) was on 25 July. On 15 August 1981, Boeing delivered the first OAS modified B-52 to Griffiss AFB.

With the delivery of the first OAS B-52, training of B-52 crews could begin and, on 15 September 1981, the first nine hour flight with an ALCM was completed. Developmental testing of the ALCM was then completed on 27 January 1982, when an ALCM coated with approximately three-quarters of an inch of ice was successfully fired against a simulated target over the Utah test range. The first of 10 operational test launches then occurred on 21 September 1982 and on 16 December an Initial Operational

Capability of 16 OAS B-52Gs was achieved at Griffiss AFB (these B-52s only carried 12 ALCMs on their underwing pylons).

In the first two years after Griffiss, ALCMs would be deployed on B-52s at Wurtsmith, Grand Forks AFB, Fairchild and Blytheville — for a 1987 total of 98 OAS B-52Gs and 34 OAS B-52Hs. Like the B-52Gs at Griffiss, these bombers only carry ALCMs on their wing Pylons, leaving their bomb bays free to carry SRAMs and free-fall bombs. In the next few years, the B-52Hs are to be modified further to incorporated the new Common Strategic Rotary Launcher. This new launcher will allow the B-52H to carry either eight ALCMs, eight SRAMs, eight bombs, or a mix of all three in its bomb bays. Flight testing of this new launcher began on 10 May 1986, when a B-52H from Carswell AFB carried a full complement of ALCMs — 12 external and eight internal — in a flight to Edwards AFB.

While production of the AGM-86B was underway, in April of 1983, the decision was made to end procurement of the ALCM at 1739 missiles and begin development of a new Advanced Cruise Missile. The last AGM-86B was delivered on 7 October 1986.

At present the ALCM is to remain in service until the mid-1990s, when it will be completely replaced by the ACM.

[1] When it was noted that the SCAD could be armed with a nuclear warhead, the name became confused to read Subsonic Cruise Armed Decoy.
[2] The missile successfully negotiated 4 TERCOM mapped areas, taking an update in each area.
[3] Suitable targets in this case means those targets that do not have a terminal air defense system. The ALCM is more vulnerable to such defenses than the earlier SRAM.

ALCM launch from bomb bay of B-52

ALCM

ALCMs on B-52 wing pylon

Air- and Ground-Launched Short Range Missiles (ALM) (GLM)

BOAR

SPECIFICATIONS

Length: 15 ft

Weight: 2000 lb
Diameter: 2 ft 6.5 in

PERFORMANCE
Speed: unknown, but probably subsonic
Range: 7.5 mi (at 40,000 ft)

PROPULSION Double base solid fuel rocket motor developed
by the Naval Weapons Center
China Lake, California

GUIDANCE Unguided; ballistic flight pattern

WARHEAD Single W-7 warhead of 20 kiloton yield

CONTRACTOR Naval Weapons Center
China Lake, California

LAUNCHING AIRCRAFT
A-1 Skyraiders and A-3 Skywarriors

The BOAR was the first nuclear tipped air-to-surface rocket ever deployed by the United States. For eight years this missile gave Navy attack aircraft the ability to attack enemy ships at standoff range.

With the detonation of the Soviet Union's first nuclear device on 29 August 1949, the US government changed its nuclear policies and gave its approval for the development of the nation's first tactical nuclear weapons. This change was extremely important to the Navy, for it meant the development of the Mk-8 penetration bomb, a weapon the service had requested for use against hardened land based Naval facilities such as underground submarine pens. At the same time, this decision put the Navy on the spot, because it now had to determine a means of delivering a tactical nuclear device against ships at sea. This was no easy task, since the development of fire directing radar had made high altitude bombing out of the question, and low level bombing did not give the aircraft enough time to escape before the bomb detonated.

The solution to the Navy's problem was found in a little known weapon called the 'Bat.' During the last few months of the war, this little radar-guided glider bomb had taken an extremely heavy toll on Japanese ships. More importantly, the Bat did this while allowing its launching aircraft to remain outside of the ship's air defense system — an example being the sinking of a Japanese destroyer at a range of 20 miles. It was this standoff capability that the Navy needed to successfully deliver nuclear weapons against ships while not subjecting its manned aircraft to either enemy fire or the bomb's highly destructive blast.

Taking into consideration the need to attack the targets with minimum warning, and the need to fill this weapons gap within the shortest possible period of time, the Navy concluded that the best design for this new weapon was a rocket-assisted bomb that was launched using the low altitude lofting technique.[1] With this conclusion, and the establishing of the military requirement by the Joint Chiefs, in the fall of 1952, the Navy Bureau of Ordnance assigned the Naval Weapons Center at China Lake, California the responsibility for the development and testing of the 30.5 inch Rocket, Mk-1, Mod-0 otherwise known as the Bureau of Ordnance Atomic Rocket-BOAR. (China Lake calls this weapon the Bombardment Aircraft Rocket.)

Development of the BOAR was very quick with field testing and evaluation having begun by June of 1953. BOAR was then released for production in 1955 and the first rounds were delivered to the Fleet in 1956.

Though BOAR had been designed as an interim weapon with a three year service life, it would remain in service over twice as long. As a result of this extended period, several of the weapon's components required redesigning or improvement in order to maintain the BOAR's effectiveness. The rocket's double based solid fuel also underwent heavy monitoring for any signs of propellant degradation. This extensive work may explain why the last BOAR was removed from the stockpile in 1963, the year before the first nuclear-capable Bullpup Bs were deployed.

An example of the BOAR known to exist by the author is on display at the National Atomic Museum in Albuquerque, New Mexico.

Rascal (GAM-63)

SPECIFICATIONS

Length: 31 ft 11.5 in   Span: 16 ft 8.25 in
Diameter: 4 ft   Weight: 13,500 lb ·

PERFORMANCE

Speed: Mach 1.5   CEP: 3000 ft radio
Range: 113 mi   1500 ft inertial

PROPULSION One Bell liquid fuel rocket engine with three
          combustion chambers each producing 4000 lb of
          thrust. Propellants: red fuming nitric acid and
          alcohol

GUIDANCE Initial models used radio command guidance; later
         models used inertial

WARHEAD Single megaton class nuclear warhead; number not
        identified

CONTRACTOR Bell Aircraft Corporation

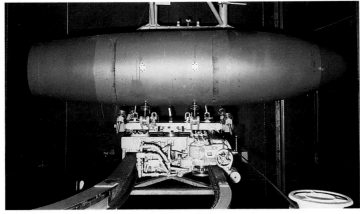

BOAR ALM

The Rascal was the first strategic missile to be deployed on US aircraft. Its purpose was to give old and obsolete bombers the ability to effectively attack heavily defended targets.

The idea of launching strategic missiles from bombers seems to have had its start during World War II. Following the D-Day invasion, the German Luftwaffe, concerned that it would soon lose its V-1 sites in France, began looking for an alternative means of striking targets in Great Britain. Manned aircraft were quickly ruled out because of the British fighters, and moving the V-1 launch sites into Germany was also out of the question because the V-1's range was limited to only 160 miles — hence it had to be launched in France. It was because of this situation that, in the summer of 1944, the Luftwaffe began modifying its obsolete Heinkel bombers to launch V-1s. Following the loss of the ground sites in August of 1944, on 1 September 1944, the first Heinkel bomber launching of a V-1 'buzz bomb' against England occurred. By 13 December 1944, a total of 865 V-1s had been thus launched.

Following the war, the US Army Air Force began several studies of the German bomber/missile combination to see if the combination could make old and obsolete US bombers militarily effective again. Using B-17s and an American version of the V-1 called a JB-2, several successful tests were achieved, proving the idea as sound. Thus, on 16 July 1945, the US Army Air Force published the first US military requirement for an air-to-surface missile. Nine months later, on 1 April 1946, Bell Aircraft was issued a letter contract for a one year study into the feasibility of a subsonic air-to-surface missile. This contract marks the beginning of the Rascal program.

Bell Aircraft was not the only company the Air Force approached with this project: McDonnell Aircraft was asked to study the feasibility of a supersonic missile and Goodyear was to study both types. When the one year study period was over, in May of 1947, the McDonnell and Goodyear studies were terminated, and Bell was issued a second contract to develop a supersonic missile capable of being carried by the B-29 bomber. This second contract also gave the program the designation Project MX-776.

With the second contract, Bell immediately went to work, and on 28 April 1949 testing began on a special test missile called the Shrike. Though smaller than the planned Rascal, and having a range of only 50 miles, this missile was instrumental in the testing of not only the Rascal's aerodynamic design, but its

Rascal ALM

radio control system, its rocket engines and even its bomber/ launcher system. A total of 22 Shrike missiles were tested from 28 April 1949 to 23 January 1953. Though only eight of the flights were successful, it was considered a very successful program. Testing of the full size Rascal then began in the summer of 1952, with the first powered flight occurring on 30 September over Holloman AFB, White Sands, New Mexico.

During flight testing, a number of changes occurred in the Rascal program. First, on 4 November 1954, the last B-29 bomber was withdrawn, leaving the Rascal with the B-36 and the B-50 as launching platforms. Following this, in June of 1955, the B-36 was also eliminated from the program, the missile's warhead requirements were revised and the all-inertial guidance system was deleted. Later that same year, on 20 October 1955, the last B-50 bomber was retired, leaving only the B-47 as a launching platform for the Rascal. Testing with this aircraft lasted two years and, on 1 November 1957, the first Rascal/DB-47 unit, the 445th Bomber Squadron, was activated at Pine Castle AFB. The first all-SAC launch of a Rascal prototype then occurred three months later, on 17 February 1958.

By the time the 445th BW was activated, the Air Force had begun development of a new air-to-surface missile called the Hound Dog. Faster, smaller and having an all-inertial guidance system, this missile was far superior against enemy air defense systems than the Rascal. More importantly, since it used jet fuel, fueling was easy and it could be kept in a ready-to-launch mode for long periods of time. To prepare the Rascal for flight required the crew to don protective clothing, and could only be done just before takeoff. As a result of these facts, on 29 November 1958, US Air Force headquarters ended the Rascal program in favor of the Hound Dog. The last Rascal was withdrawn in 1959.

Bullpup B (AGM-12C)

SPECIFICATIONS
Length: 13 ft 4 in   Span: 3 ft 10.5 in
Diameter: 1 ft 5.3 in   Weight: 1785 lb

PERFORMANCE
Speed: Mach 2 or 1520 mph   Range: 10 mi

PROPULSION One Thiokol LR-62RM2 storable liquid fuel rocket motor. Max thrust: 33,000 lb

GUIDANCE Radio command

WARHEAD Either 1000 lb of conventional explosives or a W-45 nuclear warhead of 1 to 15 kt

CONTRACTOR Martin Marietta

The Bullpup B was both the largest and the most powerful of all the Bullpup models. As with the earlier BOAR, it was developed to give Navy fighter-bombers a standoff strike capability against heavily defended ground and sea targets.

The Bullpup family of missiles had its beginning in a 1953 Navy design competition for a conventionally armed standoff

Rascal ALM launch from B-50 Superfortress

missile for attack aircraft. As one of the companies requested to submit a design, Martin Marietta's Orlando division submitted a proposal for what was essentially a 250 lb bomb attached to a solid fuel rocket motor. Though its performance capabilities were not that great, its very simplicity made it the Navy's choice, and in May, Martin Marietta was issued a development contract for the ASM-N-7 Bullpup.

The first ASM-N-7 Bullpup was deployed by the Navy in April of 1959. Like the original proposal, it was a very simple weapon consisting of a roll-stabilized airframe, a 250 lb payload, and an Aerojet General solid fuel rocket motor. Its range was not that great, and its maximum speed was only Mach 1.8, but its simplicity and aircraft compatibility made it an instant success. A large number of Navy and Marine Corps aircraft became Bullpup-equipped; this included the HUS-1 helicopter.

Guidance for all the Bullpup models was of a visual nature, with the pilot acquiring the target, launching the missile, and then guiding it to its target by means of a joystick connected to a radio transmitter: the method is the same as operating a radio control aircraft. To assist the pilot in keeping both visual contact and an up/down reference with the missile, two flares were placed on either side of the motor exhaust.

Despite its wide acceptance, the ASM-N-7 didn't last long in service, for in 1960 the improved Bullpup A was deployed. Though the same missile externally, this model had a Thiokol liquid fuel motor — giving it greater range — and an improved 250 lb warhead for greater effect. Acceptance of this model was just as swift as it was for the original Bullpup, and by 1970, 22,100 rounds, with spares, had been manufactured.

Even with these improvements, however, the Bullpup A could not meet the Navy's growing need for a nuclear-capable ASM to replace the BOAR. As a result of this, in 1960 development began on an extensively enlarged missile capable of delivering a 1000 lb conventional or nuclear warhead over a distance of 10 miles. The first of these new missiles, called Bullpup Bs (or AGM-12C), were then deployed in 1964.

Even though it could carry a larger conventional warhead than any other Navy missile, the Bullpup B was not acquired in as great a quantity as the Bullpup A. Production was, in fact, terminated in 1969, after only 4600 rounds had been produced. Regardless of this, these missiles were quite effective and, even after the nuclear warhead was removed from the Bullpup B stockpile in 1976, served with the US Navy until the early 1980s.

A-4 Skyhawk with two Bullpup ALMs

SRAM (AGM – 69A)

SPECIFICATIONS
  Length: 14 ft   Weight: 2230 lb
                                  Diameter: 1 ft 5.5 in

PERFORMANCE
  Speed: Mach 2.5   CEP: 1200 ft
                                  Range: 100 mi when
                                      launched at high altitude
                                      35 mi when launched
                                      at low altitude

PROPULSION One Lockheed Propulsion Company LPC-415
                restartable, two pulse, solid fuel rocket motor

GUIDANCE Inertial system by General Precision/Kearfott
                Terrain clearance sensor by Stewart-Warner

WARHEAD Single W-69 thermonuclear warhead of approx
                200 kt yield

CONTRACTOR Boeing Aerospace Company

NUMBER OF MISSILES 1500 manufactured, 924 in service
                as of 1984

The Short Range Attack Missile, or SRAM, is one of the most powerful weapons carried by US bombers today. As a result of the deployment of this missile, the B-52 bomber is still a viable weapon 30 years after it was deployed.

With the cancellation of the Skybolt Air-Launched Ballistic Missile on 31 December 1962, the Air Force found itself without any kind of bomber modernization program. Realizing that the Hound Dog missiles would not last forever, on 23 November 1963, the Headquarters of the Strategic Air Command submitted to the Headquarters of the US Air Force a Qualitative Operational Requirement (QOR-95) for a short range air-to-surface attack missile. HQ Air Force approved of this concept and, on 18 March 1964, submitted to the Department of Defense Specific Operational Requirement 212 for a Short Range Attack Missile. Secretary of Defense Robert S McNamara then gave his approval for initial development of the weapon on 23 March 1965, effectively starting the SRAM program.

With permission to develop the SRAM, (then called Weapon System 140), the Air Force began issuing Requests For Proposals to major industry. A total of five companies responded to this request and, following an intense design competition, on 3 November 1965, the Air Force selected the Boeing and Martin Marietta proposals for Phase II project definition. A year later, on 31 October 1966, Boeing was then awarded a $142.3 million contract to design, develop and evaluate the AGM-69A SRAM weapon system for the B-52, the FB-111 bomber and the future Advanced Manned Strategic Aircraft.

Drop testing of the SRAM from B-52s and FB-111s began on 6 December 1967. Live firing commenced on 29 July 1969, and by the summer of 1970 at least 20 flights had been completed — including the first all-SAC launch on 24 September. Following this, in demonstration of the SRAM's capabilities, on 25 November 1970, a B-52 made a single pass over White Sands Missile Range and fired, in rapid succession, two SRAMs against two separate targets.

With the success of the testing program, on 12 January 1971, the Air Force authorized Boeing to begin production of the SRAM. Testing of the SRAM was then completed on 17 July, and the first production round was delivered on 1 March 1972. Following this, on 4 August 1972, the SRAM became operational with the Strategic Air Command.

The deployment of SRAMs on the B-52 and FB-111 resulted in a major increase in the survivability of these aircraft. By firing these missiles against enemy radar and surface-to-air missile sites along its penetration route, the bomber could now physically blast a clear path to its target. And at the target site, the SRAM could be used directly against the target, even through the strongest terminal air defense systems. The SRAM's small radar cross section, quoted as the size of a .50 caliber machine gun bullet, makes it even harder to intercept than the Air-Launched Cruise Missile. The fact that the SRAM could be launched at both subsonic and supersonic speeds, from high or low altitudes, and against targets ahead, to the side and even *behind* the bomber just added to its effectiveness. Finally, since the SRAM was one of the smallest nuclear weapons in the arsenal, a single B-52 could carry a total of 20 and still have room for four freefall bombs. This was over twice the number of nuclear weapons the bomber could carry with the Hound Dog missile, making it less necessary for the bomber crew to budget its weapons use.

Because of the SRAM's capabilities, in September of 1972, Boeing received an Air Force contract to study other possible uses for this missile. In a very short time, this study concluded that because of the SRAM's high maneuverability, the missile could be used to intercept enemy fighters, surface-to-air missiles, or airborne radar planes with the addition of a radar guidance system. This study also determined that, with the addition of an anti-radiation seeker, the SRAM could be used against mobile ground based radar. (At the time only fixed sites could be engaged). None of these changes were ever implemented, however, and with the delivery of the 1500th SRAM, on 30 July 1975, production was ended.

With the implementing of new environmental regulations in the mid-1970s, certain chemicals used in the preservation of the SRAM's motors were no longer available. Since this would reduce the life span of the motors to 2.5 years (less than half that of the basic missile), the Air Force issued a contract to Thiokol for the development of a new motor. In 1977, this work was combined with a general SRAM improvement program called AGM-96B (SRAM B), in which not only would a new motor be installed, but an improved guidance package with greater nuclear hardness, and the new W-80 warhead developed for the Air-Launched Cruise Missile would also be installed. A total of $15.5 million was then allocated for the new motors, and an additional $21.3 million was allocated for the construction of 2000 SRAM Bs for use by the B-1 bomber.

The cancellation of the B-1A in 1978 also meant the end of the SRAM B program. That same year, work on the new motor was stopped because studies had shown that the old motor's life span could be extended from 2.5 to possibly five years. Following this period — according to the Carter administration — the missiles would be progressively replaced by the ALCM and a new weapon called the Advanced Strategic Air Launched Missile, or ASALM. The ASALM was cancelled in 1980.

The resurrection of the B-1 bomber in 1981 did not also result in a restart of the SRAM B program. Instead, to insure that US Air Force bombers had an effective supersonic penetrator missile, work was begun on a new weapon called the SRAM II. This new missile

is to be two-thirds the size of the operational SRAM, making it possible for a B-1B to carry up to 12 in each bomb bay (a total increase of 12 missiles per bomber). Since this missile is not to reach Initial Operational Capability until early 1992, the SRAM A will have to remain functional at least until 1995. At present, no plans exist to extensively refurbish the older SRAM As or to install a new motor.

SRAM in FB-111 bomb bay

SRAMs in B-52 bomb bay

Present Air-To-Surface Programs

Since production of the ALCM was approved, work has been under way to develop the next generation of Strategic Air to Surface missiles. These new missiles are intended to make up for shortcomings in the present Short Range Attack Missile (SRAM) and the ALCM in their ability to penetrate future air defense systems.

SRAM II

Though the present SRAM missile is capable of penetration of most Soviet air defense systems — it is even better than the newer ALCM — it has long since exceeded its solid fuel motor's design life span. Consequently, the future reliability of this motor is in question — not to mention the SRAM'S outdated nuclear warhead.

Because of these problems, and the continued development and improvement of Soviet air defense systems, in February of 1985 the Air Force issued contracts to three aerospace contractors for systems studies and risk reduction tests to establish the final design for what was then called the Advanced Air-to-Surface Missile (AASM). Following the August announcement that the weapon was to use rocket propulsion, Martin Marietta[1] dropped out of the program. McDonnell Douglas and Boeing then submitted their proposals in July of 1986, and in December Boeing was awarded the SRAM II contract.

The SRAM II will be a vastly improved weapon as compared to the SRAM. To make it even harder to detect on radar, and to allow more missiles to be carried by the rotary launcher, it will have a smaller diameter: it is stated that it will be two-thirds the size of the earlier SRAM while having the same length. It will also have a newer, safer warhead — probably variable in yield — as well as greater accuracy, speed and range. Additional attention will be paid to make the weapon easy to maintain.

The first test flight is planned for August of 1989, with the Initial Operational Capability to be achieved in early 1992. All totaled, 1633 missiles are to be manufactured: this includes test and training models.

Advanced Cruise Missile

Regardless of all the statements that the Air-Launched Cruise Missile cannot be seen on enemy radar systems, the ALCM is actually very easy to detect by airborne systems. As a result of this, in the near future when such systems are fully deployed by the Soviets, the ALCM will become nothing more than a slow moving sitting duck to enemy fighters and ground defenses. To correct this, in 1982 work was begun to develop an improved weapon using modern stealth technology.

Called the Advanced Cruise Missile, or ACM, this new weapon is to be almost invisible to enemy radar systems, making it extremely hard to detect and destroy. In addition to this, it is to have greater range, accuracy and targeting flexibility. The only other presently known fact about this weapon is that the Williams International F112 turbofan engine will be used.

One observation that can be made about the basic design of the ACM is that it must be compatible with the new Common Strategic Rotary Launcher, which fact would restrict the missile's length to approximately 20 feet.

In April of 1983 General Dynamics was given the contract for this weapon. The original plan was for the ACM to replace the ALCM in production in 1987. No information is available, as of the writing of this text, as to whether this has in fact occurred.

[1] During the 1970s Martin Marietta developed and tested a missile called the Advanced Strategic Air-Launched Missile (ASALM). This weapon was a Rocket/ Ramjet design which was not acceptable to the Air Force for the AASM.

SRAM II concept

Honest John (M-31)

SPECIFICATIONS

Length: 27 ft 3 in	Span: 9 ft 1 in
Diameter: 30 in	Weight: 5820 lb with nuclear warhead

PERFORMANCE

Speed: Mach 2.3 at burnout; .98 at impact	Apogee: 29,703 ft at max range
Range: Max — 15.4 mi Min — 3.4 mi	CEP: Azimuth — 65 ft Range: 784 ft or .15 mi

PROPULSION Single solid fuel rocket engine by Hercules Powder Company. Max Thrust: 92,500 lb

GUIDANCE Unguided, stabilized by spin rockets

WARHEAD Either a 1500 lb conventional warhead or a single 20 kt W-7, or W-31, nuclear warhead. Warhead was either detonated by timer or a radar altimeter

CONTRACTOR McDonnell Douglas

The Honest John is the second nuclear tipped ballistic missile to be deployed by the US Army and the first one to be solid fueled. At this time it is one of the oldest nuclear weapons in the US arsenal.

Development of the Honest John began in May of 1950,[1] when the Army Ordnance Corps assigned Redstone arsenal the task of developing a preliminary design for a simple rocket weapon capable of delivering a nuclear warhead against battlefield targets. The next month the Ordnance Corps asked Douglas Aircraft to submit a proposal to turn its developed Honest John solid fuel booster rocket into a weapon (the Honest John rocket program was originally begun to develop a booster, or launch motor, for other missiles). The formal proposal was submitted in the early fall and, on 26 October 1950, Douglas was issued a contract for the design and development of the Honest John rocket.

Though Douglas had been contracted to design and develop the rocket it would not be until 2 August 1951 — two months after the first flight — that the Secretary of the Army gave formal approval for its development; five days later he directed that the program be put on a crash basis. Thus in June 1952 Douglas received the initial, limited production contract for the Honest John. The first production rounds were delivered in January of 1953, and by the end of the year, the first US units began receiving the rocket. The first Honest John battalions (each consisting of two to three batteries with two launchers per battery) were deployed in Europe in the spring of 1954.

The Honest John was by far the simplest to field of all the US nuclear weapons operated during the 1950s. Starting at the ammunition supply point the three parts of the rocket — warhead, motor and fins — were shipped by truck to the battery assembly area.[2] Once there, a wrecker transferred the round to a trailer mounted handling unit and then towed the round to the launching area where it was assembled on the trailer. Mounting on the launcher proceeded to take only five minutes for the battery's six-man crew and the wrecker's crane, leaving only the setting of the proper elevation and azimuth before the rocket was launched, just like aiming a howitzer. It was this simplicity and efficiency that gave the Honest John great favor among Army units as compared to the Corporal or Lacrosse missiles.

The Improved Honest John: M-50

In November 1954 Douglas reported to the Ordnance Corp that there were ways of improving the performance of the Honest John. In response to this report, later that month the Deputy Chief of Staff for Logistics directed the start of an improvement program for Honest John; the work was to proceed with an A-1 priority. Development began in early 1955, and in 1960 the first M-50 Honest John rockets were deployed to US Army units.

The M-50 series Honest John was a vast improvement over the earlier M-31.[3] Thanks to an improved, lighter solid fuel motor (150,000 lb thrust) it had twice the range of the M-31. Additionally, this lighter weight (4332 lb with a nuclear warhead), and the fact it was 1 foot 3 inches shorter, made it easier to deploy and operate. The use of new, squared fins also gave it greater stability in flight, improving the accuracy. (The new fins extended the fin span to 11 feet 1 inch.) By the late 1960s this new model had completely replaced the earlier M-31 with US units.

In 1962 both models of the Honest John were redesignated as part of an Army, Navy and Air Force program to create a unified designation system. As a result of this the M-31 became the MGR-1A and the M-50 became the MGR-1B.

Honest John GLMs

Honest John GLM

The same year that the Honest Johns were redesignated the Army began development of the Lance missile. Though smaller and almost 2000 lb lighter than the Honest John, the Lance would be able to deliver the same payload a distance of 75 miles with reasonable accuracy. (The scatter accuracy of an Honest John at 30 miles is 250 yards; the Lance is that accurate at 46.5 miles.) Deployment of the Lance in place of both the Honest John and the Sergeant missiles began in 1972. By 1981 the only US units that still operated this rocket were National Guard.

Several nations still operate the Honest John rocket, including Greece, Turkey and South Korea. The nuclear warheads for these rockets are controlled by US personnel.

[1] The Army didn't even consider such a weapon until after the detonation of the Soviet Unions's first nuclear device on 29 August 1949.
[2] If the local temperature was below 77°F the round would be heated with electric blankets while in the truck. Though the round had firing limits from zero to 100°F, the solid fuel burned more efficiently at 77°F or more.
[3] Even before the M-50 was deployed, three improved models of the M-31 had been fielded: the M-31A1, the M-31A1C, and the M-31A2. The change was the result of minor improvements in the design of the solid fuel motor.

Corporal GLM

Corporal (M-2)

SPECIFICATIONS
    Length: 45 ft   Span: 7 ft
    Diameter: 30 in   Weight: 11,000 lb

PERFORMANCE
    Speed: Max — 2200 mph   Ceiling: 25 mi
    Impact: 1600 mph
Range: Max — 75 mi; Min — 29 mi

PROPULSION Liquid fuel rocket engine burning a mixture of red fuming nitric acid and monoethylaniline.
                Max thrust: 20,000 lb
                Firing limits temperature: -25°F to 128°F

GUIDANCE Radio control system

WARHEAD Either conventional or a single W-7 nuclear warhead of 20 kt

CONTRACTOR Firestone Tire and Rubber Co

The Corporal was the first guided missile ever deployed by the United States Army. Until the deployment of the Redstone, in 1958, it was the longest range weapon in the Army arsenal.

Throughout most of the Second World War the US Army held the view that long range missiles were not possible and that no effort should be wasted in studying them. In late 1943, however, this view changed when Allied reconnaissance discovered that Germany was constructing missile launching ramps on the northern coast of occupied France: the V-1 flying bomb ramps. Now concerned that such weapons might actually affect the course of war, the US Army decided to begin its own rocket research and asked the Jet Propulsion Laboratories (JPL) in California if they would do a feasibility study on a long range missile using their developed rocket engines. In response to this request, on 20

November 1943, JPL proposed a four stage program, the final stage of which was the construction and testing of a 10,000 lb missile capable of a 75 mile range.

The original proposal was not accepted by the Army, probably because the final missile would be shorter in range than the V-1's it was to counter. However, in June of 1944, JPL submitted a second proposal calling for a four stage program, with the final stage being the development of a 150 mile range missile called Colonel. This proposal the Army accepted and, on 1 July 1944, work officially began under the name Project GALCIT. It would be in this program that the Corporal was developed.

The first phase of the GALCIT program began with the development of a small, 530 lb, solid fuel rocket called the Private A. This rocket, capable of carrying a 60 lb payload a distance of 10 miles, was intended to be a test vehicle for the study of the effects of sustained thrust on a missile; it could also be used as a weapon if the need arose. Testing began at Ft Irwin in the Mojave desert in 1944. By spring of 1945, 24 of these rockets had been launched, with an average range of 10.3 miles per missile. By this time the war in Europe was over.

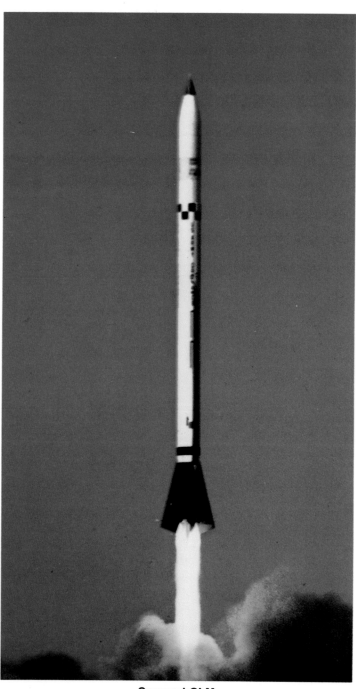

Corporal GLM

Following the war's end, the federal government sharply reduced all funding for research and development of guided missiles; as a result of this the first Corporal missile was not launched until 22 May 1947. Because the federal government felt nuclear weapons were too powerful for battlefield use, the Army had been forbidden to develop battlefield nuclear weapon systems. When the first Corporal was launched, it was not then a weapon but instead a test vehicle for the study of aerodynamics, propulsion and guidance problems associated with long range rockets. Nevertheless, the first launch was highly successful, with the missile traveling 62 miles and impacting within a half mile of its planned target.

In contrast, the next two flights were dismal failures because of problems with the rocket motor. Post flight analysis of these motors showed that the problem was in the basic design, forcing JPL, in December of 1947, to begin development of a new rocket motor. The first flight with this new motor occurred successfully on 7 June 1949, ending the program's propulsion problems.[1]

The solution to the Corporal's propulsion problems arose at just the right time in history. Following the detonation of the Soviet Union's first nuclear device, on 29 August 1949, the Federal government changed its view on the development of guided missiles and made available additional funding for this purpose. With these additional funds the Army, noting the success of the Corporal's new motor and the problems with the Hermes missile, in early 1950 ordered the program reoriented towards a weapon system. Later that year, following the start of the Korean war on 15 June 1950, Congress also changed its view on the development of tactical nuclear weapons and, in late December, gave permission for the Corporal to carry nuclear warheads.

With the issuing of the R&D contract, work on the Corporal went into high gear, and with the launch of the eleventh missile, on 10 October 1951, the missile's basic design was frozen. Firestone Tire and Rubber Company was issued the production contract in December (JPL had no production facilities) and the first production missile was delivered five months later. The first launch occurred in August of 1952, and in April of 1954 the first Army units began training with the Corporal.

Though the Corporal had been launched over 100 times since 1949, the missile JPL and Firestone delivered to the Army was not a weapon well designed for battlefield operations. Its liquid fuel motor was an extremely complex piece of machinery that was hard to maintain and prone to malfunctions. In addition, the liquid fuels the Corporal used were highly toxic and corrosive, making fueling extremely dangerous and requiring the personnel to wear hot, uncomfortable and cumbersome glass fabric suits and gas masks. (With the suits a Corporal battalion had 36 emergency showers to wash down personnel who came in contact with these liquids.) The worst problem of all was the Corporal's radar/radio control system, which was extremely difficult to service and maintain and could be seriously affected by either electronic jamming[2] or natural phenomena. Combined, these three problems reduced the reliability of the first Corporals, Type I, to only 47.1 percent. In the field the reliability was even less, as some units reported that they couldn't even successfully complete a mock launch. In February of 1955 the first battalion was deployed in West Germany and by 1956 nine battalions were in Europe.

Just as the last Type Is were being deployed, in mid-1956, the first Corporal Type IIs, with a reliability of 60.6 percent, began replacing them. The next year a revised model called the Type IIA was fielded and, in 1959, the first Type IIBs with an airturbine alternator instead of internal batteries came into service.

Even with all these improvements to the basic missile, the Corporal still had a number of limitations as a weapon. To move a

Corporal battalion was an enormous undertaking involving 35 vehicles and 250 men. Another problem was the fact that once the launch site was reached it took approximately nine hours just to get the missile ready for flight. Since there were only two launchers, or batteries, per battalion this meant that each battalion could launch only four missiles in a 24 hour period; this computation is confirmed by the Army's statement in the 1960s that each of its two Corporal battalions in Italy could launch four missiles in the first day of a crisis and one every twelve hours thereafter. It was because of these continued limitations that in 1958 the Army began development of the Sergeant missile.

With the deployment of the first Sergeant missiles in 1962 the Army began withdrawing the Corporal units from the field. The last missile was retired in 1964. A Corporal missile is on display at both the White Sands Missile Range Missile Park and the Alabama Space and Missile Center.

---

[1] The new motor and other changes in the Corporal's design cut the empty weight by 1000 lb and increased the range from 113 to 200 miles with a 1000 lb payload.
[2] Since the Corporal's warhead was armed in flight with a signal from the ground control computer any jamming could cause the missile to come down unarmed.

Lacrosse (SSM-A-12)

SPECIFICATIONS

Length: 19 ft 2.4 in.	Span: 9 ft
Diameter: 20 ft 6 in	Weight: 2300 lb

PERFORMANCE

Speed: Mach .8	Range: 10 to 12 mi

PROPULSION Single solid fuel rocket engine by Thiokol

GUIDANCE A Federal Communications Lab radio command system

WARHEAD Either a 540 lb conventional warhead or a single W-40 nuclear warhead of low kt yield

CONTRACTOR Martin Marietta

The Lacrosse was the third nuclear capable missile to be operationally deployed by the US Army. In concept it had the potential to supplement regular artillery in the role of pinpoint suppression fire. Historically, however, it proved a failure.

Development of the Lacrosse missile program began in 1947 when the Cornell Aeronautical Laboratory, of Buffalo, New York, was issued a Navy contract to investigate the feasibility of a guided missile capable of replacing conventional artillery in the role of close support for Marine Corps units. Two years later, however, the program was placed in limbo when the Joint Chiefs of Staff issued a new missile policy giving the Army control of all guided missiles used in place of field artillery. The program came to a halt on 21 March 1950 when Secretary of Defense Louis A Johnson approved of the new policy.

Following the 29 June 1950 presidential order to commit ground

troops to Korea, the Department of Defense began to take a greater interest in the development of battlefield guided missiles. As a result of this, on 31 August 1950, the Secretary of Defense transferred the Lacrosse program to the US Army Ordnance Corps. Soon after this, in February of 1951, the Army issued Cornell a formal research and development contract for the missile.

Development of the Lacrosse was extremely slow compared to the Honest John. Though the first test round was launched in August 1951, it would take four years before the design had matured enough to even consider production. In April of 1955, because Cornell could not do production work, the Army brought the Glen L Martin company into the program and, on 1 June 1955, issued Martin the initial production contract for the weapon. Tooling and other production related problems delayed things further, preventing the first prototype Lacrosse missile from coming off the production line until 26 March 1957. (Before it was sent to the Army this round was checked over and modified at Cornell so that it was not delivered until November of 1957). Testing with these missiles didn't take so long, however, and on 22 July 1959 the first Lacrosse missiles became operational within the 5th Missile Battalion, 41st Field Artillery.

Lacrosse GLM

Lacrosse GLM

The Lacrosse system was quite different from that of the related Honest John. All totalled, four vehicles were needed to operate the missile: two 2.5 ton 6X6 Army trucks (one carried the zero length launcher while the other carried the tracking antenna) and two jeeps (one carrying the missile guidance central computing unit and the other the target ranging unit).

Operating the Lacrosse was also quite different than operating the Honest John. Following the assignment of a target, the Lacrosse's forward observer would fire the missile by remote control. Then, following the acquisition of the missile's tracking beacon by the tracking antenna, guidance commands would be transmitted by radio to the missile, setting it on the proper ballistic path towards the target. Once set, Ground Control would monitor the flight, making minor course corrections for wind drift or changes in target position. (Lacrosse was supposed to be able to hit moving targets.) The end result of all this was an accuracy high enough so that the Lacrosse could bull's eye bunkers, pill boxes and other hardened point targets.

For all the Lacrosse's potential, however, it had a number of shortcomings. Its high accuracy occurred only under the best conditions with experienced personnel at the controls. (It never could hit a moving target). In the field it was a maintenance nightmare, a fact which greatly diminished the missile's reliability. Worst of all, however, because it was radio controlled, its guidance system could be jammed electronically, and the weapon made impossible to control. This last problem was of great concern to the Army because it meant there was a danger that the Lacrosse might fall on civilians or US Army units.

As a result of these shortcomings, the Army, in 1963, asked for funding to make improvements, funding which was never approved. So in the fall of 1963 the Army was forced to begin withdrawing the Lacrosse from service. The last missile was deactivated in February of 1964.

In retrospect, what can be said about the Lacrosse is that it was a great weapon in concept, but that technology was not yet ready to make it a practical weapon. A Lacrosse is on display at Redstone Arsenal.

Little John (M-51)

SPECIFICATIONS
Length: 14 ft 5.7 in
Diameter: 12.5 in

Span: 1 ft 11.75 in
Weight: 779 lb

PERFORMANCE
Speed: Mach 1.5

Range: 11.3 mi

PROPULSION One solid fuel rocket engine by Allegany Ballistics

GUIDANCE Unguided, stabilized by spin rockets and fins

WARHEAD Either conventional or a single W-45 nuclear warhead of 1-10 kt

CONTRACTOR Emerson Electric

The Little John is the smallest nuclear-capable rocket the US Army ever deployed. It was intended to give Army Airborne units like the 101st a nuclear capability.

Development of the Little John can be traced back to a proposal made in May of 1953 by the Chief of Research and Development at the Army Ordnance Corps for the development of a lightweight version of the Honest John called the Honest John Junior. Army headquarters quickly approved of the concept and, in August of that year, issued a firm requirement for the rocket now called Little John. The project was then formally established at Redstone Arsenal on 14 June 1955, with the first test launch occuring one year later, in June of 1956.

Lacrosse GLM

Little John GLM prototype

Little John GLM

The rocket that was launched was not the production version of the Little John. Called the XM-47, this 12.5 foot long missile was a propulsion test vehicle without a payload section; it would later serve duty as a live fire field training device. Design work on the definitive Little John, M-51, did not formally begin until 1957. The 101st Airborne Division conducted an evaluation of this model in 1958, and in 1961 the first rockets were deployed.

Compared to the Honest John, the Little John rocket was an extremely easy weapon to move and deploy. Starting at the ammunition supply point, a single truck could carry two fully assembled Little John rockets to the battery assembly area. Once there, using the truck's built-in crane, the rockets would be placed onto either launchers or shipping carts for towing to the launching site. Following arrival at the launching site, if the rockets were on launchers, all that was required was for the launcher to be emplaced, and the proper elevation and azimuth to be set for launch. If the Little Johns were on carts, the rockets would slide on to the launcher before emplacing. In an airborne operation, on the other hand, the round would be parachute-dropped on its launcher or cart en route to the launching site.

Regardless of its high mobility, the Little John rocket was not deployed in any great number; in fact, only two battalions were deployed, a total of eight launchers. This limited deployment may have been due to the fact that the rocket was primarily developed for airborne operations, and since there were only two Airborne units at the time — the 82nd and 101st — there was no need for any more.

On 20 August 1969, the last Little John rocket was withdrawn from service. No official reason was given, but although deployment of the Lance was not to occur for three years, the little John was not replaced. It is possible that, following the 1964 deployment of the M-48 nuclear projectile for the 155mm howitzer, the Little John became more dispensable; but if this weapon did indeed replace it, the Little John should have been withdrawn in the mid-1960s.

A Little John rocket is on display at the Alabama Space and Missile center in Huntsville, Alabama.

Little John GLM

Sergeant (MGM-29A)

SPECIFICATIONS
Length: 35 ft   Span: 5 ft
Diameter: 31 in   Weight: 10,000 lb

PERFORMANCE
Speed: supersonic
Range: Min — 28 mi   CEP: very high accuracy[1]
      Max — 85 mi

PROPULSION Single Thiokol M-53 Solid fuel rocket motor
            Max thrust: 55,000 lb

GUIDANCE Inertial system by Sperry Gyroscope

WARHEAD Either conventional or a single W-52 thermo-
          nuclear warhead

CONTRACTOR Sperry (later known as Sperry Univac)

NUMBER OF MISSILES 500 believed deployed

The Sergeant was the first solid fuel surface-to-surface missile ever deployed by the US Army. It was designed to replace the Corporal missile in the attacking of battlefield targets.

Even before the Corporal SRBM was operational, in 1951, the Army began a study to determine the feasibility of a solid fuel surface-to-surface missile. Called Hermes A-2, this program, in conjunction with Thiokol and JPL, would develop a 5000 lb weight motor that was so revolutionary it would eventually form the design basis for all follow-on solid fuel motors. In late 1953, following the completion of the Hermes A-2 program, the Army Ordnance Corps issued a request for proposal to Redstone Arsenal, General Electric and JPL for a solid fuel surface-to-surface missile. In the fall of 1954 the Army awarded JPL the R&D contract for what is now known as the Sergeant ballistic missile.

Development of the Sergeant — as opposed to that of the Corporal before it — was very fast. The first missile was launched in January 1956; later that same year, since JPL had no production facilities, the Sperry Corporation acted as co-contractor in charge of missile production. Field trials with Army units began in 1959, and in April of 1961, Initial Operational Capability was achieved. Deployment in Europe began the following year. By mid-1963, three battalions were operational in West Germany.

Like the Corporal, the Sergeant was extremely easy to operate. Because it was solid fueled, and deployed in three pieces (warhead, motor, and guidance section), an entire battery (one launcher) could be transported on three semi-trailers and a standard truck; the unit was even air-transportable. At the launch site, a well-trained six man battery crew could have the missile assembled and erected to its 75 degree launch angle in about a half an hour. After this, a 44 minute computerized countdown[2] began in which fuel preheating, final tests and guidance programming were achieved. At X-3 minutes, the crew would leave to the remote firing control, and at X-0 the missile would be launched.

Once fired, the Sergeant's guidance system would set the

Sergeant GLM

Sergeant GLM

missile on course for the target. Then, at approximately the halfway point in its flight, the guidance system commanded special drag brakes to open in order to neutralize the thrust of the motor.[3] Because Sergeant was solid fueled, its motor would not shut down until the last of the fuel had been burned. With thrust neutralized, gravity caused the missile to fall back to earth, completing a ballistic flight path to its target. Prior to impact, radio command armed the warhead from the launching site.

On 7 April 1967, Secretary of Defense Robert McNamara ordered that the Lance missile program be reoriented towards the development of a missile with the range of the Sergeant. In 1972 this new missile began replacing the US-operated Sergeants deployed in West Germany, and by 1976 the last US-operated Sergeants had been withdrawn from service. Lance began replacing the Sergeants deployed with the West Germans in 1977, and by 1979 the Sergeant was no longer in service with any nation.

Sergeant missiles are on display at the White Sands Missile Range and the Alabama Space and Rocket Center in Huntsville, Alabama.

[1] One launch was reported to have hit within four feet of its target.
[2] Five holds were programmed into the countdown to control the launch. They were at X-20 minutes, indefinite delay; X-7.5 minutes, variable delay; X-90 seconds, 10 minute delay; X-20 seconds, two minute delay; and X-0 seconds, two minute delay.
[3] These drag brakes clicked out at camera shutter speed to produce 16 tons of drag on the vehicle.

Lance (MGM-52C)

SPECIFICATIONS
   Length: 20 ft   Weight: 2850 lb
   Diameter: 22 in

PERFORMANCE
   Speed: Mach 3   Ceiling: 150,000 ft
   Range: 75 mi   CEP: 984 ft at max range

PROPULSION A coaxial Booster/Sustainer burning inhibited red fuming nitric acid and unsymmetrical dimenthylhydrazine storable liquid fuels
   Firing temp limits: -40°F to 140°F
   Thrust, booster: 42,000 lb
   Thrust, sustainer: 14 to 4400 lb (throttleable)

GUIDANCE Inertial

WARHEAD Either conventional or a single W-70[1] warhead of variable yield; fusing available for both air and ground burst

CONTRACTOR Ling Temco Vought (LTV)

NUMBER OF LAUNCHERS 36 in Europe, 12 in United States; 2133 missiles procured

The Lance is the primary battlefield nuclear weapon used by the US Army. It is the most effective weapon available for stopping massed armored units.

Development of the Lance began on 1 November 1962 when the Army announced the start of a program to develop a 30 mile range replacement missile for both the Honest John and Lacrosse weapons. Known then as Missile B, Chance Vought would then be issued the development contract on 11 January 1963. The first R&D launch of a MGM-52A took place on 15 March 1965, followed by the first successful launch from the lightweight launcher in July, the first launch from the prototype mobile launcher in August and the first successful parachute tests achieved in October of 1966.

While work on the original Lance design was under way, Rocketdyne developed a new motor design that showed the potential for giving the Lance the same range as the Sergeant. The Army took a great deal of interest in this new motor and, on 7 April 1967, announced that all work on the Lance would be redirected towards a long range model called the Extended Range Lance. Problems in the development of the new motor delayed the program for one year, postponing the launch of the first EX model until March of 1969. This launch was nevertheless a success, with the new motor increasing range over 100 percent. Testing was completed in 1971, and production of Lance MGM-52C began in September. The first rounds were deployed in 1972.

Compared to the Sergeant and Honest John weapons it replaced, the Lance is significantly easier to operate. Because its liquid fuel motor can be fired effectively at extremes in temperature, the missile doesn't require pre-launch heating as did the earlier Honest John or Little John rockets. Since the missile's guidance system automatically compensates for weather changes in flight it also becomes unnecessary for the launch crew to set up instruments to gather this data (as was done for both Honest John and Sergeant). These improvements, coupled with the fact that the Lance is carried fully assembled in its launcher, give the Lance an extremely short reaction time of approximately 15 minutes,[2] at least half that of the Sergeant.

The improved response time was not the only improvement the Lance gave the Army SRBM force. Because of its small size, a single Lance fire unit can carry three missiles into the field: one on the M752 mobile launcher and two on the MA688 auxiliary vehicle. As a result of this large number of ready missiles, the Lance unit has a very high fire rate compared to both the Honest John and Sergeant: about three rounds an hour. (A Lance battery, with two launchers and two auxiliary vehicles, can fire possibly six missiles in one hour.) It is this combination of high fire rate and short response time that makes the Lance one of the most formidable SRBMs in the world.

Because of the Lance's improved capabilities, as well as a government policy to get our European allies more involved in the defense of Europe, the Army concluded that the Honest John and Sergeant systems did not have to be replaced on a one-for-one basis. Therefore, when US deployment of Lance was completed in 1976, only 36 launchers (108 ready missiles) were deployed in Europe. Deployment with NATO units began that same year, and by 1979 56 Lance launchers were in service with British, Belgium, Dutch, Italian and West German troops[3] — for a total of 92 launchers (276 missiles). Production of the Lance missile ended in January of 1980 with the delivery of the 2133rd round.

Though Lance has greater capabilities than Honest John and Sergeant, over 500 of these earlier missiles were in operation during the 1960s and early 1970s. Even with the NATO launchers, there are only 276 lance missiles in the field.

The Lance was originally intended to have both conventional and nuclear warheads, but it was not until 1978 that Congress issued funds for the development of the conventional warheads. That same year the Army began a program, codenamed Assault Breaker, to develop a replacement for the Lance that could stop armored assaults using only conventional warheads. This research resulted in the development of what is called the Improved Lance: a 200 mile range, Lance size missile capable of delivering an effective load of conventional munitions against military targets. In 1984, however, work on this missile was put on hold and development began on a missile capable of being launched from the

Lance GLM

Lance GLM

new Multi-Launch Rocket System. Called the Advanced Tactical Missile System (ATACMS), this missile is intended for deployment in the early 1990s.

Since the ATACMS is not to begin deployment until the early 1990s, the Lance is expected to remain in service until the mid-1990s, when, unless a nuclear warhead has been developed for the ATACMS, the last nuclear tipped short range ballistic missile will have been removed from service. As of 1984, 762 Lance missiles were launched.

[1] The W-70 Mod-3 warhead with enhanced radiation capabilities (the neutron head) has been produced. All examples of this model, however, are stockpiled in the US.
[2] Launches have been completed within ten minutes of receiving the order.
[3] Israel also operates Lance, but the warheads supplied by the US are conventional. Those missiles supplied to West Germany have warheads controlled by US personnel.

Follow-On To Lance (FOTL)

SPECIFICATIONS

Improved Lance	T-12
Length: 20 ft 2 in	17 ft 5 in
Span: Unspecified	2 ft 10 in
Diameter: 22 in	1 ft 4 in
Weight: 2850 lb	3740 lb

PERFORMANCE
Speed: Mach 3
Range: 200 mi

PROPULSION Single solid fuel rocket motor

GUIDANCE Either radio command or inertial (Improved Lance 5 times more accurate than Lance)

WARHEAD Nuclear of unspecified yield (payload 30 percent larger than Lance)

FOTL GLM

The Follow-on To Lance is the next short range ballistic missile the Army hopes to develop. This missile is to improve the Army's ability to destroy large units of Soviet armor.

Since the late 1970s the Army has been trying to develop a replacement for the Lance missile developed in the early 1960s. The planned new weapon is to have twice the Lance's range, higher accuracy to allow the use of lower yield warheads, and a greater payload to make practical the use of conventional submunition warheads. Several ideas have been tried under such names as Assault Breaker, Core Support Weapon System and now the Advanced Tactical Missile System (ATACMS), but none of these systems or the missiles developed during these programs, the T-22 (improved Lance) or the T-12 (a modified Patriot), have been allowed to reach production.

With the signing of the INF agreement the Army is again asking Congress for permission to develop the FOTL using the present ATACMS program as its foundation. This program, however, based on the deployed Multi-Launch Rocket System, is currently restricted to conventional roles only by Congress. Approval for this change is still pending.

FOTL GLM

Genie (AIR-2)

SPECIFICATIONS
  Length: 9 ft 7 in   Span: 3 ft 3.5 in
  Diameter: 1 ft 5.35 in   Weight: 820 lb

PERFORMANCE
  Speed: Mach 3   Range: 6 mi

PROPULSION Single Thiokol SR49-TC-1 solid fuel rocket
            motor. Max thrust: 36,500 lb
            Firing temperature limits: 175°F to -75°F

GUIDANCE Unguided; weapon stabilized in flight by single
          gyro and flip-out fins

WARHEAD Single W-25 fission warhead of 1.5 kiloton yield[1]

CONTRACTOR McDonnell Douglas Astronautics

NUMBER OF MISSILES Several thousand reportedly pro-
                    duced; none operational as of 1987

The Genie is the world's first nuclear tipped air-to-air weapon. Throughout its 30 years of service, this weapon was the most powerful weapon available to interceptor pilots of the NORAD network.

In the first five years following the Second World War, the military restricted the use of nuclear weapons to the attacking of land and sea targets. This, because the weapons then available were viewed as too big and powerful for any other uses. With the development of small, tactical nuclear warheads in the early 1950s, however, studies were undertaken by the armed forces to determine the feasibility and capability of nuclear tipped anti-aircraft rockets. One of these studies was the 1954 Douglas Aircraft MB-1 project.

The MB-1 program was to determine the feasibility of launching a nuclear device from a US fighter aircraft against incoming enemy bombers. Initially a guided weapon was studied, but concern over the reliability of the guidance system convinced Douglas in 1955 to go with a simple gyrostabilized rocket. During these design changes, the program was successively renamed 'Bird Dog,' 'High Card' and 'Ding Dong.' Full scale development was begun that same year[2] and, in early 1956, the first test launchings were conducted from F-89Ds and the YF-102 Delta Dagger prototype. Deployment then began in January of 1957 under the new and final name of 'Genie.'

Six months after the Genie was deployed, at 0:700 hrs, on 19 July 1957, an F-89J fighter launched a Genie at 19,000 ft over the Nevada nuclear testing range. Called 'Shot John' of operation 'Plumbob,' the missile traveled a distance of 2.6 miles in 4.5 seconds in time before it was detonated by a command signal. This was the first and only live firing of the Genie missile.

Though the Genie was a simple, unguided rocket, it would have been extremely effective against enemy aircraft. Its very short flight time, a maximum of 12 seconds, and its large blast radius of 1000 feet, made it highly unlikely that enemy aircraft could avoid destruction. The fact that it was unguided just added to this, by making it impossible for the target to misdirect the Genie with flares, chaff or electronic countermeasures. Furthermore, even if the enemy aircraft was able to avoid the blast, the electromagnetic pulse produced by the weapon would effectively 'blind' the

aircraft, making it an easy target for a follow-on attack.

In the first few years following its deployment on the F-89J and F-102, the Genie was also fielded on the F-101 Voodoo and the F-106 Delta Dagger. Only these fighters, deployed with NORAD, were armed with the Genie. In the early 1960s, flight tests were also conducted on the F-4 Phantom, but no Genies were operationally deployed on this fighter. Production of the Genie was ended in 1962, after the construction of over 1000 rounds.

Soon after the last Genie was delivered, the Air Force issued Thiokol Corp. a contract to develop a new solid fuel motor with a longer lifespan and wider firing temperature limits than the Genie's earlier Aerojet motor. Production of this new motor was begun by 1965 and did not end until the year 1978.

As the years went by, the Genies were progressively withdrawn from the stockpile as their launching aircraft were retired. By 1982, only about 200 of these rockets were still in operation, deployed on about 100 F-106 and CF-101[3] fighters operated by the NORAD system. These planes were then replaced by the F-16, the F-15 and the F/A-18 as of 1985, removing the last launching aircraft for the Genie. The next year the Genie was removed from the listing of operational US Air Force weapons; it is unknown if the Genie is still in the US stockpile.

No programs are in progress to develop a replacement for the Genie.

[1] Shot John of test series Plumbob is quoted as being 2 kt in yield.
[2] On 6 April 1955, a 3 kt nuclear device, dropped from a B-36, was detonated at an altitude of 36,620 ft. Called the Ha shot, operation Teapot, it was done to determine what effect a high nuclear blast would have on airborne aircraft.
[3] Canadian operated F-101 Voodoo fighter. The Genies carried, however, were controlled by US personnel.

Genie ALM launch

Falcon (AIM-26A)

Falcon ALM (formerly GAR-II)

SPECIFICATIONS

Length: 7 ft .5 in	Span: 2 ft
Diameter: 11 in	Weight: 203 lb

PERFORMANCE

Speed: Mach 2	Range: 10 mi

PROPULSION Single Thiokol M-60 solid fuel rocket motor
Max thrust: 5800 lb

GUIDANCE Semi-active radar homing

WARHEAD Single W-54 fission warhead of sub-kiloton yield. Four active radar proximity fuzes used to trigger detonation

CONTRACTOR Hughes

NUMBER OF MISSILES 1900 AIM-26As reported produced

The AIM-26A is the only member of the Falcon family of missiles to carry a nuclear warhead. It was developed specifically to give US pilots an extremely high probability of intercepting enemy aircraft in head-on engagements.

Though the deployment, in 1957, of the Genie air-to-air rocket had given US pilots a high capability to intercept incoming Soviet bombers, by the late 1950s the Air Force had issued a new requirement for an air-to-air missile capable of successfully intercepting Soviet aircraft in head on engagements. To meet this new requirement, Hughes, the manufacturer of the operational Super Falcon missiles, began development of an improved missile using semi-active radar homing (SARH): it was decided early to use SARH because the available infrared systems required an extremely hot heat source to lock on to, namely the aircraft's exhaust. To make up for the inaccuracy of this form of guidance, a sub-kiloton class nuclear warhead was then added to give the AIM-26A, then known as the GAR-11, an extremely large kill zone. The end result of this combination of warhead and guidance was a missile capable of effectively intercepting any kind or number of aircraft, day or night, and in all kinds of weather.

Production of the AIM-26A began in 1960. Deployment began the following year on F-101, F-102 and F-106 fighter aircraft deployed with the NORAD air defense network.

By the late 1960s improvements in both radar and infared homing systems had made missiles like the Sparrow and Sidewinder effective in frontal attacks. During this same period, the type of target the NORAD defense was expecting to engage changed from high altitude to a low altitude, terrain-hugging aircraft. This change in tactics placed the AIM-26A at a disadvantage because the nuclear warhead restricted its low altitude capabilities. It is the author's opinion that this was the reason why the AIM-26A was removed from operational service in 1971.

In 1980 the conventionally armed version of the AIM-26A deployed by the Swedish and Swiss Air Forces was still operational. This tends to indicate that there was no design problem with this model of Falcon missile.

from F-106 Delta Dagger

Bombs and Warheads

Little Boy

DIMENSIONS
Length: 10 ft Weight: 8900 lb
Diameter: 2 ft 4 in

YIELD 13 kt

CARRIERS Little Boy: B-29 *Enola Gay*
Mk-1: B-29, B-50 and P2V

The 'Little Boy' bomb is the nuclear weapon that was dropped on the city of Hiroshima on 6 August 1945. In physical terms, the use of this bomb resulted in the destruction of four square miles of the city and 70,000 people killed. To history, its use served to bring about the end of the Second World War before additional hundreds of thousands of lives were lost.

The Little Boy bomb was what is called a 'gun-type' nuclear device. In this design, two subcritical masses of nuclear material are placed at opposite ends of a long tube. When detonation is desired, an explosive charge at one end of the tube is fired, shooting the subcritical mass at one end into the other mass, forming one supercritical mass. A nuclear chain reaction then occurs, releasing a large amount of energy in the form of an explosion. In the Little Boy, the material used was Uranium 235.

Because of the simplicity of its design, the Little Boy bomb was not tested prior to its use, like its brother weapon the Fat Man. At the same time, this Little Boy design required a significantly large amount of nuclear material — 135 pounds of U235. This fact, coupled with the limited amount of nuclear material available in the late 1940s, made the Little Boy the least manufactured of the early nuclear weapons.

The Little Boy bomb used essentially the same fusing system used by the Fat Man bomb. In this system, a series of small radar units ('Amos units,' developed by the University of Michigan) were placed around the weapon to determine the bomb's altitude. By design, when two of these units had determined that a prescribed altitude had been reached, a firing signal would then be sent to a series of clockwork switches which would close only if at least 15 seconds had elapsed following the bomb's release (done to prevent the bomb detonating because of radar reflections from the dropping aircraft). The signal was then sent to the bomb's fuse, detonating the weapon. Though functional, this system was susceptible to radar jamming, which could either predetonate the bomb or render it inert.

Stockpiling of the Little Boy, officially designated Mk-1, doesn't seem to have occured until mid-1948, when problems in the manufacture of the Fat Man versions began to threaten the viability of the US arsenal. Regardless of this fact, few casings were constructed[1] and no nuclear cores were manufactured.[2] By 1951, none were in stockpile.

Examples of the Mk-1 casing are on display at the National Atomic Museum and Wright-Patterson AFB. Others may also be in the Smithsonian and at Los Alamos National Laboratories.

The Little Boy bomb was not the first nuclear weapon the US tried to develop. The first device, codenamed the Thin Man, was a plutonium gun design 17 feet long and 1 foot 11 inches in diameter. Testing of full models of this bomb were begun in March of 1944, following the joining of the test B-29's two bomb bays. Problems with the release mechanism plagued these tests, however, and following the premature dropping of the device onto the bomber's own bomb bay doors, testing was understandably halted until June for repairs and revision. By the time this was done, the uranium gun design was completed, and because of its smaller size, was code named Little Boy. Development of the Thin Man was then terminated in mid-summer 1944.

[1] By 30 June 1950 28 were quoted constructed; *Bulletin of Atomic Scientists*, May 1982, pages 25-30.
[2] Following 1948, a greater use was made of U235 or 'O Ralloy' in the Fat Man bombs, making little available for the Mk-1s.

Mk-I Little Boy bomb

Fat Man (Model 1561)

DIMENSIONS
Length: 10 ft 8 in   Weight: 10,800 lb
Diameter: 5 ft

YIELD 23 kt

CARRIERS Fat Man — B-29 *Bock's Car*
           Mk-3 — B-29, B-50, B-36
           Mk-4 — B-29, B-50, B-36, P2V, AJ-1

The 'Fat Man' bomb was the second, and hopefully the last, nuclear device to be dropped in war. Because of its use, 1.5 square miles of the city of Nagasaki was destroyed and 35,000 people were killed.

Development of the Fat Man can be traced back to the summer of 1943 when Professor von Neuman of Los Alamos began urging the development of an implosion weapon. In this design a sphere of nuclear material (in Fat Man this was 13.5 pounds of plutonium) is surrounded by high explosives 'lenses' in such a manner that when they are fired — *all at once* — the resulting explosion will compress the plutonium core down until its density has been increased by a factor of two. At this increased density, the mass is now supercritical, making possible a nuclear chain reaction.

The implosion design is widely used in modern nuclear weapons because it requires a smaller amount of nuclear material than a gun design. However, it is also a more complex design, with a greater chance of having a poor yield — or a failure to explode. It was because of this that the Fat Man bomb design was tested on 16 July 1945, at White Sands, New Mexico, prior to its military use on 16 July 1945, at White Sands, New Mexico.

The firing system used by the Fat Man bomb was an extremely complicated mechanism, designed as much to prevent an accidental predetonation as to detonate the weapon. The first components of this system were four modified APS/13 tail warning radar units (called 'Archie'[1]). Used as radar altimeters, these units were to close a relay when the bomb had reached a predetermined distance from the ground. When two of these units had fired, a firing signal was then transmitted to a bank of clockwork switches set to close 15 seconds after the bomb had been released. (As a backup, a pressure switch was also installed which would close the switches at 7000 feet).[2] The switches sent the signal to the bomb's electronic switch, actuating its high voltage firing circuit.

Regardless of the fact that it worked, the basic Fat Man Model 1561 was not a very well designed weapon. Both it and the Mk-3 stockpile model (stockpiled in 1945) were aerodynamically unstable at high speeds. This caused the weapon to wobble during its drop. Terminal velocity of the weapon was .9 to .95 Mach. To keep instability at a minimum, early on, drag plates were installed in the tail box to slow the weapon down. These plates were not always reliable — an example of this being the postwar 'Crossroads Able' nuclear test, where it is believed one of the drag plates either collapsed or was lost, causing the bomb to miss the target battleship by 1000 feet or more. Following World War II, a major effort was made to rectify this problem, including extensive wind tunnel tests conducted by John Northrop of 'Flying Wing' fame.

The Mk-4 Fat Man

The aerodynamic instability was just one of the problems with the earlier Fat Man models. Because they were handmade at Los Alamos, it took an average of two days for a 39 man team to completely assemble one Mk-3. In addition, following assembly the bomb could remain ready for only 48 hours before it had to be partially disassembled to replace or recharge the batteries that

Mk-3 Fat Man bomb

powered the bomb's fuses. It was because of these problems, and a shortage of nuclear material in 1947, that development began on a greatly improved bomb called the Mk-4.[3]

With the deployment of the first Mk-4s in 1949, the Air Force began operating its first truly functional nuclear bomb. Not only did this model's improved aerodynamic design end the wobble problem, it was the first bomb that allowed the insertion of the nuclear fuel core during flight, giving it a higher safety factor and making it easier to maintain. Following the removal of the last Mk-3 from stockpile in 1950, the Mk-4 was the only nuclear weapon in service until the deployment of the Mk-6 in 1951.

The Fat Man bombs, Mk-3 and Mk-4, are the first members of that ironically elite group of US bombs that have been dropped accidentally. On 13 February 1950, a B-36 carrying a Mk-3 bomb casing and a dummy core had to drop the weapon when three of its six engines failed. (The casing exploded on impact with the ocean). Two months later, on 11 April 1950, a B-29 carrying both a bomb and a capsule crashed just three minutes after taking off from Kirkland AFB. Additional incidents are the 13 July 1950 crash of a B-50, the 5 August crash of a B-29 and the 10 November 1950 incident when, during an in-flight emergency, a B-50 jettisoned its Fat Man casing.

With the removal of the last Mk-4 from stockpile in 1953, the last of the Fat Man family of bombs was removed from service. In all, about 250 were manufactured: five were used in testing, five were lost in accidents and, of course, one was dropped on the city of Nagasaki. The rest, following their disarming, were either dismantled or are on display at museums such as the National Atomic Museum and the Air Force Museum at Wright Patterson Air Force Base.

[1] An alternative to the Archie unit was the 'Amos' unit, developed by the University of Michigan. It was a standby unit with a lower altitude range.
[2] This switch system was used to prevent the bomb from being triggered by radar signals reflected off the launching aircraft.
[3] In order to develop more efficient bombs, in 1948 three bombs were detonated in the Pacific (Operation Sandstone). One year later, the Mk-4 was deployed and the US arsenal increased from 50 bombs to just over 200.

Mark 5

DIMENSIONS
Length: 10 ft 8.5 in   Weight: 3175 lb
Diameter: 3 ft 7.75 in

YIELD 40 to 50 kt

CARRIERS Air Force: B-29, B-36, B-45, B-50, B-47, B-52,
               and Matador
        Navy: AJ-1, AJ-2, A-3 and Regulus 1

The Mk-5 was the first Lightweight Strategic nuclear weapon ever deployed by the United States.[1] Because of this it was one of the most carried nuclear weapons of the 1950s.

Like the majority of the bombs deployed between 1949 and 1955 the Mk-5 was a capsule fission weapon. What this means is that during peacetime the fission elements were kept separate from the casing in a special capsule. Right before the bomb was to be delivered against a target the capsule would be inserted into the casing.

The first three models of the Mk-5 were deployed in 1952. Model 3 (Mod-2) stayed in the stockpile until 1955, when it appears

to have been replaced by the Model 4, which was deployed that same year. (It is possible that the Model 3 casings were used with the Models 4s since at that time it was a common practice to use the casings of retired models for new model bombs, thus making unnecessary the cost of developing, testing and producing a new drop shape). The last Model 2 was retired in 1957 leaving only Models 1 and 4 in service.

The Mk-5 was not much of an improvement over the earlier Fat Man bomb. It was one-third lighter due to the use of aluminum instead of steel in the casing, and it didn't have the Fat Man's drop wobble because of an improved tail design (the fins even folded); however, it was not equipped with any form of parachute retard system — restricting it to only high altitude delivery — and it was equipped with fusing for an airburst only, restricting it for use against large, soft targets only. Also, since it could only be carried internally, and dropped at subsonic speeds, it could only be delivered by a few aircraft. Initially, since no other bomb at that time was any better, the Mk-5's limitations were of no significance.

With the deployment of the mission-flexible B-28, in 1959, the situation changed, and in 1963 both remaining Mk-5 models (Mods 0 and 3) were withdrawn from the stockpile.

[1] Lightweight in that it was half the weight of Little Boy.

Mark 6/Mark 18

DIMENSIONS
Length: 10 ft 8 in   Weight: 8500 lb
Diameter: 5 ft 1 in

YIELD Kiloton class (40 kt)[1]

CARRIERS Air Force: B-29, B-50, B-36, B-47, B-52
        Navy: AJ-1

The Mk-6 was the first atomic bomb to be mass produced by the United States. It was intended for use against strategic military targets; therefore, it was designed for carriage by bombers only.

With the deployment of the first Mk-6 (Mod-0), in 1951, the Air Force acquired its first new strategic weapon since the first Fat Man bomb was fielded in 1945. The produce of the Sandstone series of nuclear weapons test, it had twice the yield of the Fat Man while,

Mk-5 bomb

Mk-5 bomb casing

Mk-6 bomb

at the same time, it was lower in weight and had improved aerodynamics. The most important new feature of all was that the Mk-6 enabled the bomber's bombardier to change the detonation altitude while the aircraft was in flight.

The first model of the Mk-6 didn't last very long and the last model was withdrawn from the stockpile in 1952. That same year, however, four new models were deployed and, in 1953, a fifth model was deployed under the new designation of Mk-18[2]. A sixth and final model was deployed in 1955.

Being developed between 1949 and 1955 the Mk-6 was of the capsule bomb design. In this design, as a safety measure, the nuclear materials used by the weapon were kept separate from it in a special capsule; only just before the weapon was to be dropped was this capsule installed in the bomb. This particular feature may have prevented a few unplanned nuclear explosions and contaminations during the early 1950s.

The Mk-6/Mk-18 was an early fission weapon and required a great deal of expensive nuclear material to produce a large, explosive yield. With the development of thermonuclear weapons, however, it became possible to produce such high yields with a minimum amount of this material. Thus, by 1955 weapons like the Mk-6 were becoming more important as sources of fission material than as weapons. In 1955 the last Mod-1 was withdrawn from the stockpile. Following this, in 1956, the last Mods-2 and 3 were retired, and in 1957 the last Mod-4 was withdrawn.

Though probably having a greater amount of U235, or O Ralloy, the first Mk-18 model was also removed from the stockpile in 1957. The second model, Mod-5, however, was not removed until 1962. Its replacement in the stockpile seems to have been the Mk-28.

---

[1] On 15 November 1952, the US dropped from a B-36 a modified stockpile bomb over Eniwetok Atoll. Known as the King shot, of Operation Ivy, the bomb produced an explosion of 500 kt. Given the bombs in service, the size of the explosion and some photographic evidence, the author believes this was either a modified Mk-6 or possibly the prototype for the Mk-18.
[2] The Air Force sometimes redesignates an improved model of a weapon when there have been a large number of changes.

B-50 Superfortress loaded with Mk-4 bomb

Mark 7

DIMENSIONS
 Length: 15 ft 2.5 in   Weight: 1600 lb
 Diameter: 2 ft 6.5 in

YIELD 20 Kiloton class (W-7 warhead)

CARRIERS Air Force: B-45, B-57, F-84F, F-100C/D, and
    F-101
  Navy: A-1(AD-5N), A-3, F2H, F3H-2N, FJ-4B,
    and BOAR
  Army: Corporal and Honest John

The Mk-7 warhead was the first truly tactical nuclear weapon the United States ever developed. Deployed in more models than any other US bomb, and the first to be used by all three armed services, it was one of the most important of the early bombs.

The Mk-7 was of the same gun type fission weapon design as the earlier Little Boy bomb; as a result of this it was simpler and more reliable than earlier implosion designs, while also requiring a larger amount of nuclear material to produce a specific yield. Fusing was available for either air or ground burst and, through the use of a retractable fin system, the Mk-7 could be carried by a large number of aircraft, making it very versatile. Like many weapons deployed during this period the Mk-7 was also a capsule bomb — its nuclear elements stored separately from the bomb in a special container, ready for insertion.

The deployment history of the Mk-7 is one of the longest of any US free-fall bomb, spanning over 15 years. The average service life of any of these models was only 3.5 years, resulting in a very high number of models. Ten different models of this bomb were deployed.

STOCKPILE HISTORY OF THE MK-7 BOMB MODELS

Year	Models deployed	Models withdrawn
1952	Mod-0&1	
1953	Mod-2&3	Mod-0
1955	Mod-4	Mod-1&2
1956		Mod-3
1957	Mod-5	
1958	Mod-6	
1959		Mod-4
1961	Mod-7	
1963	Mod-8	Mod-6
1964	Mod-9	Mod-5&7
1966		Mod-8
1967		Mod-9

Mark 8

DIMENSIONS
 Length: 9 ft 8.5 in   Weight: 3230 lb
 Diameter: 1 ft 2.5 in

YIELD Kiloton class

CARRIERS Navy: A-1, F2H, A-4, AJ-1, A-3, FJ-4B,
    Air Force: F-84E

Mk-7 bomb

The Mk-8 was the second tactical bomb ever deployed and the first US nuclear weapon specifically designed for use against hardened military targets.

Equipped with a delayed action fuse, and designed to penetrate several feet of earth and concrete, the Mk-8 was intended for use against underground communications centers, headquarters, storage facilities and submarine pens. To allow for a large variety of launching aircraft, it was designed to be carried externally as well as internally; it was also an all-up bomb which did not require the insertion of the nuclear fuel core before takeoff.

The first model of the Mk-8 was deployed in 1951. The second model was then deployed in 1953, with the third and fourth models being deployed in 1955.

Though it was quite capable in its role as a penetration bomb, the Mk-8 could not be dropped by supersonic aircraft. Thus, following the deployment of the B-11 bomb, the Mk-8 was withdrawn from service. All four models were, in fact, withdrawn in 1956 — the same year as the deployment of the B-11.

Mark 12

DIMENSIONS
   Length: 13 ft   Weight: 1100 lb
   Diameter: 1 ft 10 in

YIELD Kiloton class

CARRIERS Navy: A-3, A-4, A-1(AD-5N), A-6, A-7, F9F, F2H-3, F2H-4, F3H-2, and FJ-4B[1]

The Mk-12 was the first US nuclear weapon that could be delivered at supersonic speeds. With its deployment, supersonic US attack aircraft could engage enemy targets with the maximum of survivability.

With the development of supersonic aircraft in the early 1950s a major increase occurred in the survivability of aircraft and the speed at which these aircraft could respond to an attack order. Initially, this increased capability was only with conventional weapons since neither the Mk-7 nor Mk-8 tactical nuclear bombs were designed for either external carriage or delivery at such speeds. Thus, in the early 1950s, in order not to restrict the capabilities, and survivability, of its aircraft, the Navy issued a requirement for a new tactical nuclear weapon capable of supersonic delivery. The result of this requirement was the Mk-12.

The Mk-12 was a major improvement over the earlier Mk-7. Though it still had the same fusing options as the Mk-7 — air and ground burst — it was both smaller and lighter, and could be delivered successfully at speeds up to Mach 1.4. (It could also be carried externally at these speeds). The first model of the Mk-12 was deployed in 1954, followed by a second model in 1957. The third and final model was deployed in 1960.

In the years following the deployment of the first Mk-12 bomb, improvements in the design of nuclear weapons, especially of small hydrogen bombs, were gradually making the Mk-12 obsolete. Following the deployment of the first B-43 bombs in 1961 withdrawal of the Mk-12 had begun. The first and third models of the Mk-12 had been completely withdrawn from stockpile by 1962. The last model 2 was removed in 1963.

Though the Mk-12 was a major improvement, it never replaced the Mk-7; it only supplemented it. In fact, the Mk-7 was still in production one year after the last Mk-12 was removed from the stockpile.

[1] Only three of these aircraft were supersonic.

Rearview of Mk-8 bomb

Mark 14

DIMENSIONS
Length: 18 ft 6 in   Weight: 29,851 lb max
Diameter: 5 ft 1.4 in

YIELD Megaton class (probably 7 mt)

CARRIERS Air Force: B-36

The Mk-14[1] was the first thermonuclear, or H bomb, to be deployed by the United States. It was designed for use by the B-36 in the attacking of large strategic targets.

Though hydrogen fusion had been scientifically proven before the Second World War, it was not until after the Soviet Union detonated its first fission device on 29 August 1949 that research to develop an operational hydrogen bomb was begun. Problems in the design of such a weapon and the start of the Korean War initially slowed down this research, but in mid-1951 a breakthrough was achieved in the design of a solid, or dry, hydrogen bomb. (For many years the research was oriented towards a bomb using liquidfied hydrogen isotopes). As a result of this breakthrough, on 22 May 1952, Los Alamos and Sandia labs put forth a proposal for a solid bomb code named Alarm Clock.

The same day the Alarm Clock bomb was proposed, an 'Emergency Capability' committee was formed to get a functional bomb in the US arsenal as soon as possible. The following month the Joint Chiefs formally established a military requirement for thermonuclear weapons, and in August engineering development began on the TX-14 bomb (the operational name for the Alarm Clock). Three months later, on 1 November 1952, the first hydrogen bomb was detonated, proving that a massive thermonuclear reaction could be created.

As work on the TX-14 progressed in August of 1953 the Soviet Union announced that it had broken the US monopoly on hydrogen weapons: a few days later, on 12 August, the Soviet Union detonated its first H bomb. With the Soviets now testing their own hydrogen weapons, the US program was expanded and by October at least five hydrogen bomb types were in development. Four months later, in February of 1954, the first Emergency Capability TX-14 bombs were deployed. An Alarm Clock bomb was then

proof fired on 26 April 1954 in Shot Union of test Series Castle (yield 6.9 mt).

Though the first hydrogen bomb that could be carried by an operational US bomber, the Mk-14 was an extremely crude and dangerous weapon to operate. Because of this only five were built, and in October of 1954 they were all withdrawn from service in favor of the Mk-17 bombs.

[1] All information in this section other than the fact the bomb was deployed was taken from *US Nuclear Weapons: The Secret History* by Chuck Hansen.

Mark 15

DIMENSIONS
Length: 11 ft 7 in   Weight: 7600 lb
Diameter: 2 ft 10.7 in

YIELD Megaton class (probably 1 – 2 mt)

CARRIERS Air Force: B-47 and B-52s
              Navy: AF-1 and A-3

The Mk-15 was one of the earliest thermonuclear or H-bombs to be deployed by the United States. It was designed for use by both heavy and medium bombers.

The Mk-15 was superior to previous bombs only in its yield and the mechanism by which it was achieved. Other than that, however, it was a highly limited weapon, with fusing for only air and ground burst, and no parachute retard system for low altitude delivery. Regardless of these limitations, following a successful test firing on 14 May 1954 during the Castle series (yield 1.69 Mt), the first Mk-15 bombs (Mod-0) were deployed in April of 1955. The second model (Mod-2) then entered the stockpile in March of 1957. Both the Mod-0 and Mod-2 remained in service until 1965.

In February of 1957, before the third model of the Mk-15 was deployed, the first model of what was called the Mk-39 free-fall bomb was fielded. Though viewed as a lightweight version of the Mk-15, this bomb was quite differently equipped with a parachute system and fusing for only contact burst. Information on this bomb is therefore listed separately under Mk-39.

Mk-12 bomb

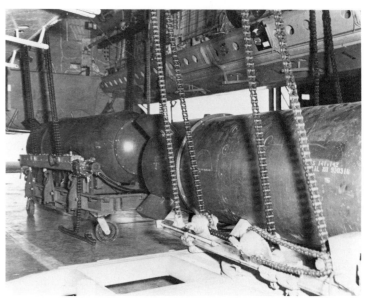

Two Mk-15 bombs

Given the time period in which the Mk-15 was developed, it is reasonable to assume that the Mk-15 was a capsule bomb in which the nuclear fission material was kept separate from the weapon's casing in peacetime.

Mark 17/ Mark 24

DIMENSIONS

Length: 24 ft 9.5 in   Weight: 41,400 lb (21 tons)
Diameter: 5 ft 1.4 in

YIELD Megaton class (probably 15 mt)

CARRIERS Air Force: B-36

The Mk-17/Mk-24 bombs were the next two drop-capable thermonuclear devices the United States ever deployed. These bombs were by far the largest nuclear devices ever operated by the US. They are described together in this section because the two bombs were identical to each other except in the design of the bombs' primary (a small fission bomb was used to start the fusion reaction).

The Mk-17/24 bombs were extremely crude weapons by comparison to contemporary nuclear devices. Equipped with only airburst fusing, they could be used effectively against large, soft targets such as cities or large military reserves. Also, though it was parachute retarded, its 64-foot ribbon chute was used more to stabilize the weapon than slow it down for a soft landing. The first

bombs, Mod-0, came into service between April and September of 1954 (five Emergency Capability or EC-17s and 10 EC-24s). Six months later the Mk-1724 Mod-1 bombs were deployed, and by September of 1955 all previous Mod-0s had been converted to the Mod-1 standard. Production of the Mk-17 Mod-2 began in June of 1956, and by 1957 all Mk-17s had been converted to Mod-2.

The Mk-24 was never converted up to Mod-2 and was instead retired from the stockpile in the fall of 1956. The following year, retirement of the Mk-17 began, and the last model was withdrawn in November of 1957.

Though no official reason has been offered for the Mk-17's short service life, it is reasonable to assume that the weapon's size was a contributing factor. Not only was it impossible for any aircraft other than the giant B-36 to carry it, but even this bomber was severely restricted in its combat capabilities when carrying this bomb. The best description of the phenomenon was the one that the pilots of the B-36, used to drop test the bomb shape, gave. According to them, the *bomb* released the *bomber* instead of the other way around!

Like most bombs developed in the early- to mid-1950s, the Mk-17/Mk-24 bombs were of the capsule design in which the bomb's fission primary was inserted just prior to the weapon's use. Intended as a safety feature, this design worked quite effectively on 22 May 1957 when a B-36 bomber, 3.5 miles from Kirkland AFB tower, dropped its Mk-17 casing from an altitude of 1700 feet. (The bomb took the bomb bay doors with it). On impact with the ground, the casing's conventional explosives went off, creating a crater 12 feet deep and 25 feet wide, and strewing debris over a mile away. Since the capsule wasn't installed, however, not only was there no nuclear explosion, but radiation contamination was limited only to the dispersal of the casing's depleted uranium shell. This casing was approximately 3.5 inches thick.

An example of the Mk-17 is on display at both the National Atomic Museum and at the Air Force Museum at Wright-Patterson AFB.

Mk-17 bomb

Hotpoint (W-34)

DIMENSIONS

Length: 8 ft internal,
        12 ft external   Weight: 1500 lb
Diameter: 1 ft 7 in

YIELD Low kiloton class

CARRIERS Navy: A-1, A-3, A-4, P-3, FJ-4B

The 'Hotpoint' bomb, designated Mk-105 by the Navy, was the first nuclear weapon designed for laydown delivery. It was the first multi-role, modular design bomb ever deployed.

The term 'Laydown' means that the bomb is to soft-land on its target, with detonation occurring only after a predetermined time interval. (This is done to give the launching aircraft enough time to escape the blast during low level bombing). To accomplish this, the Hotpoint used a 12.5-inch parachute to slow its descent and then a special inner cookie cutter-shaped nose, designed specifically to lessen the impact shock (the external nose would blow off just prior to impact).

Its laydown delivery capability was just the first unique feature of the Hotpoint. Because it used a timer for detonation, it could be used as an airburst weapon or as nuclear depth charge. Through the changing of the nose, tail or fin sections — two types were available — the Hotpoint could also be tailored for use on any type of aircraft, and for internal or external carriage.

The first Hotpoint bombs (Mod-0) came into service in June of 1958. In 1960 a second model (Mod-2) was also deployed. All models were subsequently withdrawn in 1964.

Lulu (Mk-101)

DIMENSIONS

Length: 7 ft 6 in   Weight: 1200 lb
Diameter: 1 ft 6 in

YIELD Kiloton class (W-34 warhead, probably 10 kt)

CARRIERS Navy: S-2, P-2, P-3, SH-3, A-1, A-3, A-4, FJ-4B

The 'Lulu' depth bomb is the second nuclear depth bomb to be deployed by the US Navy. It appears to have replaced the Betty depth bomb as the primary anti-submarine weapon of US aircraft.

Designated the Mk-101 by the US Navy, the Lulu was designed to destroy ships and submarines by rupturing their hulls with a massive underwater shockwave. (During the Bikini Atoll nuclear tests such a shockwave was proven more effective in sinking ships than an airburst). Detonating was handled by hydrostats (depth gauges) which triggered when a pre-set depth was attained (a timer was also present as a backup trigger to the hydrostats).

The first model of the Lulu was deployed in 1958. In 1959, a second model was deployed, followed by a third in 1960. Though

in 1961 the second model (Mod-1) was retired, in 1962 two more models, Mods 4 and 5, were deployed.

Following the deployment of the Mk-57 bomb, the Navy began to retire the Lulu from the arsenal. In 1966, the last model 1 (Mod-0) was removed from the stockpile. Following this, in 1971, the last examples of the three remaining models were withdrawn.

Betty Depth Bomb

DIMENSIONS

Length: 10 ft 2 in   Weight: 1243 lb
Diameter: 2 ft 7.5 in

YIELD 5 to 10 kt

CARRIERS Navy: A-1 (AD-5N), P-2V-5, 6, 7; S-2F-2, P5M-1, P5M-2 and the P6M

Two years after the first Mk-7s were deployed, the Navy fielded a new bomb using the same W-7 warhead. Called the 'Betty' depth bomb, it was developed to give the Navy anti-submarine aircraft a nuclear means of destroying enemy submarines: surface ships could also be destroyed by this weapon.

Though it used the same warhead as the Mk-7 bomb, the Betty was completely different in external appearance. Fusing was also different, with the Mk-7's contact or altimeter units having been replaced by hydrostatic detonators — which set the bomb off at a prescribed depth.

On 25 September 1959, a Betty depth bomb was accidentally lost in Puget Sound when its P-5M carrying aircraft had to ditch near Whidbey Island. Though the casing was never recovered, the fuel core was not installed — thus, it was impossible for any nuclear explosion or contamination to occur.

Unlike its cousin bomb the Mk-7, the Betty's time in service was not long, with the last being withdrawn in 1960. (It was probably replaced by the Lulu).

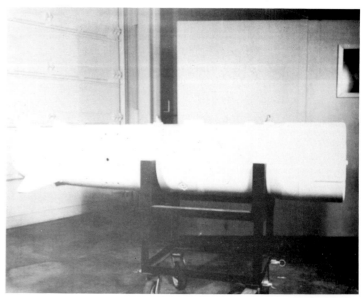

Hotpoint bomb

Mark 21/
Mark 36

DIMENSIONS
    Length: 12 ft 5.8 in   Weight: approx 17,500 lb
    Diameter: 4 ft 10.5 in

YIELD Megaton class (Mk-36 probably 10 mt)

CARRIERS Air Force: B-36, B-47 and B-52

The Mark 21/Mark 36 bombs were parachute retarded thermonuclear weapons intended for use against both hard and soft targets. For seven years they served with the US Air Force. The Mk-21, the first bomb, was deployed in 1955. For some reason, within a year of this, it was withdrawn (the author believes improvements in the design of hydrogen bombs quickly made the Mk-21 obsolete). By 1957 none were left in the stockpile. Following the withdrawal of the Mk-21 the weapons casings were reused—converted—into a new weapon called the Mk-36. The first two models of this bomb were deployed in 1956, with a third coming into service in 1958.

Though it was parachute retarded, the Mk-36 was equipped with fusing for either air or contact burst only. Thus, following the deployment of the smaller Mk-41 in 1960, the Mk-36 was no longer necessary and in 1962 all three models were withdrawn from the stockpile.

On 20 May 1956, at Eniwetok Atoll, the United States successfully dropped its first thermonuclear weapon from a B-52. Some believe that this test, known officially as Shot Cherokee of Series Redwing, was done with a Mk-17 bomb. This author believes this test actually involved the Mk-36 and bases this hypothesis on the following points: one, the Mk-36 had just entered the stockpile at the time of the test (thus it would be reasonable to live fire it); two, the last Mk-17 was being retired from the stockpile; and three, on analysis, if a Mk-17 was installed in a B-52 only three inches of clearance would exist between the front and rear of the bomb and the front or rear bulkhead of the B-52s bomb bay. (This would be too little to allow insertion of the fuel capsule). It is worth noting that during this particular weapon test the bomb was dropped prematurely and detonated 3.5 miles from the target.

Lulu depth bombs in P-2V bomb bay

Betty depth bomb

Mk-36 bomb

Mark 27

DIMENSIONS

Length: 11 ft 9.5 in   Weight: 3150 lb
Diameter: 2 ft 6.2 in

YIELD Megaton class

CARRIERS Navy: A-3, A-5, and Regulus II

The Mark 27 was the second, megaton class, strategic bomb to be deployed by the US Navy. It supplemented the Mk-15 in the Navy arsenal for six years.

Like the Mk-15 that preceded it, the Mk-27 was a high yield nuclear device designed for use against large strategic targets. Equipped with fusing for either air or ground burst, it could be used against both cities and hardened military installations. However, because it was designed for internal carriage only, it was restricted to only three carrying vehicles: the A-3 Skywarrior, the A-5 Vigilante and the Regulus II cruise missile.

Though it was probably the most powerful bomb the Navy ever deployed, the deployment of the first Mk-27 model, in 1958, was marred by the December cancellation of the Regulus II cruise missile. As a result of this the Mk-27 came into service with only two delivery vehicles: the A-3, and the A-5. The second model of the Mk-27 was then deployed in 1960.

The election of John F Kennedy to the presidency, in 1960, caused some major changes in the Navy's role in our nation's defense. A firm believer in the superiority of the ballistic missile, Kennedy began redirecting funding away from programs involving manned nuclear strike aircraft to those involving either missiles or multi-purpose aircraft. As a result of this, by 1962, the Navy had been forced to begin drawing down its nuclear bomber force. By 1965 all the A-3s had been converted into ECM aircraft or tankers, and the A-5s were reconnaissance aircraft (RA-5C).

The loss of the Mk-27's carrying aircraft led to its withdrawal from service; the first model was withdrawn in 1962. In 1963 a third model was deployed; both remaining models of the Mk-27 were withdrawn from the stockpile in 1964. The next year the last Mk-15 was withdrawn, leaving the B-43 as the only megaton class bomb deployed by the Navy.

Mk-27 bomb

Though it was not equipped with a parachute system, the Mk-27 could be successfully dropped at low altitudes using the Low Altitude Bombing System or LABS. In this method of attack the bomber pilot approached the planned target at a very low altitude and at a very high speed. Once the aircraft was a certain distance from the target the pilot put his aircraft into a hard climb releasing the bomb when the aircraft was at a pre-determined climb angle. Once released, the momentum of the bomb caused it to respond like a projectile, delivering a ballistic trajectory to its planned target. As a result of this method of bomb delivery, the launching aircraft was given enough time to escape the area before the bomb exploded. Another advantage of this bombing method was that the launching aircraft could throw the bomb over hills to attack targets on the other side without being seen.

The Mark 28 Series

The Mk-28 bomb is one of the oldest nuclear weapons in the arsenal. The first warhead design to be designated a weapon system, this bomb can be assembled into any one of five different drop shapes, allowing it to be tailored for any kind of aircraft, or attack mode. (Six different models of the warhead were also developed).

To describe accurately the different types of drop shapes in which this weapon was deployed, and the different capabilities each has, it has been necessary to write about them as if they were separate bomb types.

The first Mk-28 drop shapes to be deployed were the Internal (IN), version; the External (EX), version; and the Retarded External (RE), version.

Mk-28 External (EX)

DIMENSIONS

Length: 14 ft 2.5 in   Weight: 2040 lb
Diameter: 1 ft 8 in

YIELD High kiloton to megaton

CARRIERS Air Force: B-52, F-4, F-100, F-101, F-104, F-105,
                Mace and Hound Dog
         Navy: A-4, A-6, FJ-4B and F-4

The EX version of the Mk-28 was designed for use by both bombers and fighter bombers in the attack of strategic targets.

Like many earlier bombs the Mk-28EX could be equipped with either air or contact burst fusing only. It had no parachute system, which restricted it to medium and high altitude delivery. A special feature of this bomb was a folding fin system which allowed this weapon to be carried as close to the wing as possible, reducing aerodynamic drag and improving aircraft maneuverability.

The first two models of the MK-28EX, Mod-0 and Mod-1, were deployed in 1958. In 1961 Mod-0 was withdrawn, and was replaced the following year by the Mod-2. The Mod-3 entered the arsenal in 1963.

The last Mod-3s were retired from the stockpile in 1969. Following this the last Mod-1 was withdrawn in 1978 and the last Mod-2 was retired in 1980.

air or ground burst only. A further restriction in its capabilities is that no parachute system is deployed, making it possible to deliver this weapon from medium to high altitudes only.

The first model of the Mk-28IN was deployed in 1958. This particular model was removed from the stockpile in 1961, but in 1962 a second model (Mod-2) was deployed, which brought the Mk-28IN back into service. A third model (Mod-4) was deployed in 1964.

The second model of the Mk-28IN was removed from the inventory in 1978. Recent information reveals the third model has been withdrawn, replaced by the B-83 bomb. It is not yet known when the last model of the Mk-28IN was retired.

Mk-28 Internal (IN)

DIMENSIONS

Length: 8 ft   Weight: 1980 lb
Diameter: 1 ft 8 in

YIELD High kiloton to megaton

CARRIERS Air Force: B-52, B-66, B-47, F-105, Mace and
                    Hound Dog
         Navy: A-3 and A-5

The Mk-28IN was designed for use only by aircraft with internal bomb bays (bombers and the F-105). Like the EX version, it was intended for use against strategic targets.

Though smaller and lighter than earlier weapons, the Mk-28IN was not a better weapon, since it is equipped with fusing for either

Mk-28 Retarded External (RE)

DIMENSIONS

Length: 13 ft 9.5 in   Weight: 2170 lb
Diameter: 1 ft 8 in

YIELD High kiloton to megaton

CARRIERS Air Force: B-52, F-4, F-100, F-101, F-104 and
                    F-105
         Navy: A-4, A-6, FJ-4B and F-4

The Retarded External was basically a Mk-28EX equipped with a parachute system. Thanks to the addition of a four foot pilot chute and a 28 foot ribbon chute the Mk-28RE could be dropped from lower altitudes and at higher speeds than the IN

F-100 Super Sabre loaded with Mk-28

or EX versions. This, however, was the only improvement in this weapon since the fusing was the same as in the previous models, air or ground burst only.

The first two models of the Mk-28RE, Mod-0 and Mod-1, were deployed in 1958. The first model was withdrawn from the stockpile in 1961 and was replaced the following year with the third model. The fourth and final model was deployed in 1963.

Six years after it was first deployed, the last Mod-3, the MK-28RE, was withdrawn from the stockpile. After this the last Mod-1 was retired in 1976 and the final RE (Mod-2) was removed from the stockpile in 1980.

In order to improve the penetration capability of its bombers, following the year 1960, the Air Force began to emphasize a low level, below radar, method of attack instead of the high altitude system used in previous years. As a result of this change in tactics the last two versions of the Mk-28 were developed, the Mk-28FI and the Mk-28RI.

Mk-28 Full Fusing Internal (FI)

DIMENSIONS
Length: 12 ft 1.25 in   Weight: 2340 lb
Diameter: 1 ft 10 in

YIELD High kiloton to megaton

CARRIERS Air Force: B-52, B-66, B-47, F-105, Mace
and Hound Dog
Navy: A-3 and A-5

The FI, or Full Fusing Internal Mk-28, is the only model of this bomb to have fusing for air, ground, and delayed action burst. As a result of this, and a parachute system consisting of a four-foot pilot chute, a 16-inch extraction chute, a five-foot by four-inch main chute and a two-foot stabilizer chute, it is the only version of the Mk-28 that can be used in laydown applications. It has been reported that this model can be successfully dropped from as low as 300 feet, with a 600 foot CEP.

The first model of the Mk-28FI, Mod-2, was deployed in 1962. A gradual replacement of this model with the second model, Mod-5, began in 1977. In 1980, the last FI Mod-2 was removed from the stockpile. As of last report the Mk-28FI Mod-5 is still in service awaiting replacement with the B-83.

Mk-28 Retarded Internal (RI)

DIMENSIONS
Length: 12 ft 3 in   Weight: 2340 lb
Diameter: 1 ft 10 in

YIELD High kiloton to megaton

CARRIERS Air Force: B-52, B-66, B-47, F-105, Mace
and Hound Dog
Navy: A-3 and A-5

The Retarded Internal is the fifth and final Mk-28 drop shape to be deployed. The same externally as the Mk-28FI, this bomb differs in that it has fusing for air and contact burst only. Because of this, in order for it to be dropped at low altitudes, a different parachute system is used, consisting of a four-foot pilot

Mk-28IN and Mk-28RE bombs

Mk-28IN in B-52 bomb bay

An accident damaged Mk-28RI bomb

Mk-39 bomb

chute, a 16-foot by six-inch ribbon extraction chute, a 60-foot solid chute, and a two-foot by six-inch stabilizer chute.

Only one model of the Mk-28RI was deployed, the Mod-4, in 1964. As of last report this bomb is still operational in the US arsenal, awaiting replacement with the B-83.

Officially, the Mk-28RI is the only version of the Mk-28 to have been dropped accidentally. On 17 January 1966 a B-52 carrying four of these bombs collided with its KC-135 tanker during refueling. One of the bombs was lost at sea for three months, one parachuted to earth safely and the two remaining were destroyed when their explosives went off on contact with the ground. Several other accidents in the 1960s may have involved this bomb type.

At this moment, even as the first Mk-28 bombs are being replaced by the B-83, the remaining Mk-28s are being upgraded with new electrical and safety systems and, where possible, PBX-9502 insensitive high explosives. These enhancements will improve the safety of the bombs until the last Mk-28 has been replaced in the mid-1990s.

Mark 39

DIMENSIONS
Length: 11 ft 6 in   Weight: 6600 lb
Diameter: 2 ft 10.5 in

YIELD 4 megatons

CARRIERS Air Force: B-52, B-58, B-36 and Snark
Army: Redstone

The only weapon carried by the B-58 Hustler bomber until 1962, and the only warhead ever carried by the Snark Intercontinental cruise missile, the Mk-39 was one of the most important bombs in the US stockpile from the late 1950s to early 1960s.

Begun as a lightweight version of the Mk-15, the Mk-39 was one of the smallest megaton class bombs to be deployed in the 1950s. (Regardless of this, it was still a very large nuclear weapon). Equipped with an elaborate parachute system consisting of one six-foot pilot chute, a 28-foot ribbon canopy, a 68-foot octagonal canopy chute and, finally, a 100-foot solid, flat, canopy chute, the Mk-39 was also one of the first H bombs that could be dropped successfully from low altitudes. If a high altitude, freefall delivery was desired, the parachute system was simply jettisoned. Fusing, however, was limited to contact burst, making the Mk-39 more effective against hardened military targets.

The first model of this bomb was deployed in 1957. In the following year the model carried by the B-58 Hustler, the Mod-0-B-58 pod, was deployed — as were Models 2 and 3 of the free-fall bomb.

Though the federal government rarely informs the public when a particular bomb type is tested, we do know that, on 1 August 1956, a Redstone missile was launched from Johnston Island and detonated at an altitude of 250,000 feet (Shot Teak of test Series Hardtack 1). Since officially the Redstone only carried the Mk-39, it is reasonable to assume that the warhead used in this test was a Mk-39. (A similar test occurred later that year).

On 24 January 1961, a B-52 carrying two bombs broke up over Goldsboro, North Carolina, following a structural failure in the starboard wing. One bomb broke up on impact, while the other was recovered intact due to its parachute system's deployment. Considering the time of the accident, the fact that the weapon had a parachute system, that only two bombs were carried by the bomber and from photographic evidence at the National Atomics Museum's display on nuclear weapon accidents, the author believes that one or both of these bombs were Mk-39s. Because a portion of the other bomb was never found, no one is allowed to dig at the site without Air Force permission.

In 1964, the first model of the Mk-39, the Mod-0, was withdrawn. Following this, in 1965, the warhead for the B-58 Hustler pod was completely replaced by the Mk-53. The last two Mk-39 models were retired in 1966.

Mark 41

DIMENSIONS
Length: 12 ft 4.8 in   Weight: 10,670 lb
Diameter: 4 ft 2 in

YIELD Megaton class (possibly 24 mt)

CARRIERS Air Force: B-47 and B-52

The Mk-41 was the third largest free-fall nuclear device ever deployed by the United States. Larger than either the earlier Mk-39, or the later B-53, from 1962 until its retirement it was the largest nuclear device carried by US aircraft.

The Mk-41 was a large, thermonuclear weapon design for use against large, soft, strategic targets. Because it was designed for this purpose, it was equipped with fusing for either air or contact burst only; no delayed action. In the same way, though it was equipped with a parachute retarded system, consisting of a 5-foot pilot chute and a 16-foot by six-inch ribbon chute, laydown not possible (as with many bombs, free-fall was possible by jettisoning the parachute package). Only one model of the Mk-41 was ever deployed, with the first being stockpiled in 1960. These bombs remained in the stockpile until 1976.

Mark 53

DIMENSIONS
Length: 12 ft 4.8 in   Weight: 8800 lb
Diameter: 4 ft 2 in

YIELD 9 mt

CARRIERS Air Force: B-52, B-58, B-47, XB-70 and Titan II

The Mk-53 is the largest and most powerful free-fall bomb in the present US arsenal. Now carried only by the B-52, it is the last of the big bombs.

The Mk-53 is the most flexible of all the big bombs to be deployed by the United States, with a capability against both large,

soft, targets and hardened military facilities. Unlike the Mk-41, Mk-36 and Mk-39, the Mk-53 is equipped with full fusing options: air, contact burst and laydown. It also had available two parachute systems, a laydown system consisting of three 48-foot parachutes and a standard retard set consisting of a five-foot pilot chute and a 16-foot main chute. The selection of fusing appears to have been possible while in flight; however, selection of the parachute set must be done before the aircraft is airborne so that the ground crew can attach the required system. (If after takeoff a free-fall mode of delivery is desired, the parachute set can be jettisoned).

The first three models of the Mk-53, the Mod-0, the 53Y-1, and the BA-35-Mod-0, were deployed in 1962. A fourth model—the 53Y-Mod-2—was deployed in 1964.

The Mk-53 display at the National Atomic Museum is very extensive: it shows the clip in assembly, which allowed the bomb to be quickly and safely attached to a B-52's bomb bay rack. The bands holding the unit were released by explosive units (an integrated mechanical and electrical system prevents an inadvertant release of the weapon). Also in the display is a pie-shaped piece cut from another Mk-53 casing. This piece clearly shows the casing's thick honeycomb blanket of aluminum which acted as a shock absorber for the laydown burst option.

All models of the Mk-53 are still in the arsenal awaiting replacement by the B-83 strategic bomb. (It has been quoted that approximately one hundred-fifty examples of this bomb were in the stockpile in 1983, not counting the warheads for the now retired Titan II ICBMs).

Mk-41 bomb

Mk-53 bomb

Mark 57

DIMENSIONS
    Length: 9 ft 9.5 in   Weight: 510 lb
    Diameter: 1 ft 2.75 in

YIELD 5 to 10 kt (variable)

CARRIERS Navy: A-4, A-6, A-7, F/A-18, P-3 and SH-3

The Mk-57 is the smallest free-fall bomb in the US Nuclear arsenal. It was designed to fill a request from the Navy and Marine Corps for a small, low yield, tactical bomb.

The Mk-57 is probably the most flexible bomb in the US arsenal. Because of its small size it can be carried by every Navy attack aircraft in service, regardless of size, with little effect on the vehicle's performance. Thanks to full fusing options it can also be used in a number of different modes: from a contact burst weapon against hardened targets like beach fortifications, to an airburst weapon against large, soft targets like armor in the field, to a laydown weapon against military facilities in the enemy's rear. (A parachute system is used with this option). The Mk-57 is also equiped with hydrostatic detonators, allowing it to be used against submarines and ships at sea. The only capability this bomb doesn't have is the ability to penetrate earth or concrete.

A total of six different models of the Mk-57 have been deployed. Models 1, 2 and 5 were deployed in 1963 and are still in service. Models 3, 4 and 6, though deployed in 1966, were retired in 1972.

At present approximately 1000 Mk-57s are in the stockpile. It has been reported, however, that work is underway to replace this bomb in the ASW role with a new weapon, beginning in the 1990s.

B-11

DIMENSIONS
    Length: 12 ft 2.5 in   Weight: 3343 lb
    Diameter: 1 ft 2 in

YIELD Kiloton class

CARRIERS Navy attack and fighter aircraft (not specific)

The B-11, or Mk-91 as the Navy designated it, appears to have been the replacement weapon for the Mk-8 penetration bomb. Though it was in service for only five years, it was a major weapon of US Navy attack aircraft.

Like its predecessor the Mk-8, the B-11 was a gun-type fission weapon designed for use against hardened or underground targets. *Unlike* its predecessor, it could penetrate up to 22 feet of reinforced concrete, 90 feet of hard sand, 120 feet of clay or five inches of armor plate. Its delayed-action fuse would then fire 1.5 to two minutes after penetration. The B-11 could be carried externally and launched at supersonic speeds, *and* the fact that it was three feet longer than the Mk-8 did not effect its ability to be carried internally by Navy bomber aircraft.

The first B-11 was deployed in 1956. Only one model was ever manufactured, and the last B-11 was withdrawn in 1960.

No official reason is given for the B-11's short service life, but an understanding of the period could provide a clue. Within two years of the B-11's deployment, the first small, high-yield thermonuclear H bombs were deployed (see the B-27 and B-28). Though these early bombs were strategic weapons, they were both 10 to 100 times more powerful and, at the same time, were lighter

B-11 bomb

in weight than the B-11, making them more effective. Furthermore, one year after the retirement of the B-11, the first B-43 tactical H bombs were deployed. Though it was not intended as a replacement for the B-11, the B-43 does have some penetration capability.

A B-11 casing is in storage at the Pantex plant in Amarillo, Texas. It is part of the National Atomic Museum collection.

B-43

DIMENSIONS
Length: 12 ft 6 in
Diameter: 1 ft 6 in
Weight: 2100 lb

YIELD Low megaton class (1 to 2 mt)

CARRIERS Air Force: F-100, F-101, F-104, F-105, F-4, A-7, F-111, F-16, B-47, B-52, B-58, B-66 and FB-111
Navy: FJ-4B, A-1, A-4, A-3, A-5, A-6, A-7 and F-4

The B-43 can be carried and delivered by more aircraft than any other megaton class bomb in the US arsenal. At this time it is the primary megaton class freefall bomb in the stockpile.

The replacement for the Mk-12 tactical bomb, the B-43 is for use against either strategic targets, like cities or large military facilities; and tactical targets such as troops in the field. Designed with a steel spike in its nose, it can also be used against hardened military targets such as underground command posts, communications centers and nuclear storage facilities. (Because of this it may also be the replacement for the B-11 penetration bomb). A parachute system is also available, as well as fusing for either air or delayed action burst. (Selection of delivery mode and fusing must be done before the bomb is airborne).

The first two models of this weapon (Mods 0 and 1) were deployed in 1961 and 1962, respectively. Following this, in 1963, Mod-3 was deployed and, in 1965, both Mod-2 and Mod-4 became operational.

In 1968, the first model of the B-43, the Mod-0, was withdrawn from the arsenal. Following this, in 1976, the last of the Mod-3s was withdrawn from the stockpile, leaving only Mods 1, 2 and 4 in the stockpile. In the near future, these models are to be progressively replaced by the B-83 in the strategic role, and in the tactical role by the B-61.

B-61

DIMENSIONS
Length: 11 ft 9.5 in
Diameter: 1 ft 1.3 in
Weight: 710 lb

YIELD High kiloton class (variable from 100 to 500 kt)

CARRIERS Air Force: B-52, B-1B, FB-111, F-100, F-105 (internally), F-4, F-111, F-16 and F-15E
Navy/Marines: A-4, A-6, A-7, AV-8B and F/A-18

The B-61 is a lightweight thermonuclear weapon designed for use in tactical operations. There are more of this type of bomb in the US stockpile than any other free-fall nuclear device.

The B-61 is designed for external carriage by high speed aircraft. It can be dropped from high altitudes as a free-fall bomb or, when equipped with a special kevlar parachute, dropped from as low as 50 feet (the parachute can also slow the weapon down from 1000 mph to 35 mph in two seconds). Full fusing is also available on the newest models, allowing air, ground or delayed action burst. As a further capability, the selection of fusing and bomb yield can

B-43 bomb

Laydown landing of B-61 bomb

be done while airborne, with the pilot not having to do anything more than 'turn a knob.'

The first models of the B-61, Mods 0 and 1, were fielded in 1968. Mod-2 was then deployed in 1975, with Mod-5 entering service in 1977. The last models, Mods 3 and 4, were deployed in 1979. As of this writing, all models are still listed as in stockpile.

The B-61 Mods 3 and 4 are the safest and most versatile models of this bomb. They carry the most sophisticated security devices, PBX-9502 Insensitive High Explosive, and full fusing options. According to published information, at this time it is planned to upgrade all other B-61 models to the Mods 3 and 4 configuration.

B-83

DIMENSIONS
    Length: approx 12 ft   Weight: 2408 lb
    Diameter: Probably between 18 and 20 in

YIELD Megaton class (probably variable)

CARRIERS Air Force: B-1B, B-52, FB-111, F-111, F-4, F-16,
        F-15, and A-7
        Navy: A-4, A-6, A-7, F/A-18, and AV-8B

The B-83 is the first new type free-fall bomb to be deployed by the United States in 14 years. It is intended to 'enhance the effectiveness of the strategic nuclear gravity bomb stockpile.'

Development of the B-83 can be traced back to an earlier weapon called the B-77. Begun in 1974, this bomb was a megaton class weapon intended for low altitude delivery by the B-1A bomber. During development, the cost of this bomb rose to such an extent that, in 1978, Congress ordered the the program cancelled, and a new program begun — to develop a cheaper strategic bomb that still incorporated the B-77's important features. Development of this cheaper bomb would begin in January of 1979, and by 1981 it was known as the B-83.

The B-83 is the first megaton class free-fall bomb to be specifically designed for laydown delivery against hardened military targets such as ICBM silos, underground command posts, communications centers and nuclear weapons storage facilities. Thanks to a special parachute system, it can be delivered by aircraft making a high subsonic pass while at an altitude of 150 feet, with an accuracy of around 600 feet. Full fusing is also available, allowing either air, ground or delayed action burst — which, (as well as warhead yield), can be selected in flight by the pilot.

The B-83 is intended to replace the B-28, B-43 and B-53 bombs currently in service. This replacement will not be on a one for one basis, because the US built three times as many of these bombs as was necessary. (Each bomb type was deployed in groups of three, each having different yield and fusing.) With the deployment of this versatile bomb, this overstock will no longer be necessary.

There will also be a marked improvement in the safety of the nation's nuclear stockpile with the deployment of the B-83. Many of the older weapons to be replaced by this bomb use extremely sensitive explosives and have very old safety systems, making them susceptible to both accidental and unauthorized detonation. As for those that can be retrofitted, they are still not what is called 'one point safe,' where a detonation at one point of the high explosive

FB-111 loaded with two B-83 bombs

Walleye bomb loaded on A-7 Corsair

chain will not have a one in a million chance of causing a nuclear explosion equal to the yield of four pounds of TNT. Besides being one point safe, and having insensitive high explosives known as PBX-9502, the B-83 will have a multi-number security code with a self destruct system, which is designed to disable key components of the detonation system if the proper pass code is not transmitted within a certain number of tries.

Initial deployment of the B-83 has already occured.

Walleye (AGM-62)

SPECIFICATIONS

	WALLEYE I	WALLEYE II
Length:	11 ft 3 in	13 ft
Diameter:	1 ft 3 in	1 ft 6 in
Fin Span:	3 ft 9 in	4 ft 3 in
Weight:	1100 lb	1300 lb

PERFORMANCE

Range:	16 mi	35 mi

WARHEAD
Conventional: 850 lb
Nuclear: 2000 lb
Both could carry a W-72 warhead of approx 100 kt

POWERPLANT Ram air turbine in rear of bomb

GUIDANCE Command control; Television (Electro-Optical)

CONTRACTOR Martin Marietta

CARRIERS A-4, A-7, and F-4

The Walleye is the most accurate nuclear free-fall bomb ever deployed by the United States. Throughout the 1970s it was one of the primary weapons of US attack aircraft.

Development of the Walleye began in 1963 at the US Navy ordnance test station, China Lake, California. In July of 1964, an invitation was issued to civilian contractors to submit proposals for the project and in January of 1965 contract definition began between the designs submitted by Hughes, Martin Marietta and North American Aviation. The Martin Marietta design was selected in 1966, and with the awarding of a $12.1 million contract production began. The first bombs were ready that same year.

The Walleye is a self-guided glider bomb similar in idea to the Azon bombs of the Second World War. To utilize this weapon, all the pilot of the launching aircraft has to do is focus the Walleye's internal television camera on to the planned target. Once released, the Walleye's internal computer takes over, watches the image for any variation, corrects the glide path until the image is correct again and thus homes in on the target.

Before the year was out the Walleyes were seeing service in Vietnam attacking bridges, railways and other targets requiring pinpoint accuracy. So effective was Walleye I that by the end of 1966 the contract had been increased by $11.1 million. Early the

next year the contract was further increased, with the addition of a $34.5 million order by the US Air Force. To meet these new production requirements, in November of 1967, Hughes was made second source contractor.

By 1968 it had become apparent that a new, more powerful bomb or longer-range bomb was necessary to meet future threats. To meet these requirements, work began on a nuclear warhead (for incorporation into the Walleye if necessary) and the development of an enlarged, longer range bomb called Walleye II. (The bomb was initially known as Fat Albert and large scale Walleye). Deployment of the nuclear warhead began in 1970 and pilot production of the Walleye II commenced in March of 1971. Initial operational evaluation of the Walleye II was carried out between February and July of 1973, and service approval was granted in January of 1974. That same year, however, funding for additional production was deleted from the military budget.

In 1975 a new form of guidance known as Extended Range/ Data Link was incorporated into the Walleye II's design. In this system the launching aircraft's pilot can control and lock the bomb on target after it has been released from the aircraft. (This system also allows the weapon to be controlled by a second aircraft). Conversion of both Walleye I and Walleye II to this system began that same year.

In 1979 the nuclear warhead for the Walleye was withdrawn from the arsenal, but as of last report Walleye still appears to be in service.

Walleye bomb

Walleye bomb in flight

Strategic Bombers[1]

B-29 Superfortress

SPECIFICATIONS (B-29B)

Length: 99 ft	Span: 141 ft 3 in
Height: 27 ft 9 in	Weight: Max 137,500 lb

PERFORMANCE

Speed: Max 363 mph	Ceiling: 31,850 ft
Range: 4200 mi	

POWERPLANT Four 2200 hp Wright R-3350-51 Double Cyclone engines

MAX ARMAMENT 20,000 lb maximum bomb load plus 12 machine guns and one 37mm cannon

TYPES OF NUCLEAR ORDNANCE Mk-1, Mk-3, Mk-4, Mk-6/18 and Mk-5

CREW 13 men

MANUFACTURER Boeing Aircraft

NUMBERS MANUFACTURED 3970 built in World War II

The aircraft used to drop the Little Boy bomb on Hiroshima, 6 August 1945, the B-29 was the United States' first nuclear capable bomber. Though a slow moving, prop driven bomber, the B-29 was the nation's original 'big stick' during the late 1940s.

A great deal has been written about the B-29 since it last flew in the 1950s. Most or all of it, however, has been in regard to its use as a conventional bomber during the Second World War and the Korean conflict. This book emphasizes the bomber's operation-

al experience as a nuclear delivery aircraft.

Boeing Aircraft began development of the B-29 in 1938 as a high altitude, pressurized version of their B-17 bomber. Following the fall of France, in October of 1940, the Army Air Force began showing an interest in the plane, particularly in an improved version later called the B-50. Construction of the first B-29s was then begun in October of 1940 with the first prototype taking to the air on 21 September 1942. The first production model was then completed on 15 April 1943.

By the time the B-29 was ready, the war had turned in favor of the Allies, causing work on the long range B-50 to be halted and the B-29 itself to be reoriented for use in the Pacific theater. In September of that same year people working on the atomic bomb selected the B-29 for use as the initial drop aircraft.[2] Modifications to the first aircraft began in early 1944 (when the plane became available) and in March drop testing began using full scale models of the Thin Man and the Fat Man bombs. Problems with the Thin Man's release mechanism would cause a delay in this testing when, during a test, the bomb was released prematurely, damaging the B-29's bomb bay doors. (To carry the Thin Man the B-29s twin bomb bays had to be linked together to form one long bay.) Testing would not resume until June of 1944, by which time the Little Boy bomb had replaced the Thin Man. With the successful completion of these last tests the Air Force began assembling what would be called the 509th Composite Group.

The 509th became the Air Force's first nuclear armed bomber group, the unit that would drop the atomic bombs on Japan. In May of 1945 the squadron received its equipment, which consisted of 46 Silverplated B-29s which had been stripped of all guns and armor with the exception of the twin .50 caliber tail guns, to increase the bomber's speed. The first bombers left for the Pacific in early June with the entire force arriving on Tinian in late July. The next month, on 6 August 1945, the Bomber *Enola Gay* dropped the Little Boy atomic bomb on the city of Hiroshima. Four days later the bomber *Bock's Car* dropped the Fat Man on the city of Nagasaki. Japan opened peace negotiations the following day and on 14 August 1945 accepted the Allied surrender terms.

With the end of the war the United States Army Air Force, named the US Air Force, on 18 September 1947 set about the task of developing an effective atomic bombing force: to do this a great deal of use was made of the men, and also the B-29 bombers, of the 509th Composite Group. This task would prove exceptionally hard to accomplish, however, due to post war budget cutbacks, problems with the bombs, and the extreme cost and complexity of the Silverplate operation. In fact, by December of 1946 the number

---

[1] The B-45, B-57 and B-66 bombers were designed and considered for the strategic nuclear role, but never actually became operational with SAC. The AJ, A-3 and A-5 all represented the Navy's desire to compete with the Air Force for a strategic bomber force of its own in the form of Heavy Attack Squadrons (VAH). They reasoned that an aircraft carrier could be placed close enough to a potential target to compensate for the relatively shorter range of their aircraft. The P2V actually had a very long range and *was* the subject of carrier tests, although such operations proved impractical.

of B-29s capable of carrying a nuclear device had been cut by half.

To stop this decline, in 1947 the Air Force began Silverplating additional B-29s, as well as all new B-50 and B-36 bombers. As a result of this increased work, by 1 December 1948, the nation had 38 nuclear capable B-29s, with an additional 28 undergoing modification. (With the Silverplating these bombers were also equipped to use the British developed drogue and hose in-flight refueling system, giving them, technically, intercontinental strike capability.) Earlier that year, following the start of the Berlin Blockade in July, B-29 bomber groups began rotating out of air bases in Great Britain.[3] Silverplating of B-29s was completed sometime in 1950; by 1 January 1950 a total of 95 B-29s had been nuclear certified.

Nuclear Testing

With the exception of the two nuclear bombs dropped on Japan during the Second World War the B-29 dropped only one other live atomic bomb. This was a Fat Man (Mk-3) bomb dropped on 1 July 1947 at Bikini Atoll in a test of the effect of a nuclear blast on surface ships. Though a failure in the bomb's tail fins caused it to miss the planned target ship by over a thousand feet, a total of five ships were sunk by the blast and nine more were badly damaged. The bomber used in this test was the *Dave's Dream,* assigned to the 509th Bomber Group.

With its nuclear testing the B-29 was also involved in two accidents involving nuclear bombs. The first of these accidents occurred on 11 April 1950 when a B-29 bomber with a 13 man crew crashed into a mountain just three minutes after leaving Kirkland AFB in New Mexico. Inside the aircraft was one fully assembled bomb casing (probably a Mk-4) and one fuel capsule; they were separated for safety reasons. On impact the bombs' detonators were set off, which completely destroyed the casing. However, the nuclear capsule was recovered.

The other accident occurred four months later when, on 5 August, a B-29 crashed during an emergency landing at Travis AFB in California (the bomber had experienced two runaway propellers and landing gear problems during takeoff from Travis). A fire ensued and between 12 to 15 minutes afterward the bomb casing's high explosives were detonated. In all, 19 crew members and rescue personnel were killed in either the crash or the explosion.

Phaseout

Even though it could successfully deliver a nuclear bomb, by 1950 the B-29 was not the best aircraft for the job. The removal of their guns and armor in the Silverplating operation consistently made these bombers vulnerable to enemy fighters, bringing into question their ability to actually reach their designated targets. (The only reason the Japanese didn't shoot down the two B-29s was because they thought the planes were reconnaissance aircraft). In addition, the aircraft was badly underpowered on takeoffs and was prone to having the tail blanked out by the aircraft's fuselage during landing flairout. (Without the tail one gust of wind could push the bomber off line and off the edge of the runway.) Thus, following the deployment of the first B-47 bomber on 23 October 1951, in 1952 the Air Force began phasing out the B-29 from the nuclear deterrent force. By December of 1953 only one strategic B-29 wing

B-29 Superfortress

was still in operation and on 4 November 1954 the last SAC B-29, an A model, was withdrawn from service.

Some will argue that the previous paragraph is in error on the grounds that from December of 1950 to December of 1952 the number of operational B-29s actually increased. This increase, however, was caused by the Korean conflict and is, in its own right, evidence that only two squadrons of Silverplated B-29s ever existed—because, of the seven B-29 bomber groups the US had in 1950, five were sent to Korea to do conventional bombing missions. Given the cost of Silverplating these bombers, plus their high security nature, it is hard to believe that the Air Force would risk using nuclear capable B-29s in conventional bombing missions over Korea. In addition, following the end of the war, the number of operational B-29s dropped quickly from 417 in December of 1952 to 110 by December of 1953.

[2] For a while the British Lancaster bomber was also in the running for the job of atomic bomber.
[3] Training flights to Alaska began in October of 1946.

B-50 Superfortress

SPECIFICATIONS

Length: 99 ft Span: 141 ft 3 in
Height: 34 ft 7 in Weight: 140,000 lb max

PERFORMANCE

Speed: Max 385 mph Ceiling: 35,000 ft
Range: 6,000 mi (with 10,000 lb payload)

POWERPLANT Four 3500 hp, Pratt & Whitney R-4360-35 Wasp Majors

MAX ARMAMENT 28,000 lb of bombs plus thirteen 50 caliber machine guns; ten in four remote control turrets and three in the tail.

TYPES OF NUCLEAR ORDNANCE Mk-3, Mk-4, Mk-6/18, Mk-5 (tested with Rascal)

CREW 11

MANUFACTURER Boeing Aircraft

NUMBER MANUFACTURED 371
224 max number operational in one year.

The B-50 bomber, or the B-29D, was a souped up version of the famous B-29 bomber. Even though it was the first real nuclear bomber the Air Force ever had, this aircraft was still a very limited aircraft.

Development of the B-50 bomber began during World War II to give the United States a means of launching bombing raids against Germany even if Germany successfully invaded Great Britain. The plan was to increase the range of the already developed B-29 so that the aircraft could use Greenland as an operating base. When it

became apparent that no such invasion would occur, work on this aircraft was put on the back burner until 1944 when work resumed on the development of a longer range aircraft for use in the bombing of Japan. Production of the B-29D then began in 1945.

With the end of the war, work on the B-29D, renamed the B-50 in 1946, was again directed towards the development of a long range aircraft capable of delivering nuclear bombs. Following this change the first production model flew on 25 June 1947, and on 20 February 1948 the first aircraft was delivered to the 43rd Bomb Wing at Davis-Monthan AFB. By December a total of 35 aircraft were in service, of which 18 had been silverplated (nuclear certified).

With the deployment of the B-50, the recently formed Strategic Air Command's ability to deliver nuclear payloads over intercontinental distance improved significantly. With its range of 6000 miles and improved in-flight refueling capability, it was better suited for intercontinental bombing missions than its brother, the B-29. Its improved speed also increased the bomber's survivability by giving it the ability to successfully escape the blast from its own nuclear bomb even fully armed with guns and armor. (The B-29s had to be stripped for use.) Its more powerful engines and higher tail also improved the bomber's reliability in takeoffs and landings and gave the B-50 the ability to use shorter runways. Finally, to improve the loading and unloading of nuclear bombs, the B-50 was equipped with a jack point in its nose, allowing it to be raised so the large bomb could be easily rolled into position under the bomb bay. (On the B-29 the bomber had to be rolled over a pit where the bomb was kept.)

Even with these new capabilities the B-50 did have its problems. Though faster than the B-29 it was still one hundred miles per hour slower than the jet fighters of the period. Furthermore, even with its greater range and in-flight refueling capability,[1] for the aircraft to be used to attack a target in the Soviet Union the B-50 would first have to be flown to a forward airfield—either in Japan, Great Britain or Alaska—where it would refuel and arm its bomb before taking off on its bombing mission. In accordance with this system of operation, from 1948 until the B-50 was withdrawn, B-50 bomb wings completed 90 day rotation training operations in Great Britain, Alaska, and Japan. (When a wing completed its time another would replace it at these bases.)

Regardless of these limitations, until the advent of the B-47, the B-50 was the best medium bomber available. Thus, by December of 1952, a total of 224 B-50 bombers were operational, most of which were nuclear capable.[2] Furthermore, to demonstrate the B-50's intercontinental ability, between 26 February and 2 March 1949 the B-50 *Lucky Lady II,* flew around the world nonstop (with four in-flight refuelings). The last B-50 bomber, a D model, was delivered on 26 February 1953; by December 1952 a total of five B-50 wings were in service.

Nuclear Testing

During its time in service the B-50 was also used to drop nuclear devices in the nation's open air nuclear testing program. The first delivery by a B-50 bomber was the Able device (1 kiloton) on 27 January 1951 during Operation Ranger. By the time the B-50 was withdrawn from service it had dropped a total of 12 nuclear devices during Operations Ranger, Buster, Tumbler-Snapper, and Operation Upshot-Knothole. (The largest bomb was the 31 kiloton Charlie device dropped on 22 April 1952 during Operation Tumbler-Snapper.)

With its dropping of nuclear devices for the Atomic Energy Commission the B-50 was also involved in two accidents involving nuclear weapons. The first was on 13 July 1950, when a B-50,

A B-50 is refuelled by a KC-97

B-50 Superfortress

carrying a bomb casing but no fuel capsule, suddenly stalled at 7000 feet and then dropped to the ground, killing all 16 crewmen. The other accident occurred four months later, on 10 November, when, during an as yet unspecified in-flight emergency, the crew jettisoned an empty bomb casing (no capsule) over water at an altitude of 10,500 feet. A high explosive detonation was observed.

Phaseout

Following the delivery of the first B-47 on 23 October 1951 it became less and less necessary to retain the B-50 as a strategic bomber. With the end of the Korean War on 27 July 1953 it also became unnecessary to retain it as a conventional bomber. Thus, in 1953 the Air Force began withdrawing the B-50 from service. By December of 1954 there were only two wings still in operation with only 90 aircraft (78 B-50 and 12 RB-50 Recon planes given bombardment missions by SAC as of June 1954). The last bomber was removed from service at Biggs Air Force Base in Texas on 20 October 1955.

A B-50D bomber is on display at the US Air Force Museum at Wright-Patterson AFB.

[1] In-flight refueling during the late 1940s was very primitive and under medium to rough weather conditions was impossible.
[2] 96 B-50s are known to have been silverplated by 1 January 1950. Number deployed as of December 1949: 99.

B-36 Peacemaker

SPECIFICATIONS (B-36H)
  Length: 162 ft 1 in   Span: 230 ft
  Height: 47 ft   Weight: Max 357,500 lb

PERFORMANCE
  Speed: Max 439 mph   Ceiling: 45,200 ft
  Range: 10,000 mi with a
    10,000 lb payload

POWERPLANT
  Primary — six 3800 hp Pratt & Whitney
    R-4360-53 Wasp Majors
  Secondary — four 5200 lb thrust J47-GE-19 turbojets

MAX ARMAMENT 84,000 lb of bombs plus sixteen 20mm
                          cannons

TYPES OF NUCLEAR ORDNANCE Mk-3, Mk-4, Mk-6/18,
                          Mk-5, Mk-17/24, Mk-21,
                          Mk-36 & Mk-39 (tested
                          with Rascal air-to-
                          surface missile)[1]

CREW 16

MANUFACTURER Convair Aircraft

NUMBER MANUFACTURED 385 produced; 209 maximum
                          operational any year

The B-36 was the world's first intercontinental bomber, the largest manned bomber the United States, or any nation, has ever deployed. It was the primary delivery aircraft of the Strategic Air Command until the advent of the B-52 in 1955.

Development of the B-36 began on 11 April 1941 when, as a hedge against the possible invasion of Great Britain and the loss of its airfields, the US Army Air Force sent out a specification for a bomber with a 5000 mile combat range while carrying 10,000 lb of ordnance (total range of the aircraft was to be 10,000 miles). By October, four companies had submitted proposals for this project and on 25 October 1941 the Air Force issued Consolidated Vultee a contract for the construction of two prototypes of its proposed Model 37 bomber,[2] with the first aircraft to be ready by May of 1944. Along with this contract the planes were given the designation of XB-36.

Less than two months after development of the B-36 began, the United States entered World War II. Now, flooded with high priority orders for the B-24 and B-32 bombers, Consolidated was forced to transfer key personnel from the B-36 project, slowing down development. Development was further slowed by a lack of outside contractors willing to spend time developing components for just two aircraft. Initially, this slowdown did not concern the Air Force (the German invasion of Great Britain had yet to occur). When Japan began consolidating their holdings in the Pacific after Midway, the Air Force, faced with the possibility that any future bombing raids on Japan might have to be launched from the Aleutians, also considered the use of the B-36 in the Pacific. In September of 1942, with the planned use of this aircraft in two theaters of war, development of the B-36 program was placed on

high priority and on 23 July 1943 Consolidated was issued a letter of intent for the construction of 100 aircraft.[3]

Though the letter had been issued, Consolidated would not receive the contract for these planes until 1944, much too late for these aircraft to be used in the war. The prototype would not be rolled out of the Fort Worth facility until 8 September 1945, six days after Japan formally surrendered. By the time the war ended the US Air Force had already found a new use for the B-36, to deliver nuclear weapons over intercontinental distances. As a result of this, and the ending of B-24 and B-32 construction at Fort Worth, development of the B-36 was accelerated, with the first prototype taking to the air on 8 August 1946. A year later, on 4 December 1947, the first production prototype began flight testing and on 26 June 1948 the first bomber, a B-36A, was delivered to the Seventh Bomber Group based at Carswell AFB.

These first B-36 bombers, called model A, had no guns or armor and were used primarily for crew training. Twelve days after the first of this model was delivered the first armed B-36B began flight testing at the Fort Worth facility. By 1 December 1948 at least 13 examples of this model had been delivered to Carswell, four of them nuclear capable. Seven days later one of these B-36Bs demonstrated the combat capabilities of the B-36 by flying nonstop from Carswell AFB in Texas to Hawaii (4000 miles), dropping a simulated nuclear device, and then returning to Carswell AFB. This feat would be exceeded the following year, when a B-36B completed a 9600 mile flight on 12 March 1949.

Production of the B-36B would continue until late 1950 when, after the delivery of the 64 bomber, it was replaced on the production line by the B-36D, first flown on 26 March 1949. This

model, equipped with four auxiliary jet engines, was almost 100 mph faster than the earlier B Model (top speed of B-36D: 435 mph) making it faster than any available piston engine fighter and at least 35 mph above the competing B-50 bomber.[4] So superior was this model that on 6 April 1950, four months before the first B-36D was delivered to Eglin AFB on 19 August, the first B-36B was delivered to the Consolidated facility in San Diego, California for conversion into a D model. As a result of this and another program, in which the original B-36As were converted into RB-36E reconnaissance aircraft, from December of 1948 to December of 1950 the number of operational B-36 bombers increased by only three aircraft.

Where the conversion of the B-36Bs to B-36Ds kept the number of operational bombers in 1949 and 1950 static, the combined effect of the deployment of new production B-36D bombers, the delivery of the first converted B-36Bs, and the additional delivery of 34 B-36Fs between May and November 1951, caused the B-36 force to almost triple by December of 1951 to 98 aircraft. Production/conversion of the B-36D ended on 14 February 1952 after a total of 86 B-36Ds had been produced by Consolidated. The following year, on 5 April, the first B-36H was flown. Production of this model would begin in May of that year and by July of 1953 a total of 83 aircraft had been delivered. Production of the final model, the B-36J, then began in October of 1953, following which the last B-36 bomber was delivered to SAC on 14 August 1954.

While production was under way full operational capability was achieved with the B-36 in 1951. That same year, on 16 January, the first B-36 bombers arrived at Lakenheath Air Force Base in England during an operational deployment test. A similar deploy-

B-36 Peacemaker

ment was completed in Sidi Slimene, French Morocco on 3 December. Two years later, between August and September of 1953, the 92nd bombardment wing underwent Operation Big Stick, a 30 day exercise in which the wing flew en masse to Japan, Okinawa and Guam. Overseas rotation flights (90 day tours) to Anderson Air Force Base on Guam then began on 15 October 1954 and by mid-1955 B-36 wings were also on constant alert at Nouasseur, French Morocco, and Burton and Upper Heyford Royal Air Force stations in Great Britain.

Nuclear Testing

During its time in service the B-36 was used to drop five nuclear devices in the nation's open air testing program. The first of these bombs was the 500 kiloton Mk-18 prototype (the Super O Ralloy bomb) detonated on 15 November 1952 as Shot King of Operation Ivy. The other drops were the Climax bomb during Operation Upshot-Knothole, 4 June 1953; Wasp Prime and Ha[5] during Operation Teapot, 29 March and 6 April 1955; and the Osage fusion bomb during Operation Redwing, 16 June 1956.

When the B-36s were deployed two accidents occurred with nuclear weapons. The first was on 13 February 1950 when a B-36B, enroute from Eielson AFB in Alaska to Carswell AFB in Texas, lost three of its engines. (Since it was a B model it only had six engines.) Icy conditions made it impossible to maintain level flight, forcing the crew to head the aircraft out over the Pacific and drop their bomb casing at an altitude of 8000 feet. The bomb's high explosives detonated on impact, causing a large shockwave and a bright orange flash. The crew later bailed out over Princess Royal Isle.

The second accident occurred several years later, on 22 May 1957. A B-36 bomber ferrying a Mk-17 hydrogen bomb from Briggs AFB in Texas to Kirkland AFB accidently released the bomb while on approach to Kirkland. (The bomb took the bomb bay doors off.) On impact, 4.5 miles south of the Kirkland control tower, the bomb's high explosives detonated, producing a crater 25 feet in diameter and 12 feet deep. The bomb's primary was not installed, however, as per Strategic Air Command (SAC) flight requirements. Ironically, the bomb was probably being sent to Kirkland for dismantling. The last Mk-17 was removed from stockpile in August of 1957.

Phaseout

Prior to the delivery of the last B-36, on 16 June 1954, SAC gave the four active RB-36 reconnaissance wings a primary mission of strategic bombing (the wings were officially redesignated bomber wings on 1 October 1955). This conversion, probably prompted by the deployment of the first hydrogen bombs (a weapon only the B-36 could carry until mid-1955), would increase the number of B-36 wings from six to ten and the number of available aircraft from 209 to 342. With the deployment of the first B-52s on 29 June 1955 the Air Force began phasing out the B-36. The first wing was deactivated by December of 1955, and by December of 1958 only two wings were left. The last B-36 was retired on 12 February 1959.

Four B-36 bombers still exist. One is at the General Dynamics facility at the Fort Worth Airport in Texas; one is at the Air Force Museum at Wright Patterson AFB in Dayton, Ohio; one is at Chanute AFB in Illinois; and the final one is at Offutt AFB in Nebraska.

---

[1] Three B-36 bombers were converted into DB-36s to launch the Rascal. A month before the last plane was received on 15 July 1955, however, the B-36 had been dropped as a carrier vehicle for this missile.
[2] Northrop's XB-35 Flying Wing was also issued a contract.
[3] By the time the letter was sent the invasion of Europe had already occurred, ending the need for the B-36 in Europe.
[4] In 1946 the commander of the Strategic Air Command suggested that construction of the B-36 be stopped in favor of the then faster B-50 bomber.
[5] A 3 kt device detonated in the air is a test of the effect of a high altitude nuclear explosion on aircraft.

AJ-2 Savage

P2V Neptune

P2V-3C Neptune

SPECIFICATIONS

Length: 77 ft 11 in	Span: 100 ft
Height: 28 ft 1 in	Weight: Max 58,000 lb
Speed: Max 300 mph	Ceiling: 23,200 ft
Range: 3195 mi	

POWERPLANT Two Wright R-3350-24W engines producing 2500 hp

ARMAMENT 8000 lb of bombs and three 12.7mm machine-guns

TYPES OF NUCLEAR ORDNANCE Little Boy Mk-1 bomb, Betty or two Lulu Depth bombs

NUMBER MANUFACTURED 1051

Though it first flew on 17 May 1945, it was not until 1 January 1950 that 10 of these Navy land based bombers were operational with nuclear weapons. These early aircraft, part of VC-5 at Moffet Field in Sunnyvale, California, were designed to carry Mk-1 bombs for use against ground targets.

By the mid-1950s, however, these aircraft had been relegated to Anti-Submarine patrols and armed with nuclear depth bombs.

AJ-1 Savage

AJ-1 & AJ-2 Savage

SPECIFICATIONS

Length: 63 ft 1 in	Span: 71 ft 5 in
Height: 20 ft 4.8 in	Weight: Max 34,000 lb
Speed: Max 350 mph	Ceiling: 30,000 ft
Range: Unspecified	

POWERPLANT Two Pratt & Whitney R-2800-44W engines producing 2300 hp
One Allison J-33-A-10 of 4000 lb thrust

ARMAMENT Either conventional or free fall bombs. No defensive armament.

TYPES OF NUCLEAR ORDNANCE Mk-4, Mk-5, Mk-8, Mk-6/18, and the Mk-15

NUMBER MANUFACTURED 143; 58 AJ-1, 55 AJ-2 & 30 AJ-2P

The AJ-1 was the first Navy nuclear capable carrier aircraft. The first six planes' bombs were delivered to VC-5 at Moffet Field in Sunnyvale, California, on 13 September

1949. VC-5 then became operational on the carrier *Coral Sea* on 31 August 1950.

Following the AJ-1, on 6 March 1952, an improved model called the AJ-2 was flown. This aircraft would serve with the AJ-1s until both models were replaced by the A-3 in the mid-1950s.

B-47 Stratojet

SPECIFICATIONS (B-47E)

Length: 109 ft 10 in   Span: 116 ft
Height: 27 ft 11 in   Weight: Max 206,700 lb

PERFORMANCE

Speed: Max 606 mph   Ceiling: 40,500 ft
Range: 4000 miles without in-
flight refueling (longest
recorded with in-flight
refueling: 21,163 mi)

POWERPLANT Six 6000 lb thrust General Electric J47-GE-25 turbojet engines

MAX ARMAMENT 20,000 bomb load and two 20mm cannons in the tail

TYPES OF NUCLEAR ORDNANCE Mk-5, Mk-6/18, Mk-15, Mk-28, Mk-36, Mk-42, Mk-53, and B-43. (Four aircraft equipped to launch the Rascal)

CREW 3

MANUFACTURER Boeing Aircraft

NUMBERS MANUFACTURED 1739; 398 B-47B, 1,341 B-47Es; largest number of B-47s operational in one year: 1367, December of 1958

The B-47 was the first all jet strategic bomber the United States ever deployed. The replacement for the earlier piston engined B-29 and B-50 medium bombers, more B-47s were produced than any other post-war US bomber.

Development of the B-47 began during the Second World War when the Air Force outlined a tentative requirement for an all-jet bomber. Like many other companies at that time, Boeing initially began work on a conventional straight wing aircraft, but with the end of the war, and the acquisition of German aircraft research data, in October of 1945 Boeing dropped its earlier work in favor of a new design using a swept wing and podded engines. The mockup of this aircraft, called model 450, was then inspected by the Air Force in April of 1946 and, following a few additional changes, in May the Air Force placed an order for the construction of two prototypes. In that same month the bomber was given the designation XB-47.

Less than a year and a half after construction of the first two B-47s began on 17 December 1947 the first prototype took to the air. By July of 1948 both prototypes were undergoing flight testing, and though they were underpowered because of the use of 3750 lb thrust Allison J35-2 engines, the Air Force was pleased with the design. The J47 engines were available on 3 September and Boeing was issued an initial production contract for 10 aircraft. The two prototypes were then accepted by the Air Force in November and December, respectively, for use in advanced testing, following which, on 7 October 1949, the first XB-47 took to the air under the power of six J47-GE-3 engines.

The first production B-47, designated B-47A, was completed in mid-1950 and flown on 25 June 1950. This aircraft, and the other nine in the original Air Force order, were never deployed operationally but were used in crew training and follow-on testing.

B-47B

Two months after the initial production order was issued in November of 1948 the Air Force ordered the construction of 87 operationally configured B-47s.[1] This model, called the B-47B, would differ from the A model because of the addition of two 1500 gallon drop tanks, in-flight refueling equipment and structural changes to increase gross takeoff weight to 200,000 lb. The first example was flown at the Boeing Facility in Wichita on 26 April

XB-47 Stratojet

1951 and on 23 October 1951 this very aircraft was delivered to the 306th Bomber Wing at McDill AFB in Florida.

By December of 1951 two Air Force medium bomber wings were being equipped with the B-47B and two more being converted the following year. By December of 1952, the total number of B-47Bs delivered by Boeing was only 62, not enough even for the first two wings (each wing had 45 aircraft). The next year deliveries of the B-47B were accelerated, allowing the Air Force on 3 June 1953 to send the 306th BW to England on the first 90 day B-47 rotation training mission. From that date until 1958 at least one US B-47 wing was on alert in England at all times.

The overseas deployment of the B-47 in place of World War II B-29 bombers and post war B-50s resulted in a major increase in the capability of the US medium bomber force. Though the range of this new all jet bomber was less than that of the B-50, its smaller size, greater speed, higher flight altitude and mobility (it had the maneuverability of a fighter) made it significantly more survivable against Soviet and Eastern Block air defenses. Furthermore, because the B-47s were equipped with RATO boosters and parachute brakes it could operate out of very small fields, making it easier to deploy or disperse.

Even with its great capabilities the B-47 had several problems. At flight speeds above 490 mph control reversal was a common occurrence, one that could be fatal at low altitudes. The B-47 also suffered from roll/yaw coupling instability, a problem that made both landings and takeoffs in a crosswind difficult. This problem was at its worst when an engine was lost during takeoff and was responsible for several fatal crashes. Additionally, the design of the aircraft's landing gear system added to the difficulty of landing the B-47, with pilots having to maintain a near precise approach angle to prevent the front wheels from hitting the ground first. (If they

did a bounce would occur.) Finally, since the cockpit was not designed for flights beyond 4000 miles, the long duration flights took a heavy physical toll on the crew.

B-47E

Deployment of the B-47B came to an end in mid-1953; previously, however, on 30 January 1953, the first of the improved B-47Es was successfully flown at Wichita. This improved model not only had greater range than the B-47B, but a higher takeoff weight through the replacement of the earlier fixed/internal 18 solid fuel RATO pack with 19 to 33 jettisonable/external RATOS, and the addition of new 6000 lb thrust J47-GE-25 engines with water injection. Other changes were the addition of ejection seats for all three crew men and the installation of radar directed General Electric 20mm cannons in the tail. Deployment of this model began in late 1953 and would continue until 24 October 1956, when the last of 1241 B-47Es was delivered to the 40th BW at Schilling AFB in Kansas. This unit would become operational on 15 February 1957 giving SAC a total of 28 B-47 wings.[2]

With the large number of wings in service in 1957 the Air Force also had a large number of forward bases for use by the B-47. Under the original rotation program B-47 wings were based in England at Lakenheath, Upper Heyford, Fairford, Mildenhall, and Brize Norton; in North Africa at Benguerir and Sidi Slimene; and in Alaska at Elmendorf and Eielson AFB. Following the implementation of the Reflex program in July of 1957 the following bases were added to this list: Greenham Common, England;[3] Nouasseur, French Morroco; Moron, Spain; Torejon, Spain; Zaragoza, Spain; and, under the operation name of Air Mail, Andersen AFB in Guam. In addition to this, in the Reflex program the old 90-day

B-47A Stratojet

rotation method was dropped in favor of a new system in which each wing would send five aircraft overseas for a period of 21 days (the planes being kept on constant ground alert at these bases). From that month until the B-47 was retired, these two systems of operation, ground alert and Reflex, were used.

Phaseout

Three years after the last B-47 wing was completed in 1960 the Air Force began phasing them out in favor of the B-58 Hustler. President John F Kennedy announced the end of funding for the B-58 in a speech given on 28 March 1961. In the same speech he ordered the phaseout of the B-47 accelerated, to make more personnel available for the planned 50 percent ground alert system (50 percent of the bomber force capable of taking off in 15 minutes). This accelerated phaseout was put on hold twice, however, once for the Berlin crisis on 25 July 1961 and once during the Cuban missile crisis of 1962 (during the crisis the B-47 force was dispersed to dozens of small civilian and military airfields for protection against a first strike).

With the end of the Cuban missile crisis in 1963, retirement of the B-47 resumed, with six wings being withdrawn and operations at the North Africa bases suspended. By the end of 1964 only eight B-47 wings were still in service and the following five Reflex bases: Moron, Torrejon, Brize Norton, Upper Heyford, and Elmendorf. In 1965 the Reflex operation in Spain ended on 31 March and in October the Air Force began project 'Fast Fly' to completely phase out the B-47 by early 1966. The last two B-47s were withdrawn on 11 February 1957.

Nuclear Accidents With The B-47

The B-47 has the highest number of accidents of any US bomber. The first accident was on 10 March 1956, when a B-47, one of four that took off from McDill AFB, missed its tanker over the Mediterranean. An extensive search was made for the plane, which was carrying two nuclear capsules but neither the plane, crew nor the capsules were found.

The second accident occurred on 27 July, when a B-47 making a touch and go landing at an overseas base underwent a roll/yaw instability, slid off the runway, and crashed into a nuclear weapon storage igloo. Though the plane itself was not carrying a nuclear weapon the igloo contained several. None of the bombs exploded however, and all were later returned to the US for repairs.

The third B-47 accident occurred on 11 October 1957, when, during a takeoff, one of the plane's outrigger tires exploded, causing the plane to crash approximately 3800 feet from the runway. The bomber was carrying one bomb casing in ferry mode and one capsule in a carrying case in the cockpit. The bomb casing was heavily damaged but the capsule was recovered intact.

The fourth B-47 accident occurred on 31 January 1958 when, during a simulated strategic takeoff from an overseas base, the left rear wheel casing failed, causing the aircraft's tail to strike the ground, rupturing a fuel tank. The aircraft's one weapon was in strike configuration, but the high explosives were not detonated by the fire that resulted.

The fifth B-47 nuclear accident was on 5 February 1958, when a B-47, on a simulated combat mission from Homestead AFB in Florida, collided with an F-86 fighter. Heavily damaged, the bomber tried several times to land at Hunter AFB in Georgia, but after the third try the decision was made to jettison the bomb casing. This occurred at 7200 feet over Wassaw Sound off the shore of Tybee Beach. The bomber landed safely afterward.

The most carelessly caused B-47 accident was the sixth. On 11 March 1958 a B-47, after leaving Hunter AFB in Georgia, accidentally jettisoned its bomb casing at 15,000 feet over a sparsely populated section of Florence, South Carolina. On impact the high explosives detonated, causing property damage and injury to several people. The fuel capsule was not installed.

The seventh accident was on 4 November 1958, when a B-47 caught fire during takeoff and crashed. The fire set off the one bomb casing on board, causing an explosion that produced a crater 35 feet in diameter and 6 feet deep.

The eighth and final B-47 nuclear accident was on 26 November 1958, when a B-47, on ground alert, caught fire. The fire completely destroyed the one nuclear weapon on board.

---

[1] In 1950 the Korean War caused the order to be increased to 399 aircraft.
[2] In all, 29 B-47 wings were created, but in March of 1956, prior to the completion of the 40th BW, the 93rd BW at Castle AFB completely converted to B-52Bs.
[3] By 1962 Lakenheath and Mildenhall had been dropped from the list.

B-52 Stratofortress

SPECIFICATIONS (B-52H)

Length: 160 ft 11 in   Span: 185 ft
Height: 40 ft 8 in   Weight: Max 488,000 lb

PERFORMANCE

Speed: Max 595 mph   Ceiling: 55,000 ft
Range: 12,000 miles
(12,532.28 mi in test)[1]

POWERPLANT Eight 13,750 lb thrust Pratt & Whitney TF33 turbofan engines

ARMAMENT Unspecified bomb load, four 20mm cannons

TYPES OF NUCLEAR ORDNANCE

Free Fall bombs — Mk-5, Mk-6/18, Mk-15, Mk-28, Mk-36, Mk-39, Mk-42, B-43, Mk-53, B-61 and B-83.

Missiles — Hound Dog (AGM-28), SRAM, and ALCM (in the future the ACM)

MANUFACTURER Boeing Aircraft

NUMBERS MANUFACTURED 521, 264 operational as of 1988

The B-52 is the oldest strategic aircraft in the SAC arsenal. In service longer than any other manned bomber, this aircraft will still be in service in the year 2000.

Following the start of development of the B-47 in April of 1945, Boeing, at Air Force coaxing, began research into a turboprop powered long range bomber to replace the B-36. In June of 1946 the Air Force held a competition for this new type of aircraft, during which Boeing proposed a 350,000 lb, swept wing, turboprop bomber (essentially an enlarged B-47). Though the aircraft's range was not up to the Air Force's requirements, Boeing was

B-52 Stratofortress armed with two Hound Dog ALMs

B-52G armed with ALCMs

issued a contract for further research and, following the enlargement of the design for greater range, in July of 1948 Boeing was issued an additional contract for the construction of two prototypes, to be designated XB-52s.

Even as construction of the two prototypes was under way, Pratt and Whitney began full scale development on a new turbojet engine that would completely change the B-52 propulsion system. Called the J57, this new motor was so much more efficient than previous jet engines that Boeing proposed their use in the B-52 design in place of the planned turboprops. (Though still more efficient than the J57, these turboprops were less reliable and more mechanically complex.) The Air Force accepted the design change, which resulted in a turbojet bomber. The first XB-52 was rolled out of the facility at Seattle on 29 November 1951.

The second prototype, designated YB-52, was rolled out on 15 March 1952 and on 15 April 1952 this model took to the air in the first flight of a B-52. (The XB-52 first flew on 2 October 1953.) Long before this happened, however, in February of 1951 the Air Force issued Boeing an initial production contract for 13 B-52As. These initial production bombers would differ from the prototypes in that they would have a side by side cockpit in place of the tandem system, cross wind landing gear, new engines, and provision for in-flight refueling. The first would fly on 5 August 1954.

Only three of the planned 13 B-52As were built before production was redirected to the improved B-52B, which would become the first operational model. The first flight of this model was on 25 January 1955, following which deliveries began to the 93rd BW at Castle AFB, California on 29 June 1955. Production of the B-52B then ended at 50 aircraft in mid-1956 in favor of the B-52C, first flown on 9 March 1956. Deliveries of the B-52C (35 in all) then began on 4 June 1956 to the 42nd BW, Loring AFB, and were completed by 1 December, when the first B-52D was delivered to SAC. This model, the first B-52 designed specifically for strategic bombing, would be the first major production model with a total of 170 being deployed by mid-1958. Before deployment of this model was completed, however, on 1 July 1957 the first of 100 B-52Es was delivered to SAC. Deployment of 89 B-52Fs then began on 18 June 1958, and by December SAC had a total of 380 B-52s and nine bomber wings.

By February of 1959 SAC had a very large B-52 force, but it was not as formidable as one might think. Though they could carry larger bombs than the B-47, and their greater fuel capacity gave them greater range, these early models of the B-52s could only fly 6000 miles unrefueled. Although they could reach every military target in the Soviet Union, the number of penetration routes was limited, their time over the deepest target was short and they were restricted to flying at high altitudes for maximum fuel efficiency. In-flight refueling was of course available, but because it can be done only over friendly airspace and only during good weather, it could be used only prior to entrance into enemy airspace, and after the bombs had been dropped.

Even as production of these earlier B-52s was underway in 1957, Boeing began development on a highly improved aircraft called the B-52G. This new model would be completely different, internally, to the previous models. It incorporated integral wing tanks for greater fuel capacity, structural changes for greater strength and lighter weight, permanently affixed wing tip tanks, a new tail of shorter height and broader cord, and finally the moving of the tail gunner's position next to the radar navigator seat in the front of the aircraft. As a result of all these changes, this model of the B-52 had an unrefueled range of 10,000 miles, making it the first B-52 model to have greater range than the B-36 bombers.

In addition to these changes, the B-52G was the first B-52 model equipped to launch both Hound Dog cruise missiles and Quail ECM drones. With the addition of these missiles the B-52G could penetrate extremely heavy air defense systems, systems possibly too strong for the Mach 2 B-58 Hustler. The first flight of a B-52G was on 26 October 1958, and on 13 February 1959 the first aircraft was delivered to the 5th BW at Travis AFB in California. Production ended in mid-1961 following the delivery of the 193rd aircraft.

The B-52G was originally intended to be the last B-52 model. By 1959, however, the Air Force and Boeing had begun planning still another model for use as the launching platform for the new Skybolt air-to-surface missile system. This new model, called the B-52H, would use the recently developed TF-33 turbofan engines to give it a range of over 12,000 miles, and later it would be structurally redesigned for low altitude flight. Testing of components on a B-52G began in July of 1960, and the first B-52H flew

XB-52 prototype

from Wichita on 6 March 1961. The first aircraft was then delivered to the 379th BW at Wurtsmith AFB on 9 May.

Before the first B-52H was delivered, however, on 28 March 1961, John F Kennedy ended production funding for the aircraft. As a result of this, only 102 B-52Hs were produced, with the last one being delivered on 26 October 1962 to the 4136th Strategic Wing at Minot AFB. Peak deployment was also reached at this time, with 639 aircraft in service with 36 wings (11 Bomber, 22 Strategic, and three Heavy Strategic Aerospace wings). The following month development of the Skybolt was ended, forcing the few B-52Hs to also be armed with Hound Dog and Quail missiles.

The deployment of such a large number of B-52s specifically for nuclear strike did not last long, for in January of 1965 27 B-52Fs of the 7th and 320th BWs based at Guam were taken off nuclear strike detail and began bombing targets in Vietnam. While this was going on, on 8 March 1965, the first B-52Bs were withdrawn from service because of age; by December both B-52B wings were being phased out of service. In December of 1965, the 'Big Belly' modification program for the B-52Ds was also begun, taking these aircraft out of service for use in the Vietnam conflict. Finally, on 8 December, Secretary of Defense McNamara ordered that all B-52 models C through F were to be retired from service by June 1971.

With the phaseout order, B-52 totals began dropping very fast. By June of 1966, all the B-52Bs had been inactivated, leaving only 591 aircraft in service by December of that year. In 1967, three more squadrons were deactivated, and by December of 1969 only 505 aircraft were in service with just 24 wings, six of which were involved in Vietnam (a 21 percent drop, not counting the fact that over 100 aircraft were now tied up in South East Asia).

The change in administration in 1969 did not stop B-52 withdrawal, but did slow it down enough that by June of 1971 only the B-52Bs, Cs, Es and some Fs had been deactivated. It did, however, begin building up what was left, and, on 4 March 1972, SAC began arming its B-52G and H bomber with SRAM missiles. With these new missiles, both the penetration capability of the B-52s was increased — they could use them to clear a path to their target — as was also the number of nuclear weapons they could carry: from seven weapons — two Hound Dogs, four B-28s, and a Mk-53 — they went to 24 — 20 SRAMS and four B-28s. B-52D

operations in South East Asia then ended on 15 August 1973, making these aircraft again available for nuclear deterrent missions if necessary. (By the late 1970s this model was permanently assigned for conventional bombing missions in support of US troops and ships.) Thus, by December of 1974, SAC had 422 B-52s available (at least 100 more than it would have had under the McNamara phaseout order).

Phaseout of older model B-52s began again in 1978, when SAC disposed of its last B-52Fs and several B-52Ds — a total of 68 aircraft. Officially, this withdrawal has not had any effect on the number of operational nuclear equipped bombers, since the majority of these bombers were either in reserve or were assigned to conventional bombing roles. It has had a significant effect, for with the phaseout of the last B-52D on 1 October 1983, the Air Force has had to assign 69 of its remaining B-52Gs for use as Harpoon anti-ship cruise missile platforms. Because of this, as of 1988, of the 263 operational B-52s, the Strategic Air Command has only 194 aircraft devoted to the nuclear deterrent — 98 B-52Gs and all 96 remaining B-52Hs.

As of last report, all 98 B-52Gs have been equipped with ALCM. Deployment of ALCM on B-52Hs is still under way.

Nuclear Testing

The B-52 has dropped more nuclear devices in testing than any other aircraft. The first such drop was on 20 May 1956, when a B-52B dropped the first US hydrogen bomb at Bikini Atoll (Shot Cherokee of Operation Redwing). A six year hiatus then occurred, until the start of Operation Dominic I in 1962.

In operation Dominic, the B-52 would be used to drop a total of 29 megaton class nuclear devices. These shots were Adobe, 25 April 1962; Aztec, 27 April; Arkansas, 2 May; Questa, 4 May; Yukon, 8 May; Mesilla, 9 May; Muskegon, 11 May; Encino, 12 May; Swanee, 14 May; Chetco, 19 May; Tanana, 25 May; Nambe, 27 May; Alma, 8 June; Truckee, 9 June; Yeso, 10 June; Harlem, 12 June; Rinconada, 15 June; Dulce, 17 June; Petit, 19 June; Otowi, 22 June; Bighorn, 27 June; Bluestone, 30 June; Sunset, 10 July; Pamlico, 11 July; Androscoggin, 2 October; Bumping, 6 October; Chama, 18 October; Calamity, 27 October; and Housatonic, 30 October. The bomber that did many of these shots, if not

B-52H Stratofortress

all, is on display at the National Atomic Museum at Kirkland AFB in Albuquerque.

In addition to the large number of bombs the B-52 dropped in nuclear testing, the B-52 aircraft was also involved in a number of accidents.

The first was on 15 October 1959, when a B-52 collided with its refueling tanker over Hardinsberg, Kentucky. When the accident occurred, the bomber was carrying two nuclear weapons, both of which were probably of megaton class. Though one bomb was partially burned in the crash, both were recovered intact. Only four of the 12 men on the bomber and the tanker escaped alive.

The second accident was on 24 January 1961, when, during the recently started airborne alert system, a B-52 had a major structural failure in its right wing over Goldsboro, North Carolina. During breakup, the bomber's two nuclear devices broke loose, with one parachuting to earth intact. The other, however, broke up on impact. Because one piece of that bomb was never recovered from the waterlogged farmland it fell on, even after excavating the hole to 50 feet, the Air Force bought an easement on the land, requiring permission for any digging. As for the crew, only five of the eight men survived the accident.

The third accident was on 14 March 1961, when, following a failure of the pressurization system — forcing low altitude flight — a B-52 ran out of fuel at 10,000 feet over Yuba City, California. On impact, the aircraft's two nuclear weapons were torn loose. No explosion or contamination occurred. Only the aircraft commander was killed.

The fourth accident was on 13 January 1964, when, during severe turbulence a B-52D suffered a major structural failure and crashed approximately 17 miles SW of Cumberland, Maryland. The two nuclear weapons on board remained in the aircraft on impact, and were recovered relatively intact. Only the pilot and co-pilot survived, as the tail gunner and navigator died of exposure and the radar navigator did not eject from the plane.

The fifth accident is probably one of the most well-known accidents in modern history. On 17 January 1966, a B-52 collided with its KC-135 tanker over Palomares, Spain. Of the four B-28 bombs, one parachuted to earth intact, two exploded on impact, scattering radioactive material, and the fourth landed in the Mediterranean. Though recovery of the bomb that fell on land was relatively simple, the bomb that fell into the Mediterranean required an armada of midget subs to locate it, and was finally recovered on 7 April 1966, three months after it was lost (the longest time a nuclear weapon has been missing). The casing of the bomb that landed on shore is now on display at the National Atomic Museum.

The final B-52 accident occurred on 21 January 1968, when a B-52 crashed seven miles short of the runway at Thule, Greenland. All of the bomber's four B-28 bombs were destroyed in the resulting fire, scattering radioactive debris. Following this accident, Secretary of Defense Robert S McNamara issued an order stating that at no time other than a national crisis is a US aircraft to take off and fly with a live nuclear weapon on board. Since that time, there has not been a single accident involving a US aircraft and a nuclear weapon.

[1] On 10–11 January 1962, a B-52H from Minot flew from Okinawa to Torrejon, Spain, 12,532.28 miles, without refueling. The test flight was called Operation Persian Rug.

B-45 Tornado

SPECIFICATIONS

Length: 75 ft	Span: 89 ft
Height: 25 ft	Weight: Max 82,600 lb
Speed: Max 575 mph	Ceiling: 40,000 ft
Range: 1600 mi 'tactical'	

POWERPLANT Four General Electric J47A turbojet engines each of 4000 lb thrust

ARMAMENT 20,000 lb of bombs and two .50 caliber machine guns

TYPES OF NUCLEAR ORDNANCE Mk-5, and Mk-7

MANUFACTURER North American Aviation

NUMBER MANUFACTURED 143

B-45 Tornado

First flown on 24 February 1948, the Tornado was the first all jet tactical bomber to be developed by the US Air Force. Following the introduction of small nuclear bombs, from 1952 to 1958, the Tactical Air Command operated this aircraft in Europe as a nuclear light bomber.

Prior to its deployment in Europe, on 5 November 1951 (Shot Easy, Operation Buster) a B-45 dropped a 31 kiloton bomb (possible Mk-5). The next year, on 1 May 1952, another B-45 dropped a 14 kiloton bomb during a high speed, low altitude pass over the Nevada test range (Shot Dog, Operation Tumbler-Snapper).

B-57 Intruder

SPECIFICATIONS
Length: 65 ft 6 in   Span: 64 ft
Height: 15 ft 7 in   Weight: Max 55,000 lb

PERFORMANCE
Speed: Max 582 mph
     (mach 0.8)   Ceiling: 44,000 ft
Range: 4600 mi

POWERPLANT Two 7200 lb thrust Wright J65-W-5 turbojet engines

MAX ARMAMENT 6000 bomb load plus either eight 50 caliber machineguns or four 20mm cannon

TYPES OF NUCLEAR ORDNANCE Mk-7, B-43

CREW 2

MANUFACTURER Martin Marietta under license from English Electric

NUMBER MANUFACTURED 403; 8 B-57As

The B-57 was the first combat aircraft of foreign origin to be used by the United States since the First World War. This Americanized version of the British Canberra bomber was slated for four years' use against strategic targets in the Soviet Union, North Korea and China even though it was considered a medium bomber.

Early in the Korean War, the Air Force found itself in need of a new night interdiction bomber to replace the World War II B-26 bombers. Five aircraft were proposed for this mission (three American, two foreign), and following a competitive fly-off held on 26 February 1951, the British-designed Canberra bomber was selected for use as a night tactical reconnaissance aircraft. A formal request for the RB-57A was then submitted to USAF Headquarters on 2 May 1951, and by June, Martin Aircraft had begun redesigning the Canberra to meet American manufacturing methods and US Air Force standards.

After two years of redesign and construction, during which several changes had to be made in the design of the Canberra, the first B-57A took to the air on 20 July 1953; this B-57 was one of eight pre-production aircraft built by Martin to get the production line going. The first production aircraft, known as the RB-57A (recon/bomber), would be flown later that same year, with deliveries to Tactical Air Command (TAC) beginning in April of 1954 to the the 363rd Tactical Reconnaissance Wing at Shaw AFB. In all, a total of 67 RB-57As were deployed.

As planned, the B-57As were externally similar to the British Canberra B-2. This design restriction had its problems, however, particularly in that it affected the ability of the pilot and the bombardier/navigator to work together. Thus, while production of the B-57A was under way, Martin began work on a new version designed to fill the Air Force requirement for a night interdiction aircraft. The new B-57B model would differ from the B-57A in that it was equipped with either eight .50 caliber machine guns, or four 20mm cannons, mounted in its wings, the rotary bomb bay developed by Martin for its earlier B-48 medium bomber, and a tandem two seat cockpit. The first example of this new model took to the air on 28 June 1954, and seven months later the first planes were delivered to the 461st Bombardment Wing, Tactical Air Command, on 5 January 1955. Deployment to this unit and the 345th BW was completed by the end of the year, and in 1956 the

B-57 Intruder

3rd BW Pacific Air Force (PACAF) began receiving B-57s. This unit would be the last B-57 wing to be created.

In all, 202 examples of this model were produced, making the B-57B the major production model. With these bombers the Air Force also purchased 38 B-57C trainers, and, in 1956, 68 B-57Es for use as tugs for aerial targets (the planes could also be configured for recon, training, and bombing). Production of the basic B-57 was completed in 1959.

The B-57 did not last long with TAC as a strike aircraft. Following the deployment of RB-66 bombers in 1957, the RB-57As were withdrawn from service. The next year, after the deployment of the first B-66B bombers to Europe, the B-57Bs and Cs were also withdrawn from Europe for storage in the US.

As the B-57B was being retired in Europe, a different situation existed in the Pacific. Unlike the B-57Bs in Europe, which were equipped more for conventional warfare, the B-57s used by the 3rd Air Force had been specialized for the delivery of the Mk-7 tactical fission bomb against strategic targets in the Soviet Union, North Korea and China.[1] Based at Kunsan AFB in Korea (the planes were rotated there from Yokota),[2] these bombers could strike targets in North Korea, the south eastern coast of the Soviet Union, and even as far as Peking within a half hour of an alert (at least an hour before B-47s from Guam could arrive). With this close proximity, these B-57Bs were also equipped with the Low Altitude Bombing System, or LABS, allowing them to successfully deliver their nuclear devices and escape after approaching the target at 300 feet off the ground (the B-57 had no peer in its accuracy using LABS).

After almost six years of service, in April 1964 PACAF phased out the nuclear strike requirement for the B-57Bs. Following this, the aircraft were withdrawn from Japan too, and were taken to Vietnam for use in the conventional bombing role of the B-57.

---

[1] This group's specialization would force the Air Force, in the summer of 1948, to redeploy the 345th BW from Europe to Okinawa when trouble developed between China and Taiwan. Following this deployment the 345th was disbanded.
[2] The nuclear weapons were kept at Kunsan because of Japan's policy that banned nuclear weapons in its territory.

B-66 Destroyer

SPECIFICATIONS

Length: 75 ft 1 in	Span: 72 ft 6 in
Height: 23 ft 7 in	Weight: Max 78,000 lb
Speed: Max 620 mph	Ceiling: 43,000 ft
Range: 1750 mi with external tanks	

POWERPLANT Two Allison J71-A-11 turbojets
Max thrust: 10,200 lb each

ARMAMENT Five ton payload of bombs plus two 20mm canons mounted in the tail

TYPES OF NUCLEAR ORDNANCE Mk-28 and B-43

MANUFACTURER Douglas Aircraft

NUMBER MANUFACTURED 296 of all variants

The B-66 Destroyer was the replacement for the US Air Force's earlier B-45 light bomber. A derivative of the Navy's A-3 Skywarrior, this aircraft actually preceded its Navy counterpart into service on 16 March 1956.

A total of 72 B-66B bombers were deployed in Europe from 1958 to 1962. With these aircraft, over 200 RB-66B and C reconnaissance aircraft were also deployed, each capable of dropping nuclear weapons if the need arose. Following the 1962 withdrawal of the basic bomber, however, the strike capability was dropped from the RB-66s and many were subsequently converted into EB-66 electronic countermeasures aircraft. These aircraft were retained until replaced in the early 1970s by RF-4s and EF-111A electronic countermeasures variants.

B-66B Destroyer

B-57 Intruder

A-3B Skywarrior

A-3 Skywarrior

SPECIFICATIONS
Length: 74 ft 5 in   Span: 72 ft 6 in
Height: 22 ft 10 in   Weight: Max 70,000 lb
Speed: Max 621 mph   Ceiling: 45,000 ft
Range: 2300 mi 'tactical'

POWERPLANT Two Pratt & Whitney J57-P-10 turbojets
Max thrust: 10,500 lb each

ARMAMENT Five ton payload of bombs plus two 20mm
canons mounted in the tail

TYPES OF NUCLEAR ORDNANCE Mk-5, Mk-8, Mk-7,
B-11, Mk-12, Mk-15, Boar, Lulu,
Hotpoint, Mk-27, B-28 and B-43.

MANUFACTURER Douglas Aircraft

NUMBER MANUFACTURED 282

The A-3 Skywarrior was the first all jet bomber to be deployed by the US Navy. From its introduction on 30 March 1956 until the deployment of the first A-5 Vigilante bombers in the early 1960s, the A-3 was the Navy's primary strategic aircraft.

The A-3 remained operational as a nuclear bomber until the mid-1960s. Then, following the demise of the Navy strategic air arm, these aircraft were converted into in-flight refueling tankers and electronic countermeasure aircraft. The A-3 is still operated in these configurations.

A-5 Vigilante

SPECIFICATIONS
Length: 75 ft 10 in   Span: 53 ft
Height: 19 ft 4.75 in   Weight: 33,900 lb

PERFORMANCE
Speed: Mach 2.1   Ceiling: 44,000 ft
Range: 2650 mi with in-flight   (91,450 ft in test)
refueling over 4000 mi

POWERPLANT Two 17,000 lb thrust General Electric
J79-GE-8 turbojet engines

MAX ARMAMENT Unspecified (light) bomb load

TYPES OF NUCLEAR ORDNANCE Mk-27, Mk-28 and B-43

CREW 2

MANUFACTURER North American Aviation

NUMBER MANUFACTURED 199 total; 59 A-5As, 20 A-5Bs,
120 RA-5Cs (not counting
conversions)

The A-5 Vigilante was the US Navy's first and only supersonic, medium range bomber. Though its range was quite limited, its great speed and altitude, and the fact that it was launchable from carriers, gave it a world-wide strike capability equal to the B-58 Hustler.

Even before the first A-3 bombers were deployed, in 1955 the Navy began looking for an even more powerful aircraft, and issued a request for a supersonic, all-weather attack aircraft. In response to this request, North American Aviation initiated design work on the NAGPAW, the North American General Purpose Attack Weapon. After a review, the Navy accepted the design on 29 June 1956, and in August North American Aviation received a contract for the construction of two prototypes, designated YA-3Js. The first of these prototypes took to the air two years later, on 31 August 1958, and five months later, in January of 1959, the US Navy issued a large production order.

Following the issuing of the production contract, sea trials of the A-3J began in July of 1960 on the aircraft carrier USS *Saratoga*. Later that same year, on 13 December, an A-3J set an international height record by flying to 91,450 feet while carrying a 2204 lb payload (which could have been a simulated B-28 bomb). Six months later, the first production planes were delivered to the VAH-7 (Heavy Attack Squadron 7) at Sanford Naval Air Station in Florida. This unit was then declared operational in early 1962, prior to its embarking on its first sea tour on the USS *Enterprise*. Later that same year, as part of a joint Navy, Air Force and Army program to develop a uniform designation system, the A-3J was renamed the A-5A Vigilante.

While production of the A-5A was under way, North American Aviation began work on an extended range version called the A-5B (originally named the A-3J-2). This model of the A-5B, called the Interim Long Range Bomber, carried extra fuel tanks in a hump located just aft of the cockpit fairing, adding about 350 miles to its range. The prototype was flown on 29 April 1962, and by late 1963 a total of 20 aircraft had been manufactured.

Before the seventh A-5B was delivered, in mid-1962, the Navy's long range strategic bombing requirement was dropped. As a result of this, the construction of the A-5B bomber was ended in favor of the RA-5C, the reconnaissance/attack version of the A-5B Vigilante, which North American Aviation had begun developing in early 1962. The prototype of this dual purpose aircraft flew on 30 June 1962, and in January of 1964 the first production planes were assigned to VAH-2 of Heavy Attack Wing 1, based at Sanford Naval Air Station. The aircraft then became operational in July of 1964 on the USS *Ranger*, and by late 1964 it was in use in the South China Sea. In June of the following year, VAH-7 completed conversion to the RA-5C, ending the deployment of the A-5A and the short-lived A-5B. A total of 140 RA-5Cs were produced, of which 20 were converted A-5Bs.

The RA-5C would remain in service with the Navy until the early 1980s. Though equipped for long range, side angle reconnaissance, it still retained an all-weather strike capability with nuclear or conventional ordnance. Unlike the earlier A-5A, the RA-5C could not only carry ordnance in the linear bomb bay, but also had four underwing hard points. The introduction of the A-6E Intruder light bomber in the early 1970s, plus the deployment of the F-14 reconnaissance plane, have put an end to the fleet's use of this versatile aircraft.

A-5 Vigilante

B-58 Hustler

SPECIFICATIONS
Length: 96 ft 9 in   Span: 56 ft 10 in
Height: 31 ft 5 in   Weight: Max 163,000 lb

PERFORMANCE
Speed: 1345 mph (Mach 2)   Ceiling: 85,000 ft
Range: 4450 mi

POWERPLANT Four General Electric J79-GE-58 turbojet engines. Max thrust: each 62,000 lb with afterburner

ARMAMENT Unspecified bomb load plus one 20mm Vulcan cannon in tail

TYPES OF NUCLEAR ORDNANCE Mk-39, B-43 and Mk-53

MANUFACTURER Convair (now General Dynamics)

NUMBER MANUFACTURED 116

The B-58 Hustler was the Air Force's first supersonic strategic bomber. Though complex and expensive to operate, it was by far the most spectacular and effective bomber SAC had during the 1960s.

The B-58 Hustler program began in October of 1946, when the Army Air Force Air Material Command awarded Consolidated Vultee, later called Convair, a contract for a study into the feasibility of a supersonic bomber. Though Chuck Yeager would not break the sound barrier until 14 October 1947, the engineers at Convair took the project on, and in 1949 submitted a proposal for a small, delta wing, parasite bomber for use by the B-36. Functioning like a manned missile, this aircraft would be launched by the B-36 1500 miles from its target, fly to within 200 miles at a high subsonic speed, dash over the target at Mach 1.6, deliver its bomb, and then head back to the B-36 mothership for linkup and the trip back to the states. Though complex, this parasite system was already being tested as a means of allowing bombers to carry defensive fighters with them into enemy air space.

To make the bomber small enough to fit in the bomb bay of the B-36, the engineers at Convair came up with a unique two-part aircraft design. The first part of this design was the basic bomber, which carried the engines, the fuel that would be used in the flight back to the B-36 mothership, and the flight crew. The second part of this system was the weapons pod, which carried the warhead, any needed penetration aides, and the fuel the bomber would use in the flight to the target. By designing it in this manner, Convair made the parasite function like a two-stage missile.

Though the parasite system was workable, the Air Force, in the fall of 1951, ordered that the recently developed in-flight refueling system was to be used to achieve intercontinental range instead of the parasite system. As a result of this, Convair was forced to redesign the bomber, adding landing gear, two extra engines, and lengthening it to allow additional fuel for still longer range. A new

B-58 Hustler

proposal was then submitted on 18 August 1952, and in October of that year the Air Force selected the Hustler over the competing Boeing design. The contract was issued in February of 1953, beginning with the following month.

Three years after development of the B-58 began, on 11 November 1956, the first aircraft was flown at Fort Worth, Texas. One of 30 aircraft manufactured for testing, this aircraft would be flown by Convair for contractor tests and then later by the 6592th Test Squadron and the 3958th Operational Evaluation and Training Squadron of the Air Force. With the completion of these tests in 1959, the Air Force issued an order for the construction of 86 more aircraft, the first of which was flown in September of 1959. The first B-58 Hustler was delivered to the 43rd Bomber Wing at Carswell AFB on 1 August 1960 — one of 12 delivered that same day. By December of 1960, Initial Operational Capability had been achieved, with 19 aircraft in service.

With the delivery of the first B-58s, the ability of the Strategic Air Command to successfully penetrate heavy air defense systems improved drastically. Because of its high speed and flight altitude, the Hustler could fly safely above most of the air defense systems in use at that time. Those that it couldn't avoid were not any more secure, however, since the bomber's pod could carry such an extensive array of countermeasures it still couldn't be effectively stopped. Finally, for those situations where stealth was required, the bomber was also capable of making a high speed, low altitude (below radar) approach like the later B-1A. These capabilities, plus a radar signature 1/10th to 1/30th that of the B-52's, made the B-58 the most survivable bomber the US had.

Regardless of these capabilities, the B-58 Hustler also had its problems. Because of the peculiar flight characteristics the delta wing gave the aircraft, even good pilots could lose control of the aircraft: in all, 20 percent of the B-58s produced were lost in crashes, including eight of the test aircraft. (This number also includes the two B-58s that crashed at the Paris Air Shows of 1961

and 1965.) The aircraft was also susceptible to control reversal during high speed, low altitude flight, and because the delta wing had no flaps, landings were at 180 miles an hour, allowing almost no time for corrections. In addition to these airborne problems, the aircraft was also a maintenance nightmare, with extremely complex electronics and, thanks to its pod design, a floating center of gravity — meaning that, when the pod was loaded on the bomber, the aircraft's center of gravity was between the nose gear system and the main gear as it should be. However, if the pod was removed before the bomber was completely defueled, say after a flight, the center of gravity would shift behind the main gear, causing the aircraft to tip up on its tail.

The operational problems with the B-58 were, however, not as fatal to the aircraft as the changing times. With the development of surface-to-air missile systems in the late 1950s, many in the Kennedy administration came to the conclusion that no matter how high or how fast an aircraft could fly, if they could be detected by radar, they could be intercepted. On 28 March 1961, in the same speech in which he cancelled the Mach 3 XB-70 bomber (among other things), President John F Kennedy ended funding for production for the B-58. As a result of this, only 99 of the planned 224 production aircraft were ever procured, with the last being delivered to the 305th BW at Bunker Hill AFB on 26 October 1962. To build up the force following this cutback in 1961, the Air Force brought 10 of the original test aircraft up to operational standard, with eight others being designed as dual control trainers, or TB-58s. With the addition of these extra aircraft, by December of 1963 the Air force had a total of 94 aircraft in service (40 planes with each of the two squadrons and 14 for reserve). This was the highest number of B-58s that was ever operational during the Hustler's time in service.

Though it had been dropped from production, the B-58 Hustler was still the most effective bomber in the SAC arsenal. In the early 1960s, these capabilities were in fact enhanced with the addition of

B-58 Hustler

four B-43 megaton class bombs to the B-58's bomb load, allowing the aircraft to now engage five separate targets in one mission.

Regardless of the plane's capabilities, the B-58 era was quickly coming to an end. With the cancellation of the XB-70 in 1961, the Air Force had begun redirecting its research towards a high-speed, low-altitude aircraft, capable of flying under enemy radar systems. This work would not only result in the development of the B-1, but also result in the FB-111A, which would replace the B-58. It was with this aircraft in mind that, on 8 December 1965, Secretary of Defense McNamara ordered that, by 1971, all the B-58 Hustlers were to have been removed from service. Phaseout began in 1969, and on 16 January 1970 the last B-58 Hustler was retired to storage at Davis Monthan AFB: of the 116 aircraft produced, only 86 remained, including all eight TB-58 trainers.

Nuclear Accidents With The B-58

The B-58 Hustler had only one nuclear accident during its time in service. On 8 December 1964 a B-58, taxiing during an exercise at Bunker Hill AFB, came up behind another B-58 just when that aircraft went to full power. Caught in the jet blast, and with ice on the runway, the plane slid off the left-hand side of the runway. After hitting a concrete electric manhole box, the plane caught fire, forcing the crew to abandon the aircraft: the pilot and defensive systems operator escaped with minor injuries; the navigator was killed when he activated his ejection pod. On board the aircraft were five bombs, four B-43s and either a W-39 or a W-53 warhead in the pod. No explosion occurred, though radioactive contamination was present at the crash site.

Though its time in service was short, the B-58 was a very important aircraft. In less than three years, it set 12 world records and won the Mackay, the Bendix and the Thompson Trophies, as well as France's Bleriot Cup for the shortest time from New York

to Paris. These records were used in the selection of the only two B-58s that were retained for museums. These aircraft were B-58 59-2458, which won the Bendix and Mackay trophies in 1962, and B-58 61-2059, which was the one that set the official world speed record for a nonstop flight from Kadena Air Base in Japan to Greenham Common, England. The 59-2458 is now on display in the annex at the Air Force Museum at Wright Patterson AFB in Ohio. The 61-2059 is on display at the Strategic Air Command Museum at Offutt AFB in Nebraska.

FB-111A Aardvark

SPECIFICATIONS

Length: 73 ft 6 in	Span: full swept – 33 ft 11 in full span – 70 ft
Height: 17 ft 1.4 in	Weight: Max 100,000 lb

PERFORMANCE

Speed: 1450 mph (Mach 2.5)   Ceiling: over 60,000 ft
Range: 4100 miles with external fuel

POWERPLANT Two Pratt & Whitney TF30-P-7 turbofan engines. Max thrust: each 20,350 lb with afterburner, 12,500 lb without

ARMAMENT Up to 31,500 lb of ordnance (up to six B-61 bombs or SRAM missiles)

TYPES OF NUCLEAR ORDNANCE B-43, B-61, B-83 and SRAM

MANUFACTURER General Dynamics

NUMBER MANUFACTURED 79

The FB-111A was the United States' only operational supersonic bomber during the 1970s. The replacement for the B-58 Hustlers, and a large number of medium range B-52s, it is one of the most effective combat aircraft in the present strategic bomber force.

Stung by the cancellation of the XB-70 bomber and the Skybolt ALBM, plus the ending of production of the B-52 and the B-58 Hustler, the Air Force, in 1963, began looking for an interim bomber design for deployment in case of either an extensive delay in the development of the Advanced Manned Strategic Aircraft or a sooner-than-expected retirement of older model B-52s. Two vehicles were studied for this, the B-58 Hustler and a 'minimum modified' version of the F-111 fighter/bomber then in development. On 2 June 1965 the Air Force selected the F-111 modification project. Six months later, on 10 December 1965, Secretary of Defense McNamara announced to the nation that 263 FB-111As would be purchased as replacements for the older model B-52s and the B-58 Hustlers. (Two days before this, McNamara announced that all B-52 models C through F, and all B-58 Hustlers, were to have been retired by June of 1971.)

FB-111A armed with FLU-43 bomb

FB-111 Aardvark armed with B-43 bomb

Though the Air Force planned to deploy 263 FB-111As as an interim aircraft until the AMSA or B-1A was deployed, Secretary McNamara saw it as a full replacement for the AMSA and the operating force of B-52s and B-58s. As a result of this, he postponed the start of FB-111A production (in November of 1965) until the following year, in order that the aircraft could be equipped with more advanced avionics and the SRAM missiles (AGM-69A) being developed for the B-1. This change in the program caused some political controversy, but was still implemented and development began in February 1966.

The FB-111A prototype, a modified F-111, first flew on 31 July 1967. A year later, the first production aircraft was flown on 13 July 1968. Acceptance by the Air Force occurred on 30 August. (This plane was using TF30-P-12 engines developed for the earlier Navy F-111B variant.) The second plane was accepted for testing by the Air Force on 25 October. The first operational aircraft was then accepted by the Air Force on 8 October 1969 at Carswell AFB in Texas.

Before the first FB-111A was delivered on 19 March 1969, the new Secretary of Defense Melvin R Laird presented a revised 1969/70 budget in which the number of FB-111As to be procured was reduced from 126 to 79 aircraft. (The original procurement number of 263 was dropped on 28 November 1968.) Of these 79 aircraft, 60 were for deployment, with the remaining 19 for replacement. The money previously intended for these aircraft was spent on the resurrected B-1 bomber project.

After the third aircraft was delivered, on 24 December 1969, deliveries of the FB-111A to the 340th BG were suspended, and following the crash of an F-111 at Nellis AFB, the planes were grounded. Following the completion of some needed modifications, deliveries to the 340th BG resumed in mid-1970. The first aircraft was delivered to the 509th BW at Pease AFB, and the first combat wing (30 aircraft) on 16 December 1970 with operational capability being achieved by October of 1971. The last FB-111A was delivered to the 340th BG on 30 June 1971, following which, in early September, this wing began transferring its aircraft to the 380th Strategic Aerospace wing at Plattsburg AFB (36 aircraft).

With the transfer of its last FB-111, the 340th BG was then inactivated on 31 December 1971.[1]

Since its deployment, the FB-111's nuclear history has been uneventful. Because they were deployed after open air nuclear testing was suspended, and after airborne alert was ended, they have neither been involved in any nuclear accidents nor have they ever dropped a live nuclear device. Furthermore, with the exception of improvements to their ECM systems, the FB-111As have not had their nuclear ordnance significantly enhanced since the aircraft were equipped to carry and launch SRAMs in April of 1972.

While its nuclear history has been uneventful, the aircraft's operational history has not. Called by one Air Force officer 'one of the most unforgiving aircraft in service,' the FB-111A has one of the worst accident records of any operational strategic aircraft. The first known crash of a FB-111A was on 7 October 1970, to be followed by two more before the last plane was delivered in June of 1971. (One of these planes was the 76th FB-111A, which crashed before delivery to the Air Force.) These crashes initially did not seriously affect deployment — 72 aircraft were in service in December of 1974 — but by December of 1977, there were only 66 aircraft, just enough aircraft for the two squadrons. As a result of this, in 1978 the number of planes allocated to the two squadrons was dropped from 36 to 34 at Plattsburg, and from 30 to 26 at Pease. As of December 1984, at least six more aircraft have been lost, leaving the Air Force with only 60 aircraft (a 21 percent reduction).[2] As a result of this reduction, the number of aircraft allocated for combat are, as of 1988, only 48 (28 for Plattsburg, 20 to Pease): the remaining 12 are for training and reserve.

At present, there are no plans in the works to develop or procure a new medium range bomber to replace the FB-111. Thus it is quite possible that this aircraft will remain in service until either the last one crashes or is withdrawn from service because it is unsafe to operate.

[1] The 340th was more of a training wing for the FB-111A program than an operational combat wing.
[2] Of these last six accidents, three were ground mishaps and three in-flight, according to the Air Force. Six fatalities have ensued.

A B-61 practice bomb is loaded on to a FB-111

B-1B

SPECIFICATIONS

Length: 147 ft   Span: full spread – 136 ft 8.5 in
Height: 34 ft   full swept – 78 ft 2.5 in
                        Weight: Max 477,000 lb

PERFORMANCE

Speed: Mach 1.25 approx (at 200 ft
        altitude maximum 600 mph)
Range: 7455 mi, unrefueled

POWERPLANT Four 30,000 lb thrust General Electric
              F101-GE-102 turbofan engines

ARMAMENT 125,000 lb of ordnance; maximum of
              36 nuclear weapons (24 internal, 12 external)

TYPES OF NUCLEAR ORDNANCE B-28, B-43, B-61, B-83,
              SRAM, ALCM and, in the
              future, ACM and the
              SRAM II

CREW 4; pilot, co-pilot, and two systems operators
       (can carry six for training)

MANUFACTURER Rockwell International

NUMBER MANUFACTURED 100; 99 operational as of
                       December 1988

The B-1B is the newest strategic bomber the US Air Force fleet has. It is by far the most powerful and survivable bomber in US service at this time. It is for use against high value, heavily defended, hardened military targets.

Development of the B-1 began in 1963 under the title of Advanced Manned Strategic Aircraft, or AMSA. The reason the program began was more a political move by the Kennedy Administration to end calls for the resurrection of the XB-70 bomber than a true attempt to develop a new manned bomber. Evidence of this can be seen in the fact that, for the first five years, the DOD held up development by continually changing the performance and the mission requirements for the aircraft. At the same time, Secretary of Defense McNamara also began grooming his pet aircraft, the FB-111A, into a reasonable facsimile of a strategic bomber as an alternative to the AMSA.[1] As a result of this, by 1967 construction of a mockup had *not* begun.

Following the election of Richard Nixon, work on the AMSA, or the B-1, as it then became known, was taken out of the study stage. Funding was increased on 19 March 1969, most of this coming from cutbacks in the FB-111A program. On 3 November the Air Force issued a request for proposals to North American, Rockwell, General Dynamics, and Boeing. The following year, on 5 June, North American was issued the development contract, with a construction order for seven aircraft. (This was reduced to 3 in February of 1971.) The mockup was inspected in October of 1971, with construction of the first aircraft beginning in 1973. The first B-1A rolled out of Rockwell's Palmdale facility in October 1974.

Following rollout, the first flight of the B-1 occurred on 23 December 1974. The first supersonic flight and in-flight refueling occurred on 10 April 1975, with the first flight by a SAC pilot being completed on 19 September. Development was going so well

B-1B

that Congress authorized the construction of a fourth B-1 for use as a defensive avionics aircraft in 1975. Testing of the second and third B-1A bombers began on 14 June and 16 January 1976, respectively. The initial flight test program was completed on 30 September 1976.

As the B-1A was proving itself in its flight test program, political controversy surrounded it. Ever since the bomber was taken out of the study stage in 1969, members of Congress and leading members of the Democratic party had been making statements and accusations regarding its capabilities and costs in an attempt to build public opinion against the aircraft. By 1976 the situation had become critical, with Jimmy Carter, the Democratic presidential candidate, calling for an end to the program in his campaign. Thus, following his election, in an action that is all too similar to the 1961 cancellation of the XB-70 in favor of the Skybolt, on 30 June 1977, Jimmy Carter cancelled the B-1A in favor of the air-launched cruise missile. As a hedge against a failure of the cruise missile, several alternative aircraft, ranging from a stripped down B-1, to a stretched FB-111A, to a souped-up B-52, were also to be studied, but nothing came of this effort.

In the next four years, the political situation surrounding the B-1 shifted with the nation's political situation. With the problems of the ratification of the Salt II Treaty, the invasion of Afghanistan by the Soviet Union, and the problems in the Middle East and Central America, the nation became concerned with the condition of our armed forces.[2] These issues, plus major economic problems, resulted in the election of Ronald Reagan to office in 1980. One of his campaign pledges was to bring back the B-1.

To resurrect the B-1 would prove much harder than killing it. As per an early government law, the jigs and construction fixtures were still intact. Congress had to be convinced that the bomber should be built, when development was already under way on a new aircraft called the Advanced Technology Bomber; now B-2 was to be invisible to Soviet radar systems. As a result of this situation, on 2 October 1981, President Reagan announced his decision to build 100 B-1B bombers to serve as an interim penetration bomber until the deployment of 132 B-2 bombers in the early 1990s. The proposal was accepted by Congress and, on 20 January 1982, Rockwell International received the production contract.

The reduction in the number of planes to be built was not the only change the B-1 program had incurred: the aircraft itself had undergone several changes in the previous five years, making it literally a new aircraft. Gone was the Mach 2 supersonic dash capability, as well as the pod ejection system used on the first three prototypes. The aircraft had also undergone structural changes, allowing a 21 percent increase in its maximum takeoff weight. Its aluminum bomb bay doors had been replaced with composite ones, and the bulkhead between the first and second bomb bays had been made adjustable to allow the internal carriage of cruise missiles or other long weapons. Finally, with the addition of radar absorbing materials to the engine vanes and other areas of the bomber, the B-1B had a radar image one-tenth that of the original B-1 and one-one-hundredth that of the B-52H.

Flight testing of the first B-1B prototype, B-1A No 2, began in March of 1983. The first production bomber was rolled out on 4 September 1984, with its first flight occurring on 18 October. This aircraft was accepted by SAC and the 96th Bomb Wing on 7 July 1985 at Dyess AFB in Texas. (The aircraft that was actually accepted was B-1A No 4, which was flown to Dyess following the 29 June grounding of the original production aircraft at Offutt AFB after one of its engines ingested several nuts and bolts from a faulty air conditioning unit).[3]

B-1B prototype

The B-1B achieved Initial Operational Capability (15 aircraft) at Dyess AFB in September of 1986. Since that time, the 96th BW has achieved its full operational complement of 29 aircraft, with deliveries beginning to Ellsworth, Grand Forks and McConnell AFBs. By April of 1988 these squadrons had also achieved full operational complement, giving the Air Force 98 operational B-1B bombers.

The B-1B bombers are to remain operational as penetration bombers until the mid-1990s, when they are to be replaced in this role by the B-2 or 'Stealth' bomber. In order to meet this requirement, at this time the B-1B bombers are undergoing a modification program to improve the strength of the engine pod section following the loss of a B-1B over Colorado in September of 1987. (A pelican hit the engine pod, severing hydraulic and fuel lines.) In the near future, additional modifications may be done to the aircraft's ECM system to increase its capability to counter Soviet radar systems.

[1] McNamara wanted to eventually end the AMSA program in favor of an enlarged FB-111A force based in Europe.
[2] The failed attempt to rescue the hostages in Iran had a great deal to do with the concern regarding the capability of our military.
[3] The original prototype, B-1A No.2, crashed on 29 August 1984.

images, for the use of new high efficiency engines for low heat emissions, and in modern electronics. Flight testing of this technology began in 1977, when Lockheed began testing a possible replacement aircraft for the SR-71 Blackbird.

Though initially conceived more for recon and fighter aircraft applications, Jimmy Carter called for the use of Stealth Technology for the development of a Stealth bomber in 1980.[1] Contracts for the Advanced Technology Bomber, as it was then called, were issued to Northrop in 1981, and by 1983 a subscale model was reported to be in testing. The mockup was supposedly inspected in 1985 and as of last report the first flight of the prototype is planned for late 1988. Deployment is then to begin in early 1990 at Whiteman AFB in Missouri.

Though it has been stated for some time that the ATB, or B-2 as it is now called, was of a flying wing design similar to the YB-49 of the early 1950s it was only in mid-1988 that this was confirmed by the Air Force. The first six ATBs produced will be test flown at Edwards AFB in California. Five of these aircraft will enter operational service. A total of 132 B-2/ATBs will be built, and initial operating capability is anticipated for the mid-1990s. The B-2 will be capable of both conventional and nuclear payloads.

[1] The question that still exists today is whether he actually intended to build such an advanced aircraft or whether this was just an election year ploy to kill the B-1B (Author's comment).

B-2 (ATB)

SPECIFICATIONS
Length: 69 ft   Span: 172 ft
Height: 17 ft

PERFORMANCE
Speed: high subsonic   Ceiling: unspecified
Range: intercontinental

POWERPLANT Four General Electric F118 turbofan
                        engines

ARMAMENT Approximately 16 nuclear warheads

TYPES OF NUCLEAR ORDNANCE Probably B-61, B-83 and
                                    ACM

CREW 2

MANUFACTURER Northrop Aircraf,t with Boeing and LTV
                    as major associates

NUMBERS MANUFACTURED 132 planned

The B-2 is the next strategic bomber the US Air Force intends to deploy. If all goes as predicted with its deployment in the late 1990s, the Strategic Air Command will be able to fly into the Soviet Union without being detected by radar.

Since 1975, work has been under way to develop the technology and materials to make an aircraft virtually invisible to radar, infrared, and optical tracking systems. This technology is called Stealth Technology and it involves the use of radar absorbing materials — composites and plastics — in place of steel and titanium. The ATB's construction combines these materials with smooth angles, curves and serrated edges for lower radar and visual

YB-49 experimental bomber

B-2 ATB concept

Attack Aircraft

A-1 Skyraider

SPECIFICATIONS

Length: 39 ft 4 in	Span: 50 ft
Height: 9 ft	Weight: Max 16,649 lb
Speed: Max 360 mph	Ceiling: 25,000 ft
Range: 1935 mi 'tactical'	

POWERPLANT Single Wright R-3350-26 of 27,000 lb thrust

ARMAMENT 6000 lb of bombs and two 20mm machine guns

TYPES OF NUCLEAR ORDNANCE
Mk-8, Mk-7 & Betty, BOAR, Hotpoint,
Lulu, B-11, Mk-12, and the B-43

MANUFACTURER Douglas Aircraft

NUMBER MANUFACTURED 3155 aircraft in 21 variations

The A-1 Skyraider, also known as the AD-1, was one of the first Navy aircraft fighter bombers to be nuclear armed. Though slow compared to jet aircraft, it was a very versatile and rugged attack aircraft capable of effectively delivering a nuclear device against lightly defended land targets. When equipped with a Betty, Lulu or a Hotpoint bomb, the A-1 was also effective against surface ships and even could be used against submarines.

The A-1 Skyraider served with the US Navy from 6 December 1946 to 31 December 1971. It was not, however, until 1951 that it became nuclear capable.

F2H Banshee

SPECIFICATIONS

Length: 39 ft	Span: 41 ft 7.4 in
Height: 14 ft 5 in	Weight: Max 14,234 lb
Speed: Max 600 mph	Ceiling: 56,000 ft
Range: 1278 mi 'tactical'	

POWERPLANT Two Westinghouse J34-WE-22 turbojets each producing 3000 lb thrust

ARMAMENT 6000 lb of bombs

TYPES OF NUCLEAR ORDNANCE Mk-8, Mk-7 and Mk-12

MANUFACTURER McDonnell Aircraft

NUMBER MANUFACTURED 895 total, 25 known modified to deliver nuclear weapons

The Banshee was the first all jet Navy fighter/bomber. Though not as rugged as the A-1, it was extremely fast, giving it the ability to penetrate very strong air defense systems. Though the first squadron of F2Hs was delivered in March of 1949, it was not until the deployment of the first light nuclear bomb in 1951 (the Mk-8), that this aircraft became nuclear capable. It would remain nuclear capable until its retirement on 30 September 1959.

F-84G Thunderjet

SPECIFICATIONS

Length: 38 ft 1.2 in	Span: 36 ft 6 in
Height: 12 ft 6 in	Weight: Max 23,525 lb
Speed: Max 621 mph	Ceiling: 40,500 ft
Range: 2000 mi 'tactical'	

POWERPLANT A single Allison J-35-A-29 turbojet engine. Max thrust: 5600 lb

ARMAMENT 4000 lb of bombs and six 50 caliber machine guns. Total of 6000 lb of ordnance

TYPES OF NUCLEAR ORDNANCE Mk-8 & Mk-7

MANUFACTURER Republic Aviation

NUMBER MANUFACTURED Total of 3025 aircraft; 789 for the USAF and 2236 for MDAP

Before the B-45 dropped its first nuclear device, the Air Force had begun testing Mk-7 drop casings from F-84E fighter/bombers (see Mk-7). As a result of these tests, in late 1951, the Air Force began equipping the more capable F-84G fighter/bomber to carry tactical nuclear weapons.

AD-2 Skyraider

F-84G Thunderjets

F2H Banshee

Initially, the F-84G could only drop bombs from high altitude. In mid-1953, however, a Low Altitude bombing system was added, allowing the safe low altitude delivery of a nuclear bomb. Following this, the 81st Fighter/Bomber Group was deployed to Brentwater England to give tactical nuclear support to NATO field forces.

Though obsolete as a fighter escort in the mid-1950s, the F-84G would serve with the Tactical Air Command into the mid-1960s. By that time, however, it had been completely replaced by more capable fighter/bombers.

F-84F Thunderstreak

SPECIFICATIONS

Length: 43 ft 4 in
Height: 14 ft 4 in
Speed: 650 mph
Range: 2000 mi 'tactical'

Span: 33 ft 6 in
Weight: Max 25,000 lb
Ceiling: 45,000 ft

POWERPLANT One Wright J65-W-3 turbojet engine
Max thrust: 7200 lb

ARMAMENT 1620 lb of bombs and six 50 caliber machine guns

TYPES OF NUCLEAR ORDNANCE Mk-7

MANUFACTURER Republic Aircraft

NUMBER MANUFACTURED 1496 Air Force

The F-84F was an attempt to improve the capability of the basic F-84 design. Unlike its earlier brother, the F-84G, this fighter was not successful.

Though intended to be in service in 1952, production problems prevented the F-84F from become operational until 12 May 1954. Additional problems with the aircraft's motor would then ground

the fighter until mid-1955: after this, flying restrictions were imposed. As a result of these problems, the aircraft were quickly transferred to the Air National Guard (ANG) with the last being delivered on 10 January 1958.

During the Berlin crisis of 1961-62, some of these F-84F ANG squadrons were made active. These aircraft would remain operational until mid-1963, when they were again returned to inactive status. These planes were then retired in 1972.

F9F-8 Cougar

SPECIFICATIONS

Length: 41 ft 7 in
Height: 12 ft 3 in
Speed: 690 mph sea level
Range: 1278 mi 'tactical'

Span: 34 ft 6 in
Weight: Max 20,000 lb
Ceiling: 56,000 ft

POWERPLANT One Pratt & Whitney J48-P-8 turbojet
Max thrust: 3000 lb

ARMAMENT Two 1000 lb bombs and two 20mm cannons

TYPES OF NUCLEAR ORDNANCE Mk-12

MANUFACTURER Grumman Aircraft

NUMBER MANUFACTURED Unspecified

The F9F Cougar was the next Navy fighter/bomber to be armed with a nuclear device. Unlike the F2H Banshee, this aircraft's limited bomb load prevented it from carrying any nuclear device heavier than the Mk-12 bomb.

The swept wing F9F Cougar was developed to give Navy pilots an aircraft equal in capability to the Soviet swept-wing MiGs that were encountered during the Korean War. They would not be in service before the war was over, however, and with the introduction of supersonic aircraft in the mid-1950s they were obsolete as interceptors. Regardless of this, from 1954 to the early 1960s these aircraft would serve the US Navy as fighter/bombers and advanced trainers for Navy pilots.

F-84F Thunderstreaks

F9F-8 Cougar

F-100 Super Sabre

SPECIFICATIONS (F-100D)
Length: 47 ft 11 in	Span: 38 ft 9 in
Height: 16 ft 2 in	Weight: Max 34,832 lb
Speed: Mach 1.3 (864 mph)	Ceiling: 44,000 ft
Range: 1500 mi	

POWERPLANT One Pratt & Whitney J57-P-21A turbojet
Max thrust: 16,950 lb with afterburner

ARMAMENT 7040 lb of bombs and four 20mm cannons

TYPES OF NUCLEAR ORDNANCE on center line pylon
F-100A/C — one Mk-7
F-100D — one Mk-28 or Bullpup,
B-43, Mk-57, B-61

MANUFACTURER North American Aviation.

NUMBER MANUFACTURED 476 C; 1274 D

The F-100 Super Sabre was the world's first production supersonic fighter. Though it suffered from aerodynamic problems, it was one of the most important fighters ever deployed.

The original F-100A fighters, deployed on 27 September 1954, were primarily interceptors with a limited bombing capability. The first true fighter/bomber was the F-100C, fielded on 14 July of 1955. This model, and the two seater version known as the F-100D, would serve with the US Air Force until 1973, when the last F-100 was transferred to the Air National Guard. During a practice alert at a US pacific base, on 18 January 1959, an F-100 was destroyed by fire, when on engine start, its three auxiliary fuel tanks jettisoned. At that time this F-100 was carrying a nuclear device, probably a Mk-7, on its left intermediate station. The bomb's fuel capsule was not inserted, however, and this prevented any contamination.

F-100C Super Sabre

F-101A/C Voodoo

SPECIFICATIONS

Length: 67 ft 5 in	Span: 39 ft 8 in
Height: 18 ft	Weight: Max 48,001 lb
Speed: Max 1207 mph	Ceiling: 50,300 ft
Range: 1300 mi	

POWERPLANT Two Pratt & Whitney J57-P-13 turbojet
Max thrust: 7700 lb

ARMAMENT Unspecified bomb load, four 20mm cannons

TYPES OF NUCLEAR ORDNANCE
F-101A/C — one Mk-7
or Mk-28, B-43
F-101B — two Genie Air-
to-Air Rockets

MANUFACTURER McDonnell Aircraft

NUMBER MANUFACTURED 77 As, 47 Cs

Though primarily remembered as an interceptor, the F-101 Voodoo fighter was also one of the earliest jet fighter/bombers employed by TAC.

Conceived as a fighter escort, the original Voodoo model, F-101A, entered service as a fighter/bomber with the 27th SAC fighter/bomber wing on 2 May 1954. Because it had a very limited bomber capability, production was ended at 77 aircraft in favor of a structurally strengthened model designated the F-101C. By that time, however, even better fighter/bombers were becoming available, causing production of this fighter to end at 47.

The last F-101Cs were withdrawn to the ANG in mid-1966. After this, the only F-101 fighters in service were the long range F-101B fighters armed with Genie missiles.

FJ-4B Fury

SPECIFICATIONS

Length: 36 ft 7 in	Span: 39 ft 1 in
Height: 13 ft 11 in	Weight: Max 19,900 lb
Speed: Max 690 mph	Ceiling: 44,000 ft
Range: 1500 mi	

POWERPLANT A single Wright J-65-W4 turbojet engine
Max thrust: 7700 lb

ARMAMENT Unspecified bomb load, four 20mm cannons

TYPES OF NUCLEAR ORDNANCE Bullpup missiles or one
Mk-7, Mk-8, Lulu, Hotpoint,
B-11, Mk-12, Mk-28, or B-43 bomb

MANUFACTURER North American Aviation

NUMBER MANUFACTURED 222

The Fury models 2 through 4 were some of the most important fighters ever deployed by the US Navy. Essentially navalised versions of famed F-86 Sabre Jet, these aircraft were the first Navy fighters that were equal in performance to operational Air Force aircraft.

Fielded in late 1957, the FJ-4B was the last version of the Fury to be produced. Designed for higher altitudes and, at the same time, equipped with a Low Altitude Bombing system for the delivery of nuclear weapons, it was the most capable Fury model —even exceeding the performance of the F-86H. Though it was quickly outmoded by new, faster, longer range aircraft this model would remain in service into the mid-1960s.

F3H-2 Demon

SPECIFICATIONS

Length: 58 ft 11 in	Span: 35 ft 4 in
Height: 14 ft 7 in	Weight: Max 33,900 lb
Speed: Max 730 mph	Ceiling: 44,000 ft
Range: 1500 mi	

POWERPLANT A single Allison J-71-A-2 turbojet engine
Max thrust: 14,250 lb with afterburner

ARMAMENT Unspecified bomb load, four 20mm cannons

TYPES OF NUCLEAR ORDNANCE Mk-12 and Mk-7

MANUFACTURER McDonnell Aircraft

NUMBER MANUFACTURED 521

The F3H-2 was an improved version of the original F3H-1 fighter. With the deployment of these fighters on 7 March 1956, the US Navy had its first transonic fighter.

The F3H-2 was designed more for the intercepting of enemy aircraft than the dropping of bombs; as such it had a very limited bomb load. However, it was an effective fighter which remained in the inventory until 31 August 1964.

FJ-4B Fury

F3H-2 Demon

A-4 Skyhawk

SPECIFICATIONS (A-4M)
Length: 40 ft 4 in	Span: 27 ft 6 in
Height: 15 ft 4 in	Weight: Max 19,833 lb
Speed: Max 687 mph	Ceiling: 44,000 ft
Range: 1500 mi	

POWERPLANT A single Pratt & Whitney J52-P-408 turbojet.
Max thrust: 11,200 lb

ARMAMENT 6750 lb of bombs and two 20mm cannons in
wing roots

TYPES OF NUCLEAR ORDNANCE
Mk-8, Mk-12, Hotpoint, Lulu, Mk-28,
B-43, Mk-57, Bullpup B and B-61

MANUFACTURER Douglas Aircraft

NUMBER MANUFACTURED 2960 total;
2519 for US, 439 for export

A-4M Skyhawks

The first A-4A Skyhawks (then called A-4D-1) were delivered to Navy squadron VA-62 on 26 October 1956. Since that time, this little fighter/bomber has set an impressive record for maintainability and reliability in three wars.

Though the Skyhawk is still in service with the US Navy and Marine Corps, it is being progressively replaced by the new AV-8B Harrier 'jump jet' and the F/A-18 fighter. As to when the last of these fighters will be retired, however, is anyone's guess.

On 5 December 1965, an A-4 Skyhawk carrying one nuclear weapon rolled off the elevator of a US Navy carrier into the Pacific Ocean. Not only were the bomb and the aircraft lost but the pilot himself died in the accident.

F-101 Voodoos

F-105 Thunderchief

SPECIFICATIONS

Length: 64 ft	Span: 34 ft 11.25 in
Height: 19 ft 8 in	Weight: Max 52,838 lb
Speed: Max Mach 2.1	Ceiling: 44,000 ft
Range: 1800 mi	

POWERPLANT A single Pratt & Whitney J75-P- 19W turbojet
Max thrust: 7700 lb

ARMAMENT 14,000 lb bomb load and one 20mm M-61
Vulcan cannon

TYPES OF NUCLEAR ORDNANCE
F-105B: one Mk-28 or Mk-43 bomb (internal)
F-105D/F: one Mk-28 or B-43 (internal)
with two Mk-28s or B-43s or B-61s
(external)

MANUFACTURER Republic Aircraft

NUMBER MANUFACTURED 883 aircraft

The F-105 Thunderchief was the replacement for the earlier F-84 fighter/bombers. Though initially designed to deliver only nuclear payloads, in Vietnam it would become well known for its conventional bombing capability.

The first F-105B was delivered to the Tactical Air Command in August of 1958. Though there were some problems with this model, the later F-105D proved quite successful, becoming the major production model. In Vietnam, one wing of F-105Ds, the 335 TFW, dropped a total of 202,596 tons of bombs in five years (they also shot down 23 MiGs).

By 1970, the F-105G Wild Weasel model had become more important than the nuclear-capable fighter/bomber variant. Thus, by 1975 the remaining F-105s had either been converted into F-105Gs or had been withdrawn from service.

F-104C/D Starfighter

SPECIFICATIONS

Length: 54 ft 9 in	Span: 21 ft 11 in
Height: 13 ft 6 in	Weight: Max 28,779 lb
Speed: Max 1500 mph	Ceiling: 55,000 ft
Range: 1380 mi	

POWERPLANT One GE J79-GE-11A turbojet engine
Max thrust: 15,800 lb with afterburner

ARMAMENT 920 lb of bombs and one 20mm M-61 Vulcan
cannon

TYPES OF NUCLEAR ORDNANCE One Mk-28 or B-43

MANUFACTURER Lockheed Aircraft

NUMBER MANUFACTURED 741 aircraft total, 77 Cs

The F-104 was the first double sonic fighter to be deployed by the US Air Force. Regardless of this, the fighter only served with the active Air Force from November of 1958 to 1965, though its 1500 mph speed set a standard.

The F-104C/D Starfighter fighter/bomber is the enigma aircraft of this section. Though the F-104 C model is listed as nuclear capable, its listed maximum payload is half the weight of the smallest nuclear weapon it was to carry. Now it is true that the later F-104G could carry up to two bombs, but this model was built entirely in Europe and operated only by European Air Forces.

To add additional smoke to this question, in 1961 the Air Force initiated Operation Grindstone to upgrade the ground attack capability of the F-104C/D aircraft. It is possible that in this program the aircraft payload was increased to allow the carriage of nuclear weapons.

Regardless of this, the F-104C is an interesting aircraft with a number of achievements to its credit. It set seven 'time to climb' records and an altitude record of 103,395 feet.

F-105D Thunderchief

KB-50 tanker and F-104 Starfighter

F-105G Thunderchief

F-4 Phantom II

SPECIFICATIONS (F-4C)

Length: 58 ft 3 in	Span: 38 ft 5 in
Height: 16 ft 6 in	Weight: Max 38,328 lb
Speed: Max 1433 mph	Ceiling: 56,000 ft
Range: 1770 mi with nuclear ordnance	

POWERPLANT Two GE J79-GE-15 turbojet engines. Max thrust: 17,000 lb with afterburner

ARMAMENT 8250 lb of bombs and one 20mm M-61 Vulcan cannon. One nuclear device

TYPES OF NUCLEAR ORDNANCE Walleye, Mk-28, B-43, B-61 or B-83 bomb. Genie also tested

MANUFACTURER McDonnell Aircraft (McDonnell Douglas)

NUMBER MANUFACTURED 5195 aircraft

First flown on 27 May 1958, the F-4 Phantom is one of the most flown aircraft in the world today. In use by 12 nations, it is second only to the F-86 Sabre jet in the total number manufactured.

To list the Phantom's achievements would fill a good size book, and many people have already done this. For the purpose of this section, however, it is to be noted that the first F-4s became operational with the US Navy in June of 1961, the Marine Corps in 1962 and the Air Force in 1963. Since that time, these planes have bagged a total of 280 air to air victories.

Though production ended at 13 models in 1981, the Phantom is still evolving. At the present time, the operational fighters are being upgraded to keep them effective into the year 2000.

A-6 Intruder

SPECIFICATIONS (A-6E)

Length: 58 ft 11 in	Span: 35 ft 4 in
Height: 14 ft 7 in	Weight: Max 33,900 lb
Speed: Max 730 mph	Ceiling: 44,000 ft
Range: 1500 mi	

POWERPLANT Two Pratt & Whitney J52-P-8B turbojets Max thrust: 9300 lb

ARMAMENT Maximum of 17,280 lb of conventional bombs or 5 nuclear devices

TYPES OF NUCLEAR ORDNANCE Mk-12, Mk-28, B-43, Mk-57, B-61 or B-83

MANUFACTURER Grumman Aircraft

NUMBER MANUFACTURED over 350 A-6Es

The A-6 Intruder is the Navy's primary long range all weather strike aircraft. Though smaller than the A-3 and A-5 bombers it replaced, this aircraft can carry a conventional bomb load equal to that of a World War II B-17 bomber.

The first A-6A was delivered to Navy Squadron VA-42 on 1 February 1963. Two years later the A-6 was in combat over Vietnam where its bombing capability earned it the nickname 'the mini-B-52' bestowed by the Vietcong. Since Vietnam, this aircraft has also seen combat over Grenada, Libya and Lebanon.

The present production version of the A-6, the A-6E, is a highly improved model incorporating modern micro-electronics. As of last report, further improvements are to be done to this model to keep it effective until the Advanced Tactical Aircraft is deployed in the late 1990s.

F-4G Phantom II

A-7 Corsair II

SPECIFICATIONS (A-7E)

Length: 46 ft 1.5 in   Span: 38 ft 9 in
Height: 16 ft .75 in   Weight: Max 42,000 lb
Speed: Max 691 mph   Ceiling: 52,500 ft
Range: 2240 mi

POWERPLANT One Allison/Rolls Royce TF41-A-2 turbofan
Max thrust: 15,000 lb

ARMAMENT 15,000 lb of bombs, sidewinders and one 20mm
M-61 Vulcan cannon. Maximum of 4 bombs

TYPES OF NUCLEAR ORDNANCE Either Walleye, Mk-28,
B-43, Mk-57, B-61 or B-83

MANUFACTURER Ling Temco Vought

NUMBER MANUFACTURED 1500 aircraft

Derived from the earlier supersonic F-8 Crusader, the A-7 Corsair II was developed to supplement the Navy's A-4 Skyhawk force. The first aircraft was delivered on 14 October 1966 and, on 3 December 1967, the A-7 received its baptism of fire over the Gulf of Tonkin. The following year, the Air Force also began operating the A-7Ds in place of the A-1 Skyraiders and to supplement the F-105s.

The A-7 was originally intended as a low cost interim aircraft. Regardless of this fact, however, 20 years after it was deployed, the Navy still operates it in front line units (A-7Es), and the Air Force has many in reserve units. Though at this time the Navy planes are being replaced by F/A-18 Hornets, there is an Air Force program underway to turn the A-7 into a supersonic fighter like the F-8. The A-7 should still be operational in the year 2000.

F-111 Aardvark

SPECIFICATIONS (F-111C)

Length: 73 ft 6 in   Span: 63 ft extended
Height: 17 ft 1.5 in   Weight: Max 91,500 lb
Speed: Mach 1.2   Ceiling: 60,000 ft
Range: 2925 mi 'combat radius'

POWERPLANT Two Pratt & Whitney TF30-P-100 turbojets
Max thrust: 25,000 lb with afterburner

ARMAMENT 29,000 lb of bombs. A 20mm M-61 Vulcan
cannon can also be carried in the bomb bay

TYPES OF NUCLEAR ORDNANCE Two B-43, B-61 or B-83
bombs

MANUFACTURER General Dynamics

NUMBER MANUFACTURED 437 aircraft total,
340 operational in 1984

The F-111 is the Tactical Air Command's primary long range strike aircraft. It was the replacement for the B-66 and F-105 aircraft.

The F-111 is one of the best, and one of the worst aircraft to be developed in the last 20 years. On the good side, not only is this aircraft the world's first production variable-wing fighter, when it was fielded in October of 1967 it gave the Tactical Air Command its first *fighter/bomber* with a *superior range* and *payload* to that of the World War II B-29 *heavy bombers*. At the same time however, because of its accident rate and the politics of the 1960s, this fighter has one of the worst records any operational aircraft (one Air Force officer called it very unforgiving).

At present the Air Force plans to replace the F-111 with the new F-15E in the late 1980s.

A-6 Intruder

A-7 Corsair

F-111A Aardvark

History of the US Nuclear Arsenal

F-16 Falcon

SPECIFICATIONS
Length: 47 ft 7.75 in   Span: 32 ft 10 in
Height: 16 ft 5.25 in   Weight: Max 33,000 lb
Speed: Max 730 mph   Ceiling: 44,000 ft
Range: 1270 mi

POWERPLANT One Pratt & Whitney F100-PW-200 turbofan
Max thrust: 25,000 lb with afterburner

ARMAMENT 12,000 lb of bombs and one 20mm M-61
Vulcan cannon. Five nuclear bombs maximum

TYPES OF NUCLEAR ORDNANCE B-43, B-61 or B-83

MANUFACTURER General Dynamics

NUMBER MANUFACTURED Still in production, over 800 in
operation with USAF

More maneuverable than many other fighters and capable of carrying its own weight in ordnance the F-16 Fighting Falcon is one of the most effective lightweight fighters in service in the world.

The F-16 was developed to replace the F-4 Phantom in active units and to modernize the Air Force reserve. It entered operational service in January of 1979 with the 388th TFW at Hill AFB. By 1984 a total of eight wings were equipped with 827 aircraft in the inventory (this included the last F-105 squadron in the ANG). Production of the F-16 is continuing to a total of 2651.

F/A-18 Hornet

F-15 Eagle

SPECIFICATIONS
Length: 63 ft 9 in   Span: 42 ft 10 in
Height: 18 ft 8 in   Weight: Max 68,000 lb
Speed: Mach 2.5   Ceiling: 44,000 ft
Range: approx 3000 mi

POWERPLANT Two Pratt & Whitney F100-PW-100 turbofan
engines
Max thrust: 23,930 lb with afterburner

ARMAMENT 16,000 lb of bombs and one 20mm M-61
Vulcan cannon. Five nuclear bombs maximum

TYPES OF NUCLEAR ORDNANCE B-43, B-61 or B-83

MANUFACTURER McDonnell Douglas

NUMBER MANUFACTURED Still in production, over 1000
planned

The F-15 Eagle is the most powerful air-superiority fighter in use by the US Air Force. In use by four nations this fighter has already earned itself an excellent combat record in two conflicts.

F-15 Eagle

Though the first F-15 was delivered in November of 1974 the first truly nuclear capable model was the F-15C deployed in the June of 1979. This fighter, strengthened for heavier loads and equipped with conformal external fuel tanks, has a tremendous ground attack capability as well as a greater range compared to the earlier model.

In 1987, the new two seat model called the F-15E was deployed. This new model (60 percent new components) has new F100-PW-220 engines, an increased payload capacity of 24,500 lb, and still greater range than the F-15C.

F/A-18 Hornet

SPECIFICATIONS

Length: 56 ft
Height: 15 ft 3. in
Speed: Mach 1.7
Range: 1260 mi

Span: 40 ft 4.8 in
Weight: Max 44,000 lb
Ceiling: 44,000 ft

POWERPLANT Two GE F404-GE-400 turbofan engines
Max thrust: 16,000 lb with afterburner

ARMAMENT 17,000 lb of bombs and one 20mm M-61
Vulcan cannon. Two nuclear bombs maximum

TYPES OF NUCLEAR ORDNANCE B-57 or B-61

MANUFACTURER McDonnell Douglas

NUMBER MANUFACTURED 1366 planned

Developed to replace the A-7 Corsair II and the F-4 Phantom, the F/A-18 Hornet is the newest all weather fighter in use by the US Navy.

Derived from the earlier Northrop F-17 lightweight fighter, the F/A-18 Hornet has been designed to serve both as an interceptor and as an attack aircraft from Navy carriers. Unlike previous multirole aircraft, however, the fighter and attack F/A-18s are identical in every aspect with the exception of the external pylons, sensors and weapons. An F/A-18 configured as a fighter can in fact be reconfigured as an attack bomber in less than an hour: hence the duo designation on this aircraft.

The first F/A-18 fighters were delivered to the Navy in the summer of 1983. At this time the Navy plans to equip six fighter and 24 attack squadrons with this aircraft, the Marines plan to equip 12 fighter and 24 attack squadrons with the Hornet.

F-16 Falcons

AV-8B Harrier II

SPECIFICATIONS

Length: 46 ft 4 in	Span: 40 ft 4.8 in
Height: 11 ft 7.2 in	Weight: Max 29,750 lb
Speed: Mach 1.1	Ceiling: 44,000 ft
Range: 691 mi STOL with 7 bombs	

POWERPLANT One Rolls Royce Pegasus 11 turbofan engine
Max thrust: 21,180 lb

ARMAMENT 9200 lb of bombs and one 20mm M-61 Vulcan
cannon. One nuclear device

TYPES OF NUCLEAR ORDNANCE B-57 or B-61

MANUFACTURER McDonnell Douglas

NUMBER MANUFACTURED Unspecified

The AV-8B is the first vertical-launch aircraft capable of delivering a nuclear payload. An Americanized model of the original AV-8A developed by Great Britain, this fighter/bomber is intended to replace earlier AV-8As in use with the Marine Corps and older model A-4 Skyhawks.

Due to the use of a new lightweight composite wing, improved avionics, and other changes the AV-8B is superior to its predecessor in range, speed, payload and handling. These new capabilities, coupled with the vertical or short take-off ability it inherited from the AV-8A, give the Harrier II a strike/response capability beyond that of any operational Navy fighter.

The first AV-8Bs were delivered to the Marine Corps in late 1983. As of 1985, one squadron was operational with seven more planned. This plane has formidable agility.

ATF/ATA

The Advanced Tactical Fighter/ Advanced Tactical Aircraft is a combined Air Force and Navy program to develop the next generation of tactical interceptor/attack aircraft to replace the F/A-18, F-16, F-15 and the A-6E.

For several years now, both the Air Force and the Navy have been doing research on advance aircraft designs. Studies have been done on improving the aircraft's mobility (swept forward wings and canards), cutting its weight with composite materials, making it invisible to radar, improving the cockpit control system, and even vectoring the engine thrust as in the extremely agile Harrier design. Now work is underway to combine these different technologies to create an extraordinary fighter aircraft.

At the present time Lockheed and Northrop are each building two flying prototypes of their ATF design. Called the YF-22A (Lockheed) and the YF-23A (Northrop), these aircraft are to begin flight testing in Fiscal Year 1990.

AV-8B Harrier II

YF-22A ATF concept

US Strategic Nuclear Bases and Probable Targets in the Soviet Union

T his map shows the rough location for every US bomber base, ICBM field, and support harbor for ballistic missile submarines and their probable targets in the Soviet Union. This map is not quite complete, however, for certain key installations have been left out. These places are as follows.

United States Nuclear Forces

According to SAC, there are at least 30 airfields in the United States, separate from the main bomber bases, that have been designated for use by the manned bomber force as emergency bases in time of war. The idea is that, in a time of high political tension, the bomber force would be dispersed to these fields—thus increasing the number of targets a Soviet force would have to engage, and increasing the survivability of the bomber force. These fields would also be used as recovery points for the bombers after they had completed their intial bombing missions. Additional recovery fields exists in England, Spain and Australia. One such US field is Amarillo Airport in Texas.

Soviet Targets

In addition to the large number of targets shown, there are a number of additional installations and military facilities that would probably be targeted for destruction by US forces. Such targeted facilities would include Soviet ammunition depots, which cumulatively contain close to 12 million metric tons of ammo and small arms. Other such targets includes major petroleum reserves, fields and refineries; and major underground bunkers for use by Soviet political and military leaders during nuclear conflict; these particular facilities seem to be the primary targets of a select force of B-52s armed with the 9 megaton Mk-53 bomb.

In addition to these targets, it is known that the Soviet Union has five arctic staging bases for the Backfire bomber, which would allow this aircraft to strike deep inside the US without in-flight refueling. These fields would either be attacked preemptively during a period of high tension, or would be struck *after* an attack on the US to prevent their use in a second strike. In nuclear exchange Soviet SAM sites, mobile and fixed, would also be engaged—either by US Minuteman III or Poseidon missiles, or by SRAM missiles carried by US B-52 and B-1B bombers (the SRAM is also used to improve penetration).

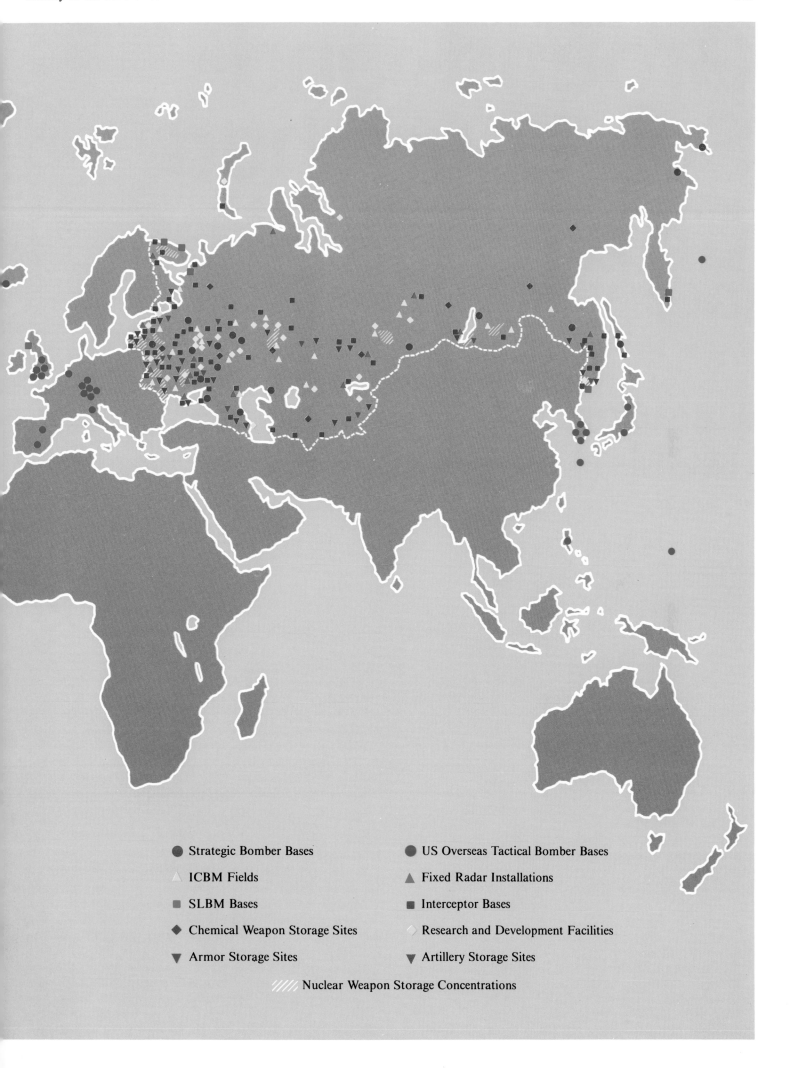

● Strategic Bomber Bases   ● US Overseas Tactical Bomber Bases

▲ ICBM Fields   ▲ Fixed Radar Installations

■ SLBM Bases   ■ Interceptor Bases

◆ Chemical Weapon Storage Sites   ◇ Research and Development Facilities

▼ Armor Storage Sites   ▼ Artillery Storage Sites

//// Nuclear Weapon Storage Concentrations

Ground- and Sea-Launched Cruise Missiles (GLCM) (SLCM)

Matador (MGM-1)

SPECIFICATIONS

Length: 39 ft 6 in	Span: 28 ft 7 in
Diameter: 4 ft 6 in	Weight: 12,000 lb

PERFORMANCE

Speed: Mach 0.9 (650 mph) over Mach 1 in terminal dive	Ceiling: 35,000 ft
Range: 700 mi	CEP: best 1700 ft

PROPULSION Sustainer — a Allison J33-A-37 Turbojet producing 4600 lb of thrust

Booster — Single Aerojet General solid fuel rocket motor producing 55,000 lb of thrust for two seconds

GUIDANCE Matador A — radar directed radio command guidance system (MSQ)

Matador C — MSQ plus Shanicle

WARHEAD Conventional or a single W-5 fission warhead of 40 to 50 kt yield

CONTRACTOR Martin Aircraft (now Martin Marietta Corp)

NUMBER OF MISSILES 1200 produced; 150 deployed to Europe, 50 to South Korea

The Matador was the first guided missile ever deployed by the United States Air Force. Almost until it was replaced by the Mace in June of 1959 this was the longest range missile in the US arsenal, superseded range-wise by the Snark.

With the ending of the second World War, the US Air Force, then known as the US Army Air Force, began several missile research and development programs to determine if the technology of the V-1 and V-2 missiles could be used to develop an alternative to the manned bomber for the deliver of nuclear bombs. One of these programs, codenamed MX-771, was the Martin missile program now known as Matador.

Following the issuing of the development contract to Martin Aircraft in March of 1946, work on the Matador began in 1947 with the construction of ten full scale, wooden, dummy missiles for use in developing the planned rocket booster/zero length launcher system. At about the same time, Martin Aircraft also began constructed of 15 XB-61 experimental missiles using available, or on the shelf, components modified as little as possible. The first flight of one of these prototype missiles occurred at White Sands Missile Range on 20 January 1949, and by 1950 testing was underway with YB-61s equipped with the planned guidance system (the XB-61s were radio controlled from the ground). By 1951, the testing location had been switched to Patrick AFB, Cape Canaveral, where on 21 June 1951 final tactical testing of the Matador began. The later part of these tests would prove certain, planned, design changes in the missile and in December of 1951 the Matador was released for mass production.[1]

While testing of the Matador was underway, on 1 October 1951, the Air Force formed the nation's first Matador squadron, the first Pilotless Bomber Squadron (light). Three months later the second PBS was formed on 10 January 1952. These squadrons were trained under the supervision of the 6555th Guided Missile Wing.

Matador A

The first production model of the Matador was the B-61A or Matador A. Though like all cruise missiles it had a basic similarity to manned aircraft, it was built to a completely different set of standards and combat requirements. First, since the missile was only to be flown once, the Matador was built using low cost, low stress materials (the engine was only designed for 10 hours of operation), which kept the cost of the weapon down to $76,000, one-fourth the price of a 1950s fighter/bomber.[2] Second, because the missile was to be launched from a wheeled, zero length launcher it was of a high wing (reverse dihedral), high tail configuration, where most fighters are of the mid-wing design.

After all these differences, however, it is interesting to note that the Matador was technically piloted by a human being, because it was guided in flight by radio commands, sent to it from a ground controller who kept track of the weapons progress via a network of land based radars. In simple terms, the Matador was a nuclear tipped, radio controlled bomber.

The first production Matador A was delivered to the Air Force in the winter of 1952, and the first launch occurred in November. Training with the two squadrons began soon afterwards,[3] and by December of 1953, both units were ready for overseas deployment. The squadrons were then transferred to the Tactical Air Command on 15 January 1954, a requirement for overseas deployment, and on 9 March 1954 the 1st PBS, with its 50 missiles, left the United States for Bitburg AFB (arriving on 20 March). The 2nd PBS would follow six months later to Hahn AFB, giving TAC a total of 100 Matador missiles in Europe.[4]

Nine months after the 2nd Pilotless Bomber Squadron arrived in Germany the US Air Force redesignated the Matador from Bomber 61A, B-61A, to Tactical Missile 61A or TM-61A. As a result of this redesignation the 1st PBS became the 1st Tactical Missile Squadron (TMS) and the 2nd PBS became the 69th TMS.

With the deployment of the Matador A, the nuclear capability of the US Tactical Air Command in Europe increased significantly. With these missiles, TAC could now strike enemy targets that were too heavily defended to use manned aircraft or manned targets that night, or bad weather, had grounded. Furthermore, because the Matador was a mobile weapon, it was not restricted to US airfields as the fighter/bombers were, and thus could be effectively hidden in the surrounding countryside against an enemy preemptive strike.

Regardless of these new capabilities, however, the Matador A also had several significant problems. One of these problems was the fact that the MSQ guidance system limited the range of the Matador to the maximum distance at which the ground based radars could keep a direct line of sight track with the missile. Another problem with the weapon was that it was deployed to the field in four separate pieces—fuselage, wings, warhead and booster—and

that it was not carried on its mobile launcher but on a towed trailer. As a result of this, once a Matador reached its launching site, it required over 10 men (and a mobile crane) close to an hour and a half to get the missile ready for launch. Because of these problems, in 1954 development was begun on a new Matador, called Matador B, which would have a self-contained guidance system, folding wings, and be deployable on its zero length launcher. When it became apparent that development of the missile would take too long, the Air Force began development of the Matador C to serve as an interim measure.

Matador C

The Matador C was essentially a Matador A equipped with the new Shanicle guidance system. In this system, two ground based transmitters, or beacons, were used to create a long range hyperbolic grid (one beacon controlling the missile's range, the other its azimuth), along which the missile would fly. As a result of this single change, the TM-61C had a greater accuracy than the earlier A model, a higher immunity to enemy electronic counter-measures, and longer range because the radar line of sight limitation was removed. One other improvement to come from Shanicle was that it allowed the ground controllers to operate more than one missile at a time.

The first Matador Cs came into service in 1957 with the deployment of the 11th TMS to Europe. Replacement of the earlier TM-61As at Hahn and Bitburg also began in 1957 and by 1958 the TM-61C was the only Matador model in service in Europe. The same year TM-61C deployment was completed in Europe the Air Force initiated 'Operation Dark Eyes' during which Matador Cs were deployed to South Korea to serve as a nuclear counter against any possible reinvasion by the North. These Korean missiles were deployed at Osan Air base, Kimpo Airport (Seoul), and Chinchon-Ni under the control of the 58th Tactical Missile Group.

As the TM-61C was finishing its deployment, however, the Air Force began preparing for the deployment of the next US

Matador GLCM

GLCM — the Mace, or Matador B. On 18 June 1958, the 1st TMS at Bitburg was replaced by the 71st Tactical Missile Squadron which served as a transition unit from Matador to Mace. By the end of the year, the 69th TMS had also been replaced by the 405th TMS and the 11th by the 822d TMS. Deployment of the Mace then began in June of 1959, and by 1961, the Matador had been completely withdrawn from Europe. Mace deployment in Asia also began in 1961, and following the launch of the 286th, and last, Matador training missile on 1 June 1961, the last TM-61C missiles were removed from South Korea in 1962.

[1] The military pressures caused by the Korean war caused the Matador to be listed as operational on 13 September 1951 prior to it being released for mass production.
[2] The Matador used neither a rudder, ailerons, or elevators for flight controls, but instead used a full flying horizontal stabilizer and special, snap action, wing spoilers for its aerobatic needs.
[3] The 2nd PBS launched its first Matador in December 1952. This may have been a production missile.
[4] One source states that each squadron originally had 100 missiles but that this number was reduced to improve maintenance.

Matador GLCM

Snark GLCM

Snark (SM-62)

SPECIFICATIONS
  Length: 69 ft   Span: 42 ft
  Height: 15 ft   Weight: 51,000 lb

PERFORMANCE
  Speed: Mach 0.94   Ceiling: over 60,000 ft
  Range: 6300 mi

PROPULSION   Sustainer — one Pratt & Whitney J57-P-17
                        Turbojet. Max thrust: 11,500 lb
                        Booster — Two Allegany Ballistics solid fuel
                        rocket motors each producing 130,000 lb
                        of thrust

GUIDANCE Inertial system with star tracker

WARHEAD One W-39 thermonuclear warhead of 4 mt yield

CONTRACTOR Northrop Aircraft

NUMBER OF MISSILES 30 known deployed

The Snark is the only intercontinental cruise missile that has ever been deployed. The first United States missile to travel over 5000 miles, it was quickly outmoded by the ICBM.

Following the end of the Second World War, in October of 1945 the Army Air Force Technical Service Command began soliciting proposals from between 15 and 30 companies for 10 year research and development efforts into four different types of guided missiles. On 9 January 1946, Northrop Aircraft responded to this request with a proposal for a subsonic, six jet, cruise missile with a range of 3000 miles. This proposal, and one other from Northrop for a supersonic missile, was accepted. On 28 March 1946, the Army Air Force awarded Northrop a one year study and research contract for both the BOOJUM (the supersonic missile)[1] and the Snark cruise missiles.

With the issuing of the contract construction began on the first of 16 N-25 missiles. A subsonic cruise missile like the later SM-62 Snark, this missile was designed to deliver a Mk-IV nuclear warhead against military targets over a distance of 5000 miles. The first launch from a rocket sled was completed at White Sands on 16 April 1951 and by March 1952 a total of 25 test launches were completed. Development of this missile had already ended by this time as the Air Force issued new range and payload requirements for the missile (possibly to allow the carriage of a hydrogen bomb).

To meet the new requirements, Northrop began development of a larger version of the N-25 missile, called the N-69A, in 1951. Lengthened from 50 feet to 68 feet and increased in weight from 28,000 lb to 49,000 lb, this new missile was the initial model of the SM-62 Snark designed to test the basic aerodynamics of the missile. Flight testing from a fixed zero length launcher at Cape Canaveral began on 6 August 1953, and by 21 July 1954 a total of seven launches had been completed (only two of the flights were successful).[2] Flight testing of the improved N-69B began on 21 September 1954, followed by the first N-69C warhead delivery test vehicle launch on 10 February 1955 (of the first three missile series only five of the 17 flights attempted could be called successful).

While testing of the N-69C was underway in May of 1955, wind tunnel tests showed that the planned terminal dive method of warhead delivery was not possible, because the missile could not maintain the prescribed dive angle with the available aerlon control: this had actually been confirmed the previous month when on 6 April a N-69C broke up during its terminal dive. As a result of this, Northrop proposed in June that the Snark be modified to incorporate a ballistic nose drop delivery system. In this method the missile's nose would actually separate from the missile and then drop like a free fall bomb onto its target. The change was approved by the Air Force in July, and on 26 October 1955 the first modified N-69C was flown (testing of the modified N-69C ended on 31 October 1956 after 10 flights, six successful).

One month after the first modified N-69C launch, on 26 November 1955, flight testing began with the N-69D. Called the 'guidance test vehicle,' the N-69D was the first Snark model to fly with the 24 hour stellar inertial guidance system that was to guide the operational Snark over intercontinental distances. Though most of the initial flights with this model would be unsuccessful, they include the 5 December 1956 flight in which an N-69D refused its destruct command and disappeared over Brazil.[3] By 20 November 1957, a total of 19 flights had been completed, 14 successful, including the first all military launch of a Snark on 1 October 1957.

Again, while testing of the N-69D was underway, on 20 June 1957 the first Operational Concept test vehicle, N-69E, was launched. Essentially the prototype for the Snark, this missile was to demonstrate the missile's operational capability, and to test the prototype mobile launcher and its associated ground support equipment. This version, however, would have one of the worst flight records of all the later models, with only eight of the 15 flights completed successfully by 19 September 1958. The N-69E flight test program was significant in that it was this model of the Snark that first reached Ascension Island, over 4400 miles from the Cape. This model was also the first Snark to be launched by the 556th Strategic Missile Squadron, the nations first strategic missile

squadron (activated on 15 December 1957).

Following the completion of the N-69E flights, on 23 October 1958, the N-69D guidance test missiles again took to the air. Three of these missiles were used for flight training with the 556th SMS, the others as part of Phase V guidance testing with the new Airborne Parabolic Arc Computer system. The last N-69D was launched on 16 December 1959.

With the completion of the N-69E test series, deployment of the Snark could now begin. On 1 January 1959 the Air Force activated the nation's first Snark missile wing, the 702nd Strategic Missile Wing at Presque Isle Maine. Three months later on 1 April the 556th SMS at Patrick was assigned to the 702nd as its first Snark squadron. The first production SM-62A missile was then launched from the Cape on 6 April, and on 27 May, the first operational missile was delivered to Presque Isle.

With the deployment of the Snark (SM-62A), the US Air Force now had an intercontinental nuclear delivery system with some rather unique capabilities. With a radar image 1/20th that of the B-52 and a low altitude approach capability, the SM-62A could come within 10 miles of a planned target before being detected by ground based radar (one minute from impact). In addition, the Snark was both air and ground mobile, allowing the missile to quickly disperse throughout the nation for protection against a preemptive strike on Presque Isle: a major capability compared to the fixed base, and at that time, soft Atlas sites. These capabilities did much to offset the missile's vulnerability to heavy turbulence (bad weather) and surface to air missiles.

Two months after the first missiles arrived at Presque Isle, on 15 July 1959, the Air Force inactivated the 556th SMS. As a result of this, and the cancellation of the 702 Missile Maintenance Squadron, from that day on all operational and maintenance functions associated with the Snark were handled by the wing's deputy commander for missiles. In addition all subsequent training and test flights for the Snark were now handled directly by the Wing.

With the 702nd SMW now completely in charge of the Snark missiles, on 6 November 1959, a production Snark was launched

Snark GLCM

carrying the new Airborne Parabolic Arc Computer or APAC. Testing of this missile modification would complete the Snark flight test program with a totaled of 14 test flights being completed by the Wing by 5 December 1960 (the Wing was given technical support for the last five flights by Northrop). Prior to this, on 18 March 1960, the first Snark went on alert at Presque Isle ('13 Snarks were at Presque Isle by December of 1959). By December 1960 a total of 30 missiles were in service at this base and on 28 February 1961 Headquarters SAC declared the 702nd SMW to be operational.

One month after the base was declared operational, on 28 March, President John F Kennedy directed that the Snark be phased out as it was 'obsolete and of marginal military value'.[4]

Withdrawal began immediately and on 25 June 1961, less than four months after the unit was declared operational the 702nd SMW was inactivated.

[1] This program was ended some time before 1954.
[2] During the N-69C test period, on 13 May 1955, the last N-69A was flown. Though a reasonably successful test, the flight was cut short when the missile collided with its T-33 photo plane.
[3] This Snark was actually found in Brazil in January of 1983 by a farmer.
[4] In the same speech Kennedy also cancelled the XB-70 bomber, ended production of the B-52 and B-58 bombers and accelerated retirement of the B-47.

Mace (MGM-13)

SPECIFICATIONS
Length: 44 ft 9 in   Span: 18 ft 2 in
Diameter: 4 ft 6 in   Weight: 13,800 lb

PERFORMANCE
Speed: Mach 2.8   Ceiling: over 40,000 ft
Range: Mace A — 800 mi
       Mace B — 1500 mi

PROPULSION Sustainer — An Allison J33-A-41 turbojet produc-
                ing 5200 lb of thrust
           Booster — Single Thiokol solid fuel rocket motor
                producing 50,000 lb of thrust

GUIDANCE Mace A — Goodyear ATRAN, Automatic Terrain
               Recognition and Navigation, system (early form
               of TERCOM)
         Mace B — AC Spark Plug inertial guidance
               system

WARHEAD Conventional or a single W-28 fusion warhead of
         2 mt yield

CONTRACTOR Martin Marietta Corporation

NUMBER OF MISSILES Over a 1000 produced; 300 deployed
                    to Europe, 100 to Okinawa, Japan

The Mace was the third GLCM to be deployed by the US Air Force. An advanced version of the earlier Matador, this weapon is even more powerful than the new Ground Launched Cruise Missile.

Though the Matador was a powerful, missile it did have several operational problems. Besides the fact that its ground based guidance system was susceptible to electronic jamming, the weapon itself was cumbersome to move and took an hour and a half to assemble for launch: this mobility problem almost caused the cancellation of the Matador in favor of the Navy's Regulus I. To rectify these problems, in 1954, Martin Aircraft began development of an improved model of the Matador, incorporating a self-contained guidance system, folding wings to improve reaction time, and a special towed launcher to improve mobility. Designated the Matador B, flight testing of this new model began in 1956 at Holloman AFB, White Sands Missile Range.

Development of the Matador B ended in 1957 with production starting in the fall of that year. The next year, the Air Force decided that there were enough differences between this missile and the Matador C to warrant a new designation. Thus in the spring of 1958, the Matador B was renamed the Mace (TM-76A) (the first launch under this new title was on 10 June 1958). The first Mace missiles were then delivered to their European based squadrons in June of 1959.

Mace A

The first Mace missiles to be deployed were the Mace As. Though similar in basic design to the earlier Matadors, these new missiles were five feet longer, to allow enough additional fuel to be carried for a maximum range of 800 miles. Along with this improved range, the Mace was also faster in responding to an attack because it was carried on its zero length launcher, not on a trailer as the Matador, and it was fielded almost fully assembled (the booster still had to be attached). Finally, the Mace also carried the lighter, yet more powerful, Mk-28 fusion bomb, giving it almost 40 times the firepower of the Matador.

Mace GLCM in hardened launcher

Probably the most significant change of all was the addition of the the ATRAN guidance system. Similar to the modern TERCOM system, in this form of radar terrain guidance the missile would, at predetermined intervals, scan the earth for certain preprogrammed topographical landmarks and then compare the image received with a film strip inside the guidance unit. Once the landmark was found the guidance system would then adjust the missile's course until the image matched the one on the film strip. Using this film map system it was possible to program the Mace to go around defensives, do evasive maneuvers, and even change its flight altitude automatically.

The first 50 Mace missiles were deployed with the 71st TMS at Bitburg AFB. By 1961, the Mace A had completely replaced the Matador missiles deployed with this unit, as well as the Matadors deployed with the 405th TMS at Hahn and the 822nd at Sembach. By 1962, the Air Force had also added three more Mace squadrons—the 89th TMS at Hahn; and the 823rd, and 887th at Sembach—making for a total Mace A force of 300 missiles.

Mace B

While the Mace A was being deployed back in 1959, work began on an even longer range missile called the Mace B. Differing primarily in that it was guided by a self-contained inertial unit, the Mace B had almost twice the range of the Mace A, allowing the missile to reach military targets deep inside the Soviet Union. This greater range would also make the Mace B a fixed missile system, because for the inertial unit to accurately guide the Mace to its target, the missile's launching point had to be accurately known—a problem neither the Mace A or the Matador had.

Because of this, the Mace B would be the only version of the Matador or Mace to be deployed in hardened surface shelters for protection against conventional strike (the hardened shelters gave the Mace B an almost instantaneous launch capability).

Following several successful test flights at White Sands Missile Range, the first Mace B launch from the prototype hardened launcher at Cape Canaveral occurred on 11 July 1960. The next year, following the activation of the 498th Tactical Missile Group 8 February 1961, the missiles were deployed to Okinawa, near Japan, as a counter to the growing Chinese nuclear force. The operating locations on Okinawa for these missiles included Bolo Point, Motobu Quarry, and the US Army Easely Range areas. Deployment of the Mace B in Europe, however, was not as swift because of problems in the construction of the hardened launchers. By September 1965, a total of 50 Mace B launchers were operational with the 71st TMS at Bitburg AFB.

Even as the Mace B was becoming operational in Europe, in 1965, Secretary of Defense Robert S McNamara issued a requirement that the Pershing missiles were to have a Quick Reaction Alert capability. The reason he gave for this new capability was that, by having a high speed launch ability, the Pershing could replace the Mace missiles in the striking of high value enemy targets, no notice seems to have been given to the fact that the Pershing I had only half the range of the Mace A and not even one-fourth the range of the B. Phase out of the Mace A began shortly after this order was given, and by September 1966, only the Mace B unit at Bitburg was operational. These Mace missiles would remain a little while longer, but on 30 April 1969, the 71st TMS was deactivated: the New Pershing 1 equipment was deployed the previous month.

Mace GLCM

Though the Mace had been withdrawn from Europe by fall of 1969, the Mace B missiles deployed in Okinawa would remain operational until the year 1971, when in preparation for the reversion of custody of Okinawa to Japan, the 498th TMG was deactivated. Japan then took custody of the island on 15 May 1972.

After retirement, most of the Mace A and Mace B missiles were disposed of as drone targets for Army Surface to Air Missile systems. Some, however, did make it to museums where they are on display today.

GLCM (BGM-109G)

SPECIFICATIONS

Length: missile — 18 ft 2 in	Weight: missile — 2650 lb
with booster — 20 ft 6 in	with booster — 3200 lb
Diameter: 1 ft 9 in	Span: 8 ft 7 in

PERFORMANCE

Speed: Approx 500 mph	Ceiling: from 10 ft to 500 ft
Range: 1500 mi	CEP: 100 ft

PROPULSION Sustainer — One F107-WR-102 turbofan producing 600 lb of thrust
Booster — Single solid fuel rocket motor producing 7000 lb of thrust

GUIDANCE McDonnell Douglas inertial system with TERCOM

WARHEAD Single W-84 fusion warhead of 80 kt yield

CONTRACTOR General Dynamics and McDonnell Douglas

NUMBER OF MISSILES 464 to be deployed

The BGM-109G is the newest Ground Launched Cruise Missile to be deployed by the US Air Force. It is designed to replace manned aircraft in the attacking of fixed military targets.

By 1971, even before the last Mace missile was being withdrawn from service, the US Air Force was considering the possibility of developing a new Ground Launched Cruise Missile using new, small turbofan motors; TERCOM precision guidance systems; and small thermonuclear warheads. The Navy's Sea-Launched Cruise Missile program and the Air Force's own ALCM project stimulated interest in a new GLCM, and by late 1976 the Air Force was actively courting congress for permission to develop such a weapon. Development was approved in January of 1977 with the stipulation that the weapon be an adaptation of the Navy's selected BGM-109 Tomahawk cruise missile for use in a theater role. As a result of this, the Air Force became actively involved in the Tomahawk cruise missile program.

The Air Force's role in the Tomahawk program was not to assist in the development of the missile, but to develop and test the mobile launcher and Launch Control Center (LCC) needed to make the Tomahawk a land mobile weapon system (for a history of the

GLCM launch

Tomahawk flight test program see SLCM section). Development of these vehicles began in October of 1977, and by early 1980, field trials were underway on the prototype mobile launcher, or TEL (Transporter/Erector/Launcher). The first launch of a Tomahawk from this vehicle was on 16 May 1980 with the first launch using guidance from a mobile LCC occurring on 25 February 1982. Operational Evaluation testing of the GLCM began on 19 May 1982.

While development of the GLCM was underway, on 12 December 1979, NATO decided to include the deployment of the GLCM as part of its theater nuclear force modernization. In this plan, a total of 464 missiles were to be deployed in several Western European countries for use against fixed base Soviet military targets both in eastern Europe and the USSR. Once these targets were covered by the missiles, NATO could re-direct its manned bombers against the new mobile SS-20 missiles or, in a conventional role, against Soviet land forces.

As part of this agreement, the deployment of the GLCM was not to constitute an increase in the number of nuclear weapons in Europe. Other US nuclear weapons were withdrawn from service as the GLCMs were deployed.

The first GLCMs arrived at Greenham Common Air base in December of 1983. Over the next three years GLCMs were also deployed to Comiso Sicily, in March of 1984; Florennes, Belgium, in March of 1985; and Hahn AFB, Germany, in March of 1986 (the squadron sent to Hahn was named the 89th TMS after the earlier Mace unit). The unit sent to Hahn has since been transferred to Wueschheim Air Station, Germany.

The GLCM is deployed in flights consisting of 69 Air Force personnel, two Launch Control Centers (one primary, one backup), 16 support vehicles, and four TEL vehicles, each carrying four missiles for a total of 16 missiles. During peacetime, these flights remain at the main base in shelters built to withstand a massive conventional attack. During times of international crisis, however, the individual flights would be dispersed to the surrounding country side for protection. Regardless, the individual vehicles of the flight stay together, and when they reach their assigned launch point, the heavily armored TELs (56 feet long, 8 feet wide and weighing 80,000 lb) would be positioned around the LCC and then physically connected to it with a secure fiberoptic cable. Once assembled, the dispersed GLCM flight takes the form of a surface-mounted US ICBM base, with a single LCC and four satellite launchers spread out around it.

As of 8 December 1987, the United States operated 96 GLCMs at Greenham Common, 18 at Molesworth AFB in Great Britain, 96 at Comiso Sicily, 16 at Florennes, and 48 at Wueschheim (a total of 17 flights). On that day, the United States and the USSR signed the treaty eliminating both intermediate and shorter-range guided missiles from Europe. According to the agreement, a three year controlled withdrawal of the GLCM units is to begin in the fall of 1988. The missiles will be destroyed by high explosives while the launchers are dismantled.

Regulus I (SSM-N-8)

SPECIFICATIONS

Length: 34 ft	Span: 21 ft
Diameter: 8 ft	Weight: 14,000 lb

PERFORMANCE

Speed: 600 mph	Ceiling: 40,000 ft
(Mach 1.1 in terminal dive)	
Range: 575 mi	

PROPULSION Sustainer—One Allison J33-A-18A turbojet engine. Max thrust: 4600 lb
Booster—Two Aerojet General solid fuel rockets. Max thrust: 33,000 lb each

GUIDANCE Radio command system

WARHEAD 1954 to 1963 one W-5 fission warhead of 40 to 50 kt yield (from 1958 to 1964 the W-27 fusion warhead of 2 mt yield was also available)

CONTRACTOR Vought Corp (now Ling Temco Vought or LTV)

NUMBER OF MISSILES 514

Regulus I SLCM aboard USS *Tunny*

The Regulus I was the first strategic missile ever deployed by the US Navy. It was intended for use against military targets that were too heavily defended to be successfully engaged by manned aircraft without excessive casualties.

During the Second World War, the Navy began studying cruise missiles as a method of striking heavily defended targets. Initially, this research centered on remote control aircraft but, following the successful use of armed drones in a raid on Bougainville on 27 September 1944, on 17 November 1944 a program was announced to determine the feasibility of launching Army JB-2 cruise missiles (an American copy of the V-2) from Navy escort carriers. In April of the following year, the program was given the official name of Loon, created to give Navy escort carriers and other surface ships a guided missile capability against both ground and seaborne targets.

Following the war, and the capture of certain German Navy documents, the Navy began to consider the possibility of also launching guided missiles from submarines. To test this concept on 5 March 1946, approval was given for the conversion of two submarines (the *Cusk* and the *Carbonero*) to carry, launch and guide the Loon. Seven days later, it was directed that the Loon be used as a test vehicle in the development of a more capable SLCM (Loon would retain an interim weapon capability).[1] Three months later Vought Corp began development of this more capable SLCM under the name Regulus.

The Loon would become the technological foundation for the Regulus cruise missile. In launches from the *Cusk* and *Carbonero*, it would test the planned zero length launcher system, the water-tight holding hangar, the radio command guidance system, and on 22 March 1950, the method of transferring guidance control to another sub or plane — an essential system for the longer-range Regulus missile. At the same time the Loon's own flaws and limitations — such as the requirement that the wings be manually attached before launch — guided the designers of the Regulus, making the resulting weapon more efficient. Testing of the Loon was then terminated in March of 1950.

After the Loon program was finished in 1950, testing began on the Regulus. Full scale dummy vehicles were used for field testing on ships, while flight testing was done with a special Regulus equipped with retractable landing gear to allow vehicle recovery. The first successful flight of one of these missiles occurred at Edwards AFB[2] on 29 March 1951, when the Regulus successfully took off, circled the field and landed under remote control from a chase aircraft. The first ship launch occurred on 3 November 1952 and, on 16 December, the carrier *Princeton* completed a simulated combat strike with the weapon. Following launch radio control of the Regulus, it was transferred to a previously launched aircraft which guided the missile to its target.

The Regulus I radio control system, though susceptible to jamming, gave this missile a very high accuracy. An excellent example is the 19 November 1957 test flight of a Regulus I from the USS *Helena*, in which the missile, after traveling 272 miles, impacted within 450 feet of its planned target. The missile was controlled by the *Helena* for the first 112 miles, then by the submarine *Cusk* for 70 miles, and finally by the submarine *Carbonero* for the final 90 miles.

Following the success of the surface ship launch program, on 30 March 1953, the Navy announced that production of the Regulus I was underway. Earlier that same month, the submarine *Tunny* completed its Regulus conversion and set the stage for the first submarine launch on 15 July 1953. Testing was completed in mid-1954, and in May, the Regulus Attack Missile (RAM) was declared operational. Guided Missile Group One (Regulus) was then commissioned on 16 September 1955. By 1957, a total of 16 ships operated the Regulus: 10 improved *Essex* class carriers;[3] the cruisers *Los Angeles*, *Helena*, *Macon*, and *Toledo*; and the submarines *Tunny* and *Barbero*.[4]

The Regulus I would not be operated for very long on the carriers. Though it did add a great deal of firepower to these ships, and was launched by both the carrier's catapults and deck mobile zero length launchers, the Regulus was soon outclassed by new naval aircraft in both range and attack speed. Furthermore, since

Regulus I SLCM

the aircraft carriers that were armed with the Regulus were too short to handle the improved manned aircraft, by 1960 all but two of them had been redesignated as either support, or anti-submarine warfare, carriers with no strategic strike requirement. As a result of this, by 1961, the only surface ships that still operated the missile were the cruisers *Los Angeles* and *Helena* (why the cruisers *Macon* and *Toledo* had their Regulus launchers removed has not been explained).

As the Regulus I was being removed from the surface ship force, the number of submarines equipped with this missile was increasing. Following the cancellation of the Regulus II program in 1959, the submarines designed for this missile the *Grayback*, *Growler*, and *Halibut* were refitted to launch the earlier Regulus I. The first subs designed specifically to launch strategic guided missiles, the *Grayback* and *Growler*, could each carry four Regulus Is, two in each of the subs' twin forward missile hangers; the *Tunny* and *Barbero* carried only two missiles in their single hanger. As for the *Halibut*, the only nuclear-powered Regulus sub, it could carry a total of five missiles in its built in hanger: a total of 17 operational submarine launched Regulus missiles in 1960. These subs were all stationed in the Pacific.

With the launch of its first Regulus missile on 25 March 1960, the *Halibut* would also become the first nuclear powered submarine to launch a nuclear capable missile (beating the USS *George Washington* by four months).

Regardless of the addition of the originally Regulus II subs, the Regulus I was rapidly becoming obsolete. Compared to the Polaris system in which the submarines remained submerged, the Regulus I's surface launch requirement placed its submarines in much greater danger from enemy ships and aircraft. Furthermore, thanks to the development of surface to air missiles and supersonic aircraft, the subsonic Regulus had become extremely vulnerable to interception. Thus, following the deployment of the first Polaris subs to the Pacific, the last Regulus missile was withdrawn from service in 1964.

At the time of its withdrawal, over 1129 Regulus Is had been

launched, most being training missiles with retractable landing gear and parachutes like the early test missiles. In the years that followed, these training missiles were used as target drones for Navy fighters and surface to air missile systems.

[1] The primary reason that the Loon was abandoned was that it was too small to carry any of the two available nuclear warheads.
[2] Because of the secrecy of the program, whenever the Regulus was outside of its hangar at Edwards, and not in the air, it sported a fake cockpit canopy.
[3] Three of these carriers are known: the *Randolph*, *Hancock*, and *Princeton*.
[4] Five other submarines were equipped with Regulus guidance units to guide the missile to its target. These subs were the *Cusk*, *Carbonero*, *Torsk*, *Argonaut*, and the *Runner*.

Regulus II (SSM-N-9)

SPECIFICATIONS

Length: 57 ft	Span: 20 ft
Diameter: 6 ft	Weight: 23,000 lb

PERFORMANCE

Speed: Mach 2	Ceiling: 60,000 ft
Range: 1200 mi	

PROPULSION Sustainer—One General Electric J79-GE-7 turbojet with afterburner. Max thrust: 15,000 lb Booster—One Aerojet General 115,000 lb thrust solid fuel motor or one Rocketdyne 135,000 lb thrust solid fuel motor

GUIDANCE Inertial system by AC Sparkplug

WARHEAD Single W-27 thermonuclear warhead of mt yield

CONTRACTOR Vought Corp (now known as Ling Temco Vought)

NUMBER OF MISSILES 54 manufactured before program terminated

The Regulus II is the only supersonic, surface to surface, cruise missile ever deployed by the US Navy. It was intended to replace the Regulus I in the role of striking heavily defended strategic targets.

Even before the Regulus II was deployed, by 1953, the Navy had become aware of several major problems with this weapon system. Besides being subsonic, and altitude limited (making it vulnerable to surface to air missiles and supersonic aircraft), a major problem with the missile was the fact that the Regulus I's radio control system could be jammed electronically by an enemy. Of additional concern were also the weapons' limited range (putting the launching ship, or sub, inside the combat envelope of enemy land based aircraft), the great amount of time it took to set up the zero length launcher system used by the submarines and the limited underwater speed of the Regulus-equipped submarines. Thus in February of 1953 the Navy began a new program designated Regulus II.

Contrary to its name, the Regulus II was not a modified version of the Regulus I but an entirely new weapon system. The missile

Regulus I being loaded aboard USS *Tunny*

was of a completely new design with supersonic speed, longer range, higher flight altitude, an inertial guidance system and a megaton-class warhead. The Regulus II would also have a more automated launch system, allowing the submarines to launch the missile within a few minutes of reaching the surface.

Testing of the Regulus II began at Edwards AFB on 29 May 1956, using special test missiles equipped with landing gear and a parachute braking system; these missiles also used a 7800 lb thrust Curtiss Wright J-65 turbojet engine, limiting their maximum speed. Testing with this model was completed in late 1957, following which, on 13 November 1959, the first Mach 2 capable, 1000 mile range, Regulus II was launched using the solid fuel booster. The first Mach 2 flight took place on 10 December.

While testing was underway the Navy also began construction of the first Regulus II submarines. The first of these ships were the conventionally powered *Grayback* and *Growler*, which had twin streamlined forward missile hangers. The third ship to be built was the nuclear powered *Halibut*, which had an enclosed hangar system capable of handling two missiles; the prototype automated launcher system for this sub began testing on the LST *King County* in May of 1958. Testing on the conventional powered *Grayback* began in July of 1958, the first submarine launch of a Regulus II occurring two months later on 18 September.

By mid-1958 the Navy planned to deploy the Regulus II on several cruisers (including the nuclear powered *Long Beach*), the conventional submarines *Grayback* and *Growler* and the nuclear submarines *Halibut*, *Permit*, *Plunger*, and *Barb*.[1] In December of that year however the Navy was forced to cancel the weapon in favor of the Polaris SLBM (the Navy was promised enough funds for both systems but this proved impossible). Construction of the submarines *Permit*, *Plunger*, and *Barb* was cancelled and the hull numbers and names transferred to three *Thresher* class attack submarines. The Regulus II launcher was also dropped from the *Long Beach*'s design (for a while the Navy considered putting the Polaris system on this ship in place of the Regulus). As for the submarines *Grayback*, *Growler* and *Halibut*, they were armed with the earlier Regulus II missile upon completion.

Though the Regulus II was cancelled in 1958, for several years afterwards the Navy and the Air Force would use the training versions of this missile as a supersonic target drone. For the BOMARC program, they completed a total of 46 target flights.

---

[1] *Permit*, *Plunger*, and *Barb* were to have four missile hangars, two in the bow and two abeam of the sail, giving these submarines twice as many Regulus missiles as the *Halibut* design.

Tomahawk (BMG-109)

SPECIFICATIONS
Length: 18 ft 2.4 in	Span: 8 ft 6 in
With Booster: 20 ft 6 in	Weight: 2650 lb
Diameter: 21 in	With Booster — 3200 lb
	With Capsule — 4200 lb

PERFORMANCE
Speed: Mach 0.7
Range: Antiship — 287 mi

PROPULSION Missile — Single Williams F107-WR-102 Turbofan engine. Max thrust: 600 lb
Booster — Atlantic Research solid fuel motor Max thrust: 7000 lb

GUIDANCE Inertial system with TERCOM and possibly DSMAC for land attack versions, modified Harpoon active radar seeking unit for anti-ship version all types manufactured by McDonnell Douglas Astronautics

WARHEAD Either a single W-80 thermonuclear warhead of 200 kt yield or up to 1000 lb of conventional explosives

CONTRACTOR General Dynamics Convair Division

NUMBER OF MISSILES 4080 missiles to be produced; 400 will be deployed with nuclear warheads

The Tomahawk cruise missile is the newest cruise type weapon to be deployed by the US Navy. With this weapon US Navy cruisers, destroyers, and attack submarines have a nuclear strike capability against strategic land targets.

Regulus II SLCM

Following the cancellation of the Regulus II in 1959, the US Navy redirected its missile research towards the development of ballistic missiles for use against both strategic and tactical targets. The Soviet Union, on the other hand, continued its dual track research into both ballistic and cruise missiles, producing a number of improvements in their sea launched cruise missiles. Though western military analysts were initially unimpressed by these improvements, the sinking of the Israeli Destroyer *Eliat* by a Soviet Styx anti-ship cruise missile in 1967 caused the Navy to begin rethinking its view on such weapons. The following year, the Navy began development of the Harpoon anti-ship cruise missile.

During the development of the Harpoon in 1970, the Navy concluded that an even more powerful, extended range Harpoon was possible. A year later, the Navy also began studying the feasibility of a 3000 mile range strategic cruise missile for use by Navy Polaris submarines and a smaller, shorter range, missile for use by Navy attack submarines. After an extensive in-house study of both systems, on 2 June 1972, the Navy selected the torpedo tube launch system on the grounds that it gave attack submarines a strategic capability with little modifications. The extended range Harpoon program was then merged with this strategic missile on 6 November, and in December the US Navy issued limited design contracts to Boeing, LTV, General Dynamics, Lockheed and McDonnell Douglas for the new weapon.

Though Boeing would soon drop out of the project to develop the ALCM for the Air Force, by August of 1973 the remaining companies had submitted their designs for the new missile. An extensive review of these proposals followed, and in January of 1974 the Navy selected the General Dynamics and LTV designs for

Tomahawk SLCM

Tomahawk SLCM

continued development. Two years later, on 17 March 1976, the Navy announced that the General Dynamics Tomahawk Sea-Launched Cruise Missile (SLCM) had been selected for advanced development.

Testing of the Tomahawk began immediately following the issuing of the Navy contract, with the first powered flight occurring on 29 March 1976. The first fully guided flight was completed on 5 June, and the first TERCOM terrain avoidance flight on 16 July. A simulated land attack then occurred on 30 September, paralleling a simulated anti-ship attack on 14 October. The first in-flight engine start was achieved on 15 November 1976, and on 31 January 1977, a Tomahawk with TERCOM demonstrated precision accuracy against a simulated ground target.[1] The first full scale booster/cruise flight was then completed on 24 February 1977.

The rest of 1977 was marred by minor technical glitches in the missile and certain testing equipment. In January of 1978, however, the Tomahawk began a 10-month, eight-flight test series to determine its survivability against present Warsaw Pact air defense systems. The following month, on 2 February, the first Tomahawk submarine launch was completed from the USS *Barb*: the *Barb* launched two Tomahawks that day, the first a land attack, the other an anti-ship. Three months later a land attack missile successfully delivered a load of submunitions against a simulated airfield at White Sands. Phase II survivability testing against improved Soviet defenses began in December of 1978, and in January of 1979 installation of the first armored box launcher began on the destroyer *Merrill* (DD-976).

Back in January of 1977, the Carter administration had consolidated the Tomahawk and the Air Force ALCM project under a single command titled the Joint Cruise Missile Project. Officially created to 'realize the cost savings inherent in common component development and testing, resource sharing and quantity manufacturing,' the JCMP unified these two missiles in both performance, and equipment, in preparation for a 10-missile-each competitive flyoff to determine which would be deployed on the Air Force's B-52 bombers (the hope was that Tomahawk would win this competition). This flyoff began on 1 July 1979 and was completed on 8 February 1979.

While the Tomahawk ALCM was competing with the Air Force ALCM, development of the Tomahawk SLCM was continued with the first successful vertical launch of a Tomahawk Anti-Ship Missile (TASM) being completed from a ground launcher on 13 December 1979. The first Digital Scene Matching Area Correlator (DSMAC) flight on 15 February 1980, followed by the first launch from the prototype armored box launcher on 13 March. Six days later, the destroyer *Merrill* inaugurated the start of Operational Evaluation (OPEVAL) of the Tomahawk weapons system with the first surface ship launch of a Tomahawk (this was the 50th Tomahawk flight).

Following the start of shipborne testing on 25 March 1980, it was announced that the AGM-86B ALCM had been selected as the Air Forces Air-Launched Cruise Missile. Though this meant an end to the Tomahawk ALCM, it also meant that work could now be concentrated on the SLCM and its land based derivative, the Ground-Launched Cruise Missile. Three months later, on 6 June 1980, the submarine *Guitarro* (SSN 665) inaugurated the start of submarine OPEVAL with the first submarine launch of a production missile. The first Tomahawk system test using flight data supplied by a Theater Mission Planning Center was then completed on 15 February 1981.

Though OPEVAL was not completed until April of 1984, in March 1983 the USS *Merrill* was released for operational duty with the Tomahawk. The Navy received its second ship on 10 May when the USS *New Jersey* launched its first Tomahawk cruise

Tomahawk SLCM test

missile. Six months later, following the completion of OPEVAL on the *Guitarro*, the Tomahawk submarine launched anti-ship cruise missile achieved Initial Operational Capability.

Though Tomahawk missiles were in service by the winter of 1983, it was not until June of 1984 that the nuclear tipped Tomahawk Land Attack Missile (TLAM/N) achieved Initial Operational Capability on submarines and surface ships.

The arming of the battleship *New Jersey*, the destroyer *Merrill*, and the submarine *Guitarro* with Tomahawk was just the beginning of this missile's deployment program. At the present time, using the Armored Box Launcher system, the Navy has either armed, or is planning to arm, the following surface ship classes: the four *Iowa* class battleships (32 missiles in eight ABLs), the guided missile cruiser *Long Beach* (eight missiles), the four *Virginia* class cruisers (16 missiles) and some *Spruance* class destroyers (4 to 8 missiles). As for the submarine force, all *Sturgeon*, *Los Angeles* and the future *Seawolf* class of subs will be equipped to launch Tomahawk from their torpedo tubes. Also in the future, following the introduction of the Vertical Launch System, Tomahawk will be deployed on the *Ticonderoga* class cruisers (24 maximum), additional *Spruance* class destroyers (16 maximum), the new *Arleigh Burk* class of destroyers, and those *Los Angeles* class submarines that are equipped with eight vertical launch tubes.

By deploying the Tomahawk, the Navy has greatly increased the combat capabilities of these ships. With the TLAM/N Navy surface ships and submarines can now engage tactical and strategic targets that previously required the use of carrier aircraft or ballistic missile submarines. With the TLAM/C (C for Conventional) these ships can now also give long range, pin point, support of US ground forces, or suppress enemy air defenses for Navy aircraft. Finally,

the TASM gives these ships a long range anti-ship capability equal to that of the carriers and the battleships. The best description of all this would be, that by deploying the Tomahawk, the Navy has turned each of these ships into a small aircraft carrier.

Integral to the Tomahawk land attack missile system are the two Theater Mission Planning Centers at Norfolk, Virginia, and Hawaii. These centers maintain huge files of data on various areas of the of the world (terrain features, known defenses, and TERCOM maps) for use in determining the most survivable route the missile can fly to a specific target: a rapid strike system is also available to convert reconnaissance photos into digital images for the DSMAC system. This data is then transmitted to the Weapons Control System of a Tomahawk ship in that area which then programs, powers and launches the Tomahawk.

Development of the Tomahawk has not ended with its deployment. In June of 1984 a Tomahawk land attack missile successfully demonstrated a terminal dive mode of attack: all previous land attacks had been limited to a horizontal impact. In February of the following year, a new sea-skimming anti-ship missile was tested with a re-attack, or circling, mode. That same year, on 31 May 1985, the first surface ship vertical launch of a Tomahawk was completed from the USS *Norton Sound*, paving the way for the planned 1989 IOC of this system. The first capsule, or vertical launch, of a Tomahawk from a *Los Angeles* class submarine was then successfully completed in November of 1986.

At the present time no plans are in the works for a replacement to the Tomahawk. Work is underway on an Advanced Cruise Missile for the Air Force, however, which may result in additional improvements to the Tomahawk.

[1] 17 Tomahawk evaluation flights were completed by January of 1977.

Tomahawk SLCM

Medium Range Ballistic Missiles (MRBM)

Redstone (SSM-A-14)

SPECIFICATIONS

Length: 69 ft   Span: 12 ft
Diameter: 70 in   Weight: 61,346 lb

PERFORMANCE

Speed: Max — Mach 5.5   Ceiling: 34 to 57 mi
        Impact — Mach 2.3
Range: 57.6 to 201.5 mi

PROPULSION One North American Rocketdyne A-6 liquid
           fuel rocket engine burning a 1.28: one
           mixture of liquid oxygen (LOX) and alcohol
           Max thrust: 75,000 lb

GUIDANCE Inertial

WARHEAD Single W-39 thermonuclear warhead of 4 megaton
        yield (payload weight 6305 lb)

CONTRACTOR Chrysler

The Redstone was the first Medium Range Ballistic Missile ever operated by the US Army. Though as a weapon it was awkward to deploy, it played a very important role in the development of guided missiles for the military and the space program.

On 20 November 1944, the Army issued General Electric a contract to study and develop long range guided missiles for the military. Called the Hermes project, this program would have many sub-projects, one of which was the Hermes C-1, a 500 mile range surface-to-surface missile, begun in June of 1946. The next year, however, the project would be greatly restricted due to a lack of basic technical data on high velocity missiles and, more importantly, a lack of funding caused by postwar cutbacks in military spending. By 1949, little work had been achieved.

With the detonation of the Soviet Union's first nuclear device on 29 August 1949, and the start of the Korean War on 25 June 1950, Congress made available additional funding for military projects.

As a result of this, the Hermes C-1 project was revitalized and, on 11 September 1950, the Ordnance Department transferred the whole project to Redstone Arsenal as part of a program to develop a 500 mile range surface to surface missile.[1] Five months later, the payload requirement for the missile was increased tenfold, reducing the range of the weapon by half. Research and development of the missile was then formally transferred to Redstone arsenal on 10 July 1951, and on 8 April 1952 the program was officially assigned the name of Redstone.[2]

The Redstone project gave Dr Werner Von Braun and his fellow Paperclip Scientists, as they were called, the chance to try some new ideas in missile technology. One of these new ideas was to manufacture and deploy the Redstone in three distinct parts, or sections, which were assembled at the launch site. Not only did this design concept improve the mobility of the weapon, it also made it possible to incorporate later improvements through the replacing of a section. Reliability was also improved by allowing a defective section to be either shipped back or replaced without requiring the

Redstone MRBM

entire Redstone unit to return to base. Another new idea was to have the Redstone's warhead section separated from the booster section after main engine cutoff. By doing this, a great deal of aerodynamic drag was removed, improving the overall range of the missile (altitude control after separation was handled by four small fins located at the rear of the warhead section).

On 22 October 1952, the Army brought the Chrysler Corporation into the Redstone program to assist in both the development and production of the missile. Flight testing then began on 20 August 1953, and by May of 1955 the design of the Redstone was frozen.[3] Following the issuing of a firm production contract to Chrysler on 15 June 1955, testing began with production missiles and by 1958 a total of 36[4] Redstones had been launched. The first Redstone unit, the 40th Field Artillery Missile Group, began training with the weapon on 14 March 1956, with the first all Army launch occurring on 16 May 1958 from Battery A. The first units were deployed to West Germany the following month.

With the deployment of the Redstone, the Army had a reliable method of attacking communication centers, headquarters, ammuni-

tion sites and staging areas deep in an enemy's rear. Before it was deployed, the Redstone had been selected to deliver a nuclear warhead to the upper atmosphere in a test of the effects of high altitude nuclear explosions on radio and radar. The first of these test missiles, code named Teak, was launched from Johnson Island on 31 July 1958, at 11:17 pm. Three minutes later, the warhead detonated, at 250,000 feet, producing an explosion that was seen 700 miles away in Honolulu and an electromagnetic pulse that blacked out Australian radio for nine hours. The second shot, code named Orange, occurred at 11:27 pm on 11 August. It was less spectacular, however, and the warhead detonated at 125,000 feet above the earth.

The reliability and power of the Redstone would also make this missile one of the most important missiles in the early US space program. Following the disastrous failure of the Vanguard missile in 1957, a modified Redstone called the Jupiter C successfully orbited the first US satellite, Explorer I, on 1 January 1959. Three years later, on 5 May 1961, a Redstone would again be used to send Alan Shepard into space, with the Mercury sub-orbital flight.

For all its capabilities, however, the Redstone would have been very cumbersome to operate in a war. A single battery — one launcher — consisted of an air servicer trailer; three semi-trailer trucks to carry the missile sections; two diesel engine generator sets; a power distribution trailer; a battery servicing trailer; a programer test station, truck mounted; a hydrogen peroxide servicer trailer; two liquid nitrogen transporters; one alcohol semi-trailer; an erector-servicer truck; a fire engine; a liquid oxygen trailer; and two 2.5 ton 6X6 trucks carrying accessories. Even during peacetime, when these units moved, traffic was tied up for miles.

While moving the weapon was difficult, setting it up for launching was time consuming. First, the launching site had to be surveyed to ascertain its exact position and this information was to be used by the missile's guidance system. Following this, the launching pad was emplaced and leveled, the three missile sections assembled and the weapon erected for launch (this alone could take up to seven hours to complete). Loading of the nonstorable propellants would begin after a launch order was received, and within 15 minutes, the Redstone could be launched.

In the late 1950s, the Army began a program to develop a battlefield surveillance TV system for the Redstone. In this system, the Redstone re-entry vehicle would be modified to eject a stabilized, high drag, television equipped, capsule on the downward arch to its target. Next, the TV camera would transmit both before and after impact pictures of the target area, giving field commanders instant strike results. A total of three flights were completed with this system in 1960 (15 March, 19 April and 2 June), but whether the system was ever deployed is not known.

Even before the Redstone was deployed, the Army was concerned about its size and slow response time and, in January 1958, began feasibility studies into a solid fuel MRBM. Eventually this work would develop into the Pershing I missile, which began replacing the Redstone in Germany in 1964. By 1966, the Redstone was no longer in service.

Though it was in service less than 10 years, the Redstone was regarded as one of the most important of the early missiles. Both Cape Canaveral and Redstone Arsenal have several Redstones on display in commemoration.

Redstone MRBM

[1] Between April and November of 1950, Von Braun and his fellow German scientists moved from Fort Bliss to Redstone Arsenal.
[2] From February 1951 to this date the program was variously known as Hermes C-1, Major, Ursa, XSSM-G-14, and XSSM-A-14.
[3] So reliable was the Redstone at that time that it was already slated for use as a test vehicle for components of the Jupiter IRBM.
[4] The first 12 Redstones were built in-house at Redstone Arsenal from components supplied by industry.

Pershing I MRBM

Pershing I (MGM-31A)

SPECIFICATIONS
Length: 34 ft 7.35 in   Weight: 10,275 lb
Diameter: 3 ft 4 in

PERFORMANCE
Speed: Mach 8   Range: 100 to 460 mi

PROPULSION First stage — Thiokol solid fuel TX-174
                    Avg thrust: 26,000 lb, burn time 38.3 sec
                    Second stage — Thiokol solid fuel TX-175
                    Avg thrust: 19,200 lb, burn time 39.0 sec

GUIDANCE Inertial

WARHEAD Single W-50 thermonuclear warhead of
              400 kt yield

CONTRACTOR Martin Marietta

NUMBER OF MISSILES 108 missiles/launchers were de-
                    ployed; only those missiles in
                    service with West German forces
                    are still operational

The Pershing I was the first solid fuel Medium Range Ballistic Missile ever deployed by the US Army. The replacement for the Redstone, it was then the Army's longest range weapon until the advent of the Pershing II in 1985.

With the Sergeant program well underway in mid-1956, the Army began a study to determine the feasibility of a solid fuel Medium Range Ballistic Missile to replace the famous Redstone MRBM. Within a few months of this, however, on 26 November 1956, Secretary of Defense Wilson put a limit on the capabilities of this proposed missile by restricting the range of all Army missiles to 200 miles maximum. By late 1957, research confirmed that not only was such a weapon possible but it was easier to move, faster reacting, and more survivable than the operational Redstone. As a result of this, following the rescinding of the range restriction in late 1957, the Army began full scale research and development on a solid fuel MRBM with a range of 400 miles in January of 1958. Two months later, the Martin Aircraft company was issued the development contract for the Pershing missile.

Development of the Pershing was very short by most standards. After just two years of research flight, testing of the Pershing began in January of 1960 (only the first stage was live, the second stage was a dummy). Eight months later, the first two-stage flight was completed following which, in December, Martin Marietta was awarded the production contract. The first tactical round was then launched on 24 January 1962, with the first simulated tactical firing from the mobile launcher occurring on 15 March 1962. The testing program was completed in October of 1963 with a total of 59 successful flights, four partial and only six failures.

Three months after the first simulated combat launch, in June 1962, the first Pershing unit, Battery A, 2nd Battalion, 44th Field Artillery, received its first Pershing missiles. The second unit, 4th Battalion 41st Field Artillery, was then activated on 14 January 1963 and in April 1964 this unit was deployed to West Germany. By 1968, a total of 250 Pershing missiles were listed as deployed in West Germany.[1]

A Pershing I battalion consisted of four batteries each having three launchers units or platoons. Each of these platoons consisted of four vehicles: one to carry the warhead, another for the programmer-test station/power station, the third for the tropospheric–scatter radio terminal and the fourth for the missile and the erector (because of its small size this unit had a minimal impact on road traffic compared to the Redstone units). Combat range of these transport vehicles was 200 miles over any kind of terrain, with a maximum road speed of 40 miles per hour.

Though compared to the Redstone, the Pershing was a fast reaction weapon system, the DOD wanted something even faster and, in 1965, assigned the weapon a Quick Reaction Alert requirement (QRA).[2] To meet this new requirement, in January 1966, the Army awarded Martin Marietta the Pershing IA contract to develop a new set of high speed ground support vehicles, incorporating solid state electronics, and a faster erector/launcher. Production of these new vehicles then began in November of 1967 with the first SWAP (replacing, in the field, the old vehicles with the new ones) occurring in August of 1969. The last US Army Pershing I unit was then retired in September of 1970: The last West German unit was in August of 1971.

During this SWAP program, the Army increased the number of launchers per Pershing battery from the original three to nine. This increase allowed a reduction in the number of operational battalions without causing a major decrease in the number of deployed missiles. By 1971, the US Army had a total of 108 missiles in Europe.[3]

The SWAP program was not the last upgrade the Pershing system has undergone. In March of 1976, deployment began of a sequential launch adapter (SLA) and an automatic reference system

(ARS). With the sequential launch adapter, a Pershing platoon could now launch its three missiles without having to shift the power and air cables for each flight. As for the automatic reference system — a ground based inertial guidance system — it removed the need for a pre-surveyed firing site allowing on-the-spot launch.

Production of the Pershing I was initially terminated in 1971 (the production line went idle in June of 1975). By 1977, it had become necessary to reopen the Pershing I production line to replace missiles that had been expended in training. Production was recommenced in 1978, with a total of 66 more missiles being produced by 1979. Further production was then terminated in favor of the Pershing II missile.

In accordance with the December 1979 NATO agreement, in December of 1983 the Army began replacing the Pershing IAs with the new, long range Pershing II. By December 1985, all 108 missiles at Neu Ulm, Schwaebisch-Gmünd, and Waldheide-Neckarsulm had been replaced: only the missiles were replaced, the launchers were structurally, and electronically modified to handle the Pershing II. The remaining 169 Pershing IA missiles were then returned to the United States, where they are now stored at Pueblo Depot, Pueblo, Colorado.[4]

At the present time, only the 72 West German Pershing IAs are in service. The signing of the INF treaty states, furthermore, that by 1991 these missiles and the US Army's Pershing IIs are to be withdrawn and destroyed by high explosive charges. As for the 169 Pershing I missiles now stored at Pueblo Depot, they will be destroyed by static firing of the boosters.

[1] This included both American and West German operated missiles.
[2] Military budgets of the period suggest this was done to allow the phaseout of the Mace missile units in the late 1960s.
[3] This doesn't include 72 missiles operated by West Germany and 36 launchers stationed at Fort Sill in the US.
[4] One standard Pershing I launcher has been reported to still exist.

Pershing I MRBM

Pershing I MRBM

Pershing II

SPECIFICATIONS

Length: 34 ft 9.7 in   Weight: 16,540 lb
Diameter: 3 ft 4 in

PERFORMANCE

Speed: Mach 8   CEP: 98 ft
Range: 1100 mi

PROPULSION Two stage solid fuel motors by Hercules Inc

GUIDANCE Inertial guidance system by Singer Kearfott
         Terminal radar area guidance by Goodyear Aero-
         space

WARHEAD One W-85 thermonuclear warhead of variable
        yield — 10 to 50 kt

CONTRACTOR Martin Marietta

NUMBER OF MISSILES 384 planned — 228 for operational
                   deployment, 24 for monitoring, and
                   132 for training. 247 known opera-
                   tional as of December of 1987, with
                   over 60 launched as of mid-1980

NUMBER OF LAUNCHERS 108 in Germany and 42 at Fort
                    Sill, Oklahoma

The Pershing II is the newest and most accurate Medium Range Ballistic Missile in the Army arsenal. Though originally developed to improve the accuracy of the Medium Range force, it is now a counter weapon to Soviet IRBMs pointed at Europe.

Following the election of John F Kennedy, the United States armed forces embarked on a new strategic policy called Flexible Response. This new policy would have a major effect on the tactical nuclear systems, for it emphasized the development of highly accurate, low yield, nuclear weapons for precision strikes against enemy bases and troops in the field. The theory was that they would allow the destruction of the military target while causing minimum damage or deaths in surrounding civilian areas. The replacement of the megaton class Redstone with the kiloton class Pershing I is an excellent example of this policy.

Even as the Pershing I was being deployed, the Air Force and Navy were busy developing the Minuteman III and the Poseidon MIRVed missiles: the first precision ballistic nuclear systems for these armed services. When these missiles were deployed in 1970–1971, a major increase occurred in the number of strategic nuclear warheads carried by the US ICBM and SLBM force. At the same time, the average yield of a strategic warhead dropped to 170 kilotons for an ICBM warhead and 50 kilotons for an SLBM warhead. Since the the Pershing I still carried its 400 kiloton warhead by 1971, it was more powerful than a strategic nuclear warhead. This fact would not be well accepted by Western Europe and by the end of the year, political pressure was placed on Washington to do something about it.

At the same time political pressure was being mounted over the Pershing IA's 'excessive yield,' the Army was asking the government for permission to modify the Pershing IA missile so that it could deliver a low yield nuclear warhead. The reason for this request was that population increases in Europe, and improvements in the speed of mechanized forces, had made it almost impossible in the Army's view to use the 400 kiloton Pershing in Europe without running a major risk of hitting civilians, or friendly units. With the political pressure from Europe as additional incentive, this request was almost immediately accepted and, in January of 1972, development of the Pershing II began.

Originally, the purpose of the Pershing II program was to improve the accuracy of the basic Pershing missile with a minimum of modifications. Within a year, work had centered on the development of a new terminally guided, maneuvering, re-entry vehicle (MARV) which, when fitted to the Pershing IA, would augment the missile's inertial guidance system. Advanced development of the terminal guidance system began in April of 1974, with development of the special re-entry vehicle beginning the following year. In 1976 and 1977, funding was issued for the design and construction of seven prototype RVs for flight testing in 1978.

In the original design, the Pershing II RV would directly replace the RV carried on operational Pershing IA missiles. From launch until second stage shutdown the missile would function as before the change with the second stage inertial guidance system releasing the warhead at the proper velocity and trajectory for a ballistic

Pershing II MRBM

Pershing II MRBM

flight to the planned target. After re-entry into the atmosphere the RVs terminal guidance system then takes over, scanning the target area with radar to acquire an image. The RV's flight computer will then compare this radar image to an image in its memory and adjust the RV's course until the images match. The result is a tenfold increase in accuracy over a standard Pershing IA flight.

By May of 1978, five successful flights had been conducted with the new Pershing II RV, with one flight resulting in the warhead landing within 80 feet of its planned target. By this time, major changes were being planned for the Pershing II.

In 1977, the Soviet Union began deploying a new IRBM designated the SS-20. This new missile's greater range, mobility and fire rate (not to mention MIRV capability) represented a major increase in the capability of the Soviet IRBM force to effectively strike targets in Europe. Because of this, in 1978, NATO requested the deployment of an IRBM capable of replacing manned NATO aircraft in the attacking of fixed targets. The freed aircraft could then be used to find and engage the mobile SS-20 units. In response to this request, in August of 1978, the Secretary of Defense directed the Pershing program to work towards the development of an extended range version. Engineering development began in February of the following year.

To meet the new range requirement while not increasing the physical size of the missile, work began on an improved booster system using the new high energy solid fuel developed in the Patriot Surface-to-Air Missile program. To improve range further, and to make up for the increased weight of this high density fuel, the motor casings were made of light weight kevlar. Regardless of the use of this lightweight material, the Pershing II weighs almost twice as much as the Pershing IA.

The first Pershing II flight on 22 July 1982 ended prematurely, when a malfunction in the first stage forced the missile to be destroyed. It was very embarrassing for the Reagan Administration because it was a televised launch. Four months later, however, on 12 November 1982, a successful flight was completed from a launch site in Texas to White Sands missile range. Further successful flights would follow and by mid-1983 the first Army unit was training with the weapon.

In December of 1979, NATO approved of the deployment of the Pershing II and the GLCM as part of its Theater Nuclear Modernization program. With this decision, however, came a requirement that the deployment of these missiles would not increase the number of nuclear weapons already deployed in Europe. As a result of this, as each Pershing II was deployed, a Pershing IA missile was withdrawn, and its launcher structurally upgraded to handle the new, heavier missile. The first battery, nine missiles, became operational in December of 1983 and by December of 1985 all three battalions, 108 missiles, had been rearmed.

In Germany combat-ready Pershing IIs are deployed at Schwaebisch-Gmünd, 40 missiles (includes four spares) and 36 launchers; Neu Ulm, 40 missiles (includes four spares) and 43 launchers (includes seven spares); and Waldheide-Neckarsulm, 40 missiles (includes four spares) and 36 launchers. In addition to these, 12 missiles are stored at Weilerbach, Germany, 111 at Pueblo Depot, Colorado, one at Redstone Arsenal (with one launcher), and three at Cape Canaveral, Florida: 39 launchers are also kept at Fort Sill, Oklahoma. These numbers date to December of 1987.

With the signing of the treaty to eliminate intermediate and short range missiles from Europe, withdrawal of the Pershing II was to begin in the fall of 1988. The missiles are to be destroyed by explosive charges and the launchers are to be cut up at specific points in their structure (15 missiles and their launchers, however, will be retained for static displays). This withdrawal is to be completed by the year 1991.

Surface-to-Air and Anti-Ballistic Missiles (SAM) (ABM)

Talos (RIM-8)

SPECIFICATIONS (RIM-8E)
Length: Interceptor — 21 ft 2.2 in
Booster — 10 ft 0.8 in
Span: 9 ft 0.6 in
Diameter: 2 ft 4 in   Weight: 7000 lb

PERFORMANCE
Speed: Mach 2.5   Ceiling: 86,941 ft
Range: 75 mi

PROPULSION Sustainer — one Bendix ramjet engine
Max thrust: 9000 lb
Booster — single solid fuel booster
Max thrust: 20,000 lb

GUIDANCE Beam rider with semiactive radar homing

WARHEAD Conventional or a W-30 nuclear warhead of
approx 5 kt yield

CONTRACTOR Bendix Aerospace

NUMBER OF MISSILES 2500 manufactured by 1970

The Talos missile is by far the most powerful missile to come out of the Bumblebee program. Until the recent deployment of the SM-2, it was the longest range surface-to-air missile the Navy had ever operated.

Development of the Talos missile system began on 1 September 1944 when, in an attempt to find an effective weapon against kamikaze attacks, the Navy created the Bumblebee program to investigate the feasibility of using a ramjet for guided missile propulsion. Four months later, on 11 June 1945, the Applied Physics Lab of Johns Hopkins University was assigned Bumblebee Project 1 to develop a ramjet powered surface-to-air missile by the year 1948. With the issuing of this order, work on the propulsion system began immediately, and on 13 June, the APL/JHU success-fully flew a six inch diameter ramjet, made from the exhaust tubing of a P-47 fighter, a distance of 6.25 miles. So successful was this test (later called a Burner test vehicle), that by September of 1946, testing had begun with a larger, 18 inch missile called Cobra.

Though testing of large ramjets was underway by late 1946, it would still be many years before an operational missile system was ready. In 1947, booster system problems delayed the program, forcing many of the guidance system tests to be done by aircraft and, in 1948, by a special rocket powered Supersonic Test Vehicle (this STV would later be developed into the Terrier missile). Testing of the ramjet vehicles did resume in September of 1949 with a six inch burner vehicle reaching an altitude of 60,000 feet, but it would not be until 1950 that a pretactical Talos missile was successfully flown.

With testing already behind schedule, the Navy drastically increased the missile's operational requirements in December of 1950. Now the missile was to have a 57 mile range, a 60,000 foot ceiling, and accuracy to within 70 feet of its target. Also, the missile was to be ready for service testing by June of 1953.

With these new requirements, on 6 March 1951, the first prototype Talos missile (a Ramjet Test Vehicle RTV-N-6A3) successfully flew for a total of 2 minutes (at Mach 2, it would have covered a distance of approx 40 miles). The first full scale Talos flight (X-SAM-N-6) then occurred in October of 1952, with a successful homing intercept completed that same month by RTV-N-6A4. Two years later, in May of 1954, a Talos set a record by hitting a QB-17 drone 32 miles from the missile's launch point. Two more years passed, however, until in November of 1956 a Talos successfully intercepted a target at the required range of 57 miles (100,000 yards). Finally, in March of 1957, a full scale Talos intercept ended when a missile carrying a live warhead completely destroyed a target drone.

Even if the Talos had been ready by June of 1953, it could not have been field tested. Like the Terrier missiles, conversion of the cruiser Galveston to carry Talos was started late, resulting in the ship not being ready until mid-1957. When evaluation did begin in May of 1957, it didn't take long, and by 1958 the Talos operated with the US fleet.

Once in service, the Talos proved itself to be the most powerful guided missile in the Navy's cruiser arsenal. Unlike the earlier Terrier, Talos' greater range allowed it to intercept enemy aircraft before they could launch their own anti-ship missiles. In addition to this, because the Talos flew a high-efficiency trajectory to its target, the missile tended to attack its targets from above (achieving tactical surprise). In Vietnam, the Talos missiles proved quite successful against Vietnamese aircraft. Finally, following the deployment of the nuclear tipped SAM-N-6BW in March of 1959, the Talos became extremely effective against large formations of enemy aircraft and, as a surface-to-surface missile, against large enemy ships.

In the years that followed, the Talos missile system was gradually improved. In October of 1960, an improved missile designated SAM-N-6BL was deployed with greater range and a new continuous-rod warhead that was lethal out to 100 feet: a nuclear version of this model was deployed the following month. In December of 1962, following the redesignating of the Talos system as RIM-8, the RIM-8E was deployed with greater altitude, continuous wave semiactive terminal homing, and the ability to have either conventional or nuclear warheads (the previous models did not have interchangeable warheads). In September of 1966, an improved beam rider, designated RIM-8G, was fielded, and in 1968, the RIM-8J with improved guidance became operational (some earlier Talos missiles were converted into anti-radiation RIM-8H starting in June of 1968).

These enhancements to the Talos system, however, were more band-aid actions than anything else. Following the start of the *Typhoon* SAM program in 1960, most of the funding left for Talos went to improve its reliability instead of its capability. Work on this program also put an end to the deployment of the Talos, with the conversion of only seven ships: the *Long Beach*, three *Cleveland* cruisers, and three *Baltimore* cruisers (more *Baltimore* conversions were planned before the start of *Typhoon*). Even after *Typhoon* was cancelled in 1964, there was no interest in increasing the number of Talos ships, as the Navy had already begun work on the Standard Missile. The final blow then came in the early 1970s when the Navy began work on short range, fast reaction missiles for use against low flying anti-ship cruise missiles. For all its great range, the Talos was slow to respond to an attack. Thus in the late 1970s, the Talos missiles were withdrawn from service. The last operational ship was the USS *Oklahoma City*, which was retired in late 1979.

Following its withdrawal, many of the remaining Talos missiles were expended as Vandal or LAST supersonic targets for the Aegis missile system.

Talos SAM

BOMARC (CIM-10)

SPECIFICATIONS

	CIM-10A	CIM-10B
Length:	46 ft 9 in	45 ft 1 in
Span:	18 ft 2 in	
Diameter:	2 ft 11 in	
Weight:	approx 15,500 lb	approx 16,032 lb

PERFORMANCE

Speed:	Mach 2.8	
Range:	250 mi	Range: 440 mi
Ceiling:	60,000 ft	Ceiling: 100,000 ft

PROPULSION

CIM-10A Sustainer — Two Marquardt RJ43 MA-7 Ramjets each producing 11,500 lb of thrust

Booster — Single Aerojet General LR59-AJ-13 liquid fuel rocket motor burning nitric acid and kerosene. Max thrust: 35,000 lb

CIM-10B Sustainer — Two Marquardt RJ43-MA-7 Ramjets each producing 12,000 lb of thrust

Booster — Single Thiokol XM-51 solid fuel rocket motor producing 50,000 lb of thrust

GUIDANCE
Cruise phase handled by Westinghouse Command guidance system connected to the SAGE or Semi-Automatic Ground Environment air defense network. Terminal guidance handled by Westinghouse active homing radar system

WARHEAD
CIM-10A — conventional or a single W-40 fission warhead of 7 to 10 kt yield

CIM-10B — single W-40 fission warhead of 7 to 10 kt yield

CONTRACTOR
Boeing and Michigan Aeronautical Research Center

NUMBER OF MISSILES
570 produced: 269 CIM-10A, 301 CIM-10B

The BOMARC is the only surface-to-air missile the US Air Force has ever developed. Though a cruise missile of limited speed and mobility, this weapon is second only to the Spartan as the longest range air defense missile ever deployed by the United States.

Immediately following the Second World War, Boeing Aircraft began the GAPA, or Ground-to-Air Pilotless Aircraft, program to determine the feasibility of surface-to-air missiles. Like the Navy's Bumblebee program, this project would study both rocket and ramjet propelled missiles and, by 1950, a total of 112 missiles — of three different configurations (two rocket powered, one ramjet) — had been tested with the last version reaching speeds of Mach 2.5 and having a kill altitude of 80,000 feet. So successful was this program that, in 1949, the Air Force would authorize Boeing Aircraft to begin development of a more powerful, longer range, pilotless interceptor capable of intercepting enemy long range bombers and intercontinental cruise missiles. Two months later, the Michigan Aerospace Research Center began participating in the project, giving the program its strange name of BOMARC (BO for BOeing and MARC for Michigan Aerospace Research Center).

Three years after development of the BOMARC began, the first prototype missiles, XIM-99s,[1] were delivered to the Air Force for testing. Designed for testing the planned liquid fuel booster system, these early missiles were not equipped with a guidance system, warhead *or* ramjets. There were 41 of these missiles delivered before flight testing of the prototypes began in February of 1955. Testing of the XIM-99, all 38 of them, would continue until 1957 when the first of the guided production variant, designated YIM-99A, were delivered. On 16 May, Boeing received the production contract for the BOMARC and on 7 November 1957, an order was placed for 23 production model IM-99As.

BOMARC B in launcher

BOMARC A

The IM-99A (BOMARC A) was the first production model of the BOMARC series. Essentially an unmanned aircraft, or cruise missile, it was launched vertically, using a liquid fuel rocket engine built into its tail. Once airborne, and traveling at supersonic speed, guidance commands from a ground station would ignite the ramjet engines and then rotate the missile so that the top of the BOMARC faced its target. Following this, once the missile reached its planned cruise altitude (about 80,000 ft), additional commands would be sent to the BOMARC to pull itself over to horizontal flight and then half roll to place it in the planned tail-up cruise configuration. After that, all the ground station had left to do was monitor the BOMARC's flight, and, if necessary, update or change its course, until the missile was within 10 miles of its target. Once there, the BOMARC's own internal radar system would take over to guide the missile to its intercept.

The first BOMARC A became operational on 19 September 1959 with the 46th Air Defense Missile Squadron at McGuire AFB. By September, all 28 missiles in this squadron were operational, and by December of 1960, four more squadrons had been deployed: the 6th ADMS at Suffolk County, New York; the 22nd ADMS at Langley AFB, Virginia; the 26th ADMS at Otis AFB, Mass; and the 30th ADMS at Dow AFB, Maine. All totalled, 140 missiles.

Though the BOMARC A allowed the Air Force to literally defend the entire eastern sea board (each site could defend almost 200,000 square miles), the missile had a major problem with its liquid fuel booster motor. First, because the fuels used by this motor were too corrosive to be stored for long periods in the missile's fuel tanks, the BOMARC As had to be fueled before launch, keeping them on the ground for approximately two minutes. Another problem with these fuels was that they were hypergolic (they ignited when mixed), making the system extremely prone to fire. An example of this fire danger was the accident at McGuire AFB on 7 June 1960, in which a nuclear armed BOMARC A burst into flames after its fuel tank was ruptured by the explosion of a high pressure helium tank. Luckily the warhead's safety systems functioned properly, and the bomb simply melted in the inferno.

Even though the problems with the BOMARC A were known by the Air Force as far back as the mid-1950s it wasn't until the development of large, high thrust, solid fuel rocket motors in the Minuteman and Polaris programs that it was possible to do something about them. Thus, in February of 1958, Boeing

BOMARC A SAM

announced that development was underway on a new model using a solid fuel booster motor. This model would be called the BOMARC B or Super BOMARC.

BOMARC B

Though similar in design to the original BOMARC A, the BOMARC B was by far the most effective of the two BOMARC models. Because it used a solid fuel booster, this model not only eliminated the fire problems of the earlier A model, it could also be launched in 30 seconds: the time needed to elevate the missile. In addition to this, since the solid fuel booster took up less room compared to the liquid motor, the BOMARC B had more internal room available for jet fuel, increasing the range of the missile to 440 miles. Other changes incorporated into the BOMARC B were improved ramjets (tested to speeds of Mach 4 and altitudes of 100,000 feet) and an enhanced radar seeker which could search from sea level to the missile's ceiling.

The first BOMARC B was launched on 27 May 1959. Though propulsion problems marred the first seven flights, by mid-1960 all the bugs had been found, and on 8 July 1960, a BOMARC B intercepted a supersonic Regulus II drone. A more complicated intercept was then completed on 23 March 1961, when a BOMARC first intercepted a Regulus II at Mach 2, ignored it by command of the ground station, and then intercepted a second one at an altitude of 100,000 feet, 375 miles downrange. On 1 June 1961, the first BOMARC B site became operational with the 37th ADMS based at Kincheloe AFB in Michigan.

Following the deployment of the first Super BOMARCs at Kincheloe, BOMARC Bs were also deployed with the following units: the 74th ADMS, Duluth Municipal Airport, Minnesota (August of 1961); the 22nd ADMS, Langley AFB (October of 1961); the 35th ADMS, Niagara Falls (46 missiles deployed on the Michigan side) (December of 1961); the 26th ADMS, Otis AFB (September of 1962); the 46th ADMS, McGuire AFB (October of 1962); the first Canadian BOMARC squadrons, the 446SAM, North Bay, Ontario (November of 1963); and the 447th SAM, La Macaza, Quebec (December of 1963). Only the 6th ADMS at Suffolk County and the 30th ADMS at Dow AFB were not rearmed with the BOMARC Bs. Testing and training with the BOMARC A subsequently ended on 10 March 1962, and on 1 December 1964, both Dow and Suffolk County shut down. Prior to this, in June, the Air Force had an operational force of 242 BOMARC B sites.

During the deployment of the BOMARC B, on 27 June 1963, the missile was redesignated as part of an Air Force, Navy and Army program to achieve a uniform designation system. As a result of this, the BOMARC's designation was changed from IM-99, or Interceptor Missile 99, to CIM-10 or Coffin-launched Interceptor Missile 10.

Soon after it achieved its 242 missile force, in the fall of 1964, the Air Force began withdrawing the BOMARCs based at Niagara Falls. In three years, 16 of the original 46 launchers had been shut down and by June of 1969, only 22 missiles were still operational. All operations at Niagara ended on 1 December 1969 and the 35th ADMS was deactivated on 31 December. The next year, the US Congress decided that, since the Soviet Union did not have a major bomber force, there was no need to continue operating a continental surface-to-air missile defense system. As a result of this decision, on 1 April 1972, operations ended at Duluth, La Macaza, North Bay, and Otis AFB. Kincheloe was deactivated on 1 July 1972, and on 1 October, the last BOMARC missile was deactivated and withdrawn at McGuire AFB.

---

[1] Originally, the missile was designated XF-99, for experimental Fighter 99.

Terrier BT-3A/N (RIM-2D)

SPECIFICATIONS

Length: 26 ft 4 in	Span: 2.4 in
Diameter: Missile — 1 ft 1 in	Weight; 3000 lb
Booster — 1 ft 6 in	

PERFORMANCE

Speed: Mach 2.5	Ceiling: 65,000 ft
Range: 36 mi	

POWERPLANT Two stage solid fuel motor system developed by Atlantic Research

GUIDANCE Beam rider with semi-active radar homing

WARHEAD conventional or a W-45-0 fission warhead of 1 kt yield

CONTRACTOR General Dynamics

NUMBER OF MISSILES Unknown number produced; approx 310 armed with nuclear warheads in 1983

The Terrier BT-3A/N is the only member of the Terrier family of surface-to-air missiles that was designed to carry a nuclear warhead. At this time, it is the only version of the Terrier still in service.

The Terrier family of surface-to-air missiles had its beginnings in the US Navy Bumblebee program. Designed using data from the Talos program's Supersonic Test Vehicle, and the earlier Lark surface-to-air missile, work on the Terrier tactical prototype began in February of 1949, with the first flight occurring on 16 February 1950. The start of the Korean War on 25 June 1950 accelerated development and, following the conversion of the cruiser *Canberra*, the first Terrier BW-1 missiles became operational on 15 June 1956. That same year, development began on the BT-3, the first Terrier to be effective against supersonic aircraft at both high and low altitude.

Terrier SAM

As a result of the the BT-3's low altitude capability, General Dynamics initiated a study to determine the feasibility of turning it into a surface-to-surface weapon: this to meet a Navy requirement for a long range, tactical, surface-to-surface missile. These studies indicated that such a model was feasible with only minor modifications and, in 1958, development was begun on the first nuclear capable Terrier, the BT-3A/N (RIM-2D).

By using a longer burning solid fuel auxiliary power source, and an end-burning sustainer motor, the BT-3A/N has twice the range of the earlier BT-3. In addition to this longer range the W-45 nuclear warhead was incorporated into the missile to give it maximum effectiveness against surface targets. The US Navy's deployment of this model began in 1962.

Though in a very short time the RIM-2D would become both impractical and ineffective as a standoff missile — its range became too short — its ability to stop large waves of enemy planes, and anti-ship cruise missiles, would soon make it the most effective surface-to-air missile in the Navy arsenal. Even the deployment of the SM-1 in the 1970s, and the recent deployment of the SM-2 have not changed this situation, since neither missile has the ability to stop more than one missile or aircraft. It is for this reason alone that the BT-3A/N is the only Terrier version still in service.

In an attempt to develop a replacement for the Terrier, a nuclear warhead has been developed for use by the SM-2. Production of this warhead, however, was deferred by Congress in 1986, making it uncertain as to when the BT-3A/N will be phased out of the Navy arsenal[1].

[1] Deployment of the SM-2 nuclear warhead was originally planned for the mid-1980s. No information about actual deployment is available.

Nike Zeus

Following the issuing of the production contract for the Nike Hercules, in June of 1955 the US Army began a study to determine the feasibility of Nike system-based surface to air missile that could intercept hypersonic aircraft and Inter-Continental Ballistic Missiles. Initially, this project was called Nike II but, on 15 November 1956, Army ordnance issued the project the new name of Nike Zeus.

Originally, the Army had intended the Nike Zeus to be a long range weapon, possibly capable of intercepting enemy nuclear warheads in space. Twelve days after the project was renamed, however, Secretary of Defense Wilson issued a directive restricting all Army missiles to a maximum range of 200 miles. But this restriction did not remove the need for such a missile, and as of that December, a contract was issued for the development of a missile specifically designed to intercept ICBM warheads inside the earth's atmosphere while retaining compatibility with the Nike launcher/radar system. Called the Nike Zeus A, the resulting missile was nothing more than an enhanced version of the Nike Hercules, designed for greater range and speed.

Nike Zeus (XLIM-49A)

SPECIFICATIONS
Length: 44 ft 3 in   Span: 9 ft 9.6 in
Diameter: 3 ft   Weight: 11,000 lb ·

PERFORMANCE
Speed: Supersonic   Range: 200 mi

PROPULSION Two stage solid fuel rocket motors; first stage producing 400,000 lb of thrust

GUIDANCE Radio command

WARHEAD Would have probably carried a nuclear warhead of 20 kt

CONTRACTOR Western Electric

Nike Zeus A ABM

Nike Zeus B ABM

Flight testing of the Nike Zeus A, using only the first stage, began on 26 August 1959: the missile exploded following launch. The second attempt on 14 October, however, was highly successful and paved the way for the first two-stage attempt on 16 December. This flight was also unsuccessful, but in February of 1960, a two-stage flight was completed with a full range flight occurring on 9 March 1960. The last missile of this model was launched on 25 May 1960.[1]

Following the orbiting of the Soviet Satellite 'Sputnik' on 4 October 1957, the range restriction on the US Army's missiles was rescinded, allowing the development of an even longer range Nike Zeus capable of intercepting enemy ICBM warheads outside the earth's atmosphere. This new missile would be called the Nike Zeus B.

Nike Zeus (XLIM-49B)

SPECIFICATIONS

Length: 48 ft 4 in	Span: 8 ft
Diameter: 3 ft	Weight: 22,800 lb

PERFORMANCE

Speed: supersonic	Ceiling: 174 mi[2]
Range: 250 mi	

PROPULSION
First stage a Thiokol TX-135 solid fuel rocket motor
   Max thrust: 450,000 lb
Second stage a Thiokol TX-238 solid fuel rocket motor
Third stage a Thiokol TX-239 solid fuel rocket motor

GUIDANCE Radio command

WARHEAD One W-50 thermonuclear warhead of 400 kt yield

CONTRACTOR Western Electric

Because it was designed to intercept targets in space, the Nike Zeus B was significantly different in design compared to the earlier Nike Zeus A. Since it was not really intended to intercept targets in the atmosphere, this missile did not require fins as large as the earlier Zeus—only small fins to control it until it reached space. Once there, a special third stage with small control jet ports (similar to control rockets on a space craft) was used to make the interception. As a result of this, the only thing the Nike Zeus B had in common with the Nike Zeus A was its method of guidance and use of the same solid fuel motor for the first stage. This use of the same first stage motor would later cause the Nike Zeus A to be labeled a 'motor test vehicle.'

The first flight of a Nike Zeus B (only the first stage was live) occurred on 28 April 1960. Testing of two stage versions was completed in the summer of 1961 and, on 9 September, the first full three-stage flight was completed at Point Mugu Naval station. Several months later, testing was again transferred to Kwajalein Atoll where, on 19 July 1962, a Zeus B missile intercepted the nose cone of an Atlas D ICBM, launched from Vandenberg AFB. A similar intercept would be achieved on 12 December, and by the end of 1963, a total of 13 RVs had been technically destroyed.[3]

Even though the Nike Zeus B had proven it could intercept an ICBM RV, the system still had some problems. First, the planned mechanical radar systems were extremely expensive to deploy, very slow in operation, limited in the number of targets they could track and totally inefficient at filtering out decoys. The second problem, more of a concern, was that, because the Nike Zeus was designed for space, it could not intercept short range SLBMs or any ICBM warhead that had penetrated the space defence. As a result of this, in January of 1963, the original mechanical radar system was dropped in favor of a new, high speed, phase-array system and a new endo-atmospheric[4] interceptor missile was added to the system for use against Submarine-Launched Ballistic Missiles. That same day, because of these changes, the Nike Zeus system was re-named Nike-X.

Soon after the Nike-X system was created, Western Electric, Bell and Douglas began development of an even longer range version of the Nike Zeus. Initially called Extended Range Nike Zeus, this model's greater range would quickly catch the attention of the DOD as an effective method of improving the area coverage of the Nike-X sites. As a result of this, on 29 September 1965, Western Electric was given the contract for the development of this missile. Two years later, on 18 September 1967, the DOD scrapped the Nike-X program and replaced it with a thinner ABM defense called Sentinel; the basic equipment was still the same. That same day, the Nike Zeus EX missile was issued the new name of Spartan.

Even though the Nike Zeus would never be operationally deployed as an Anti-Ballistic Missile, it would become an operational nuclear weapon. Back in April of 1962, Secretary of Defense McNamara ordered a Nike Zeus attempted intercept of an orbiting satellite. Code named Mudflap, this intercept was accomplished in May of 1963, using a modified Nike Zeus missile designated a DM-15S. The next month, on 27 June, McNamara ordered that a Nike Zeus with a live nuclear warhead be kept ready at all times at the Kwajalein complex for use against Soviet satellites. From that day until sometime in 1964, at least one missile with a live nuclear warhead was on 24 hour launch alert at this base. This deployment was ended completely in May of 1966.

[1] One source says there were only five flights of the Nike Zeus A.
[2] This was the altitude a Nike Zeus reached during an anti-satellite test launch.
[3] The Zeus missile didn't hit the RV, but came so close that if the Zeus was carrying a nuclear warhead the RV would have been destroyed.
[4] Endo-atmospheric is a term describing the missile's ability to intercept its targets inside the earth's atmosphere.

Nike Zeus B ABM

Sprint

SPECIFICATIONS
    Length: 26 ft 11 in   Weight: 7700 lb
    Diameter: 4 ft 5 in

PERFORMANCE
    Speed: Hypersonic (test vehicles to Mach 10)
    Range: 25 mi
    Ceiling: around 100,000 ft

POWERPLANT Solid fuel rocket engines by Hercules (possibly
                X-271s).
                First stage produces 300,000 lb of thrust static
                Second stage thrust unknown
                Firing temperatures limits: 700°F to 900°F

GUIDANCE Radio command

WARHEAD Single W-66 thermonuclear warhead of 20 kt
            yield; the target was destroyed by the neutron flux
            produced by the warhead (early neutron warhead)

CONTRACTOR Martin Marietta

NUMBER OF MISSILES 70 known to have been deployed;
                over 150 missiles were manufac-
                tured, of which 48 are known to
                have been expended in Safeguard
                system testing

Sprint ABM

The Sprint is the third anti-ballistic missile to be developed by the United States. It was designed to intercept tipped, ballistic missile, re-entry vehicles in the last few seconds before they reached their targets.

Following the removal of the 1956 range restriction, the Army ended development of the Nike Zeus A atmospheric interceptor missile in favor of the longer range Nike Zeus B space interceptor. To many in the government, this was an intelligent move because it meant that the intercepts, and subsequent nuclear explosions, would be in space — where they would not endanger the health of the nation's population. Others, however, knowing that radar problems made the space defense imperfect and that the Nike Zeus B was incapable of intercepting targets in the earth's atmosphere, called for the development of terminal defense missiles to destroy any warheads that leaked through the space defense. The development of submarine launched ballistic missiles, with their short flight time, added additional weight to the idea of a fast reaction atmospheric interceptor and, in late 1959, a study was begun to determine the feasibility of a such a missile.

After three years of research it was concluded that, by using high speed phased-array radars and computers, and recent developments in heat shielding, it was possible to develop the proposed high speed interceptor missile. As a result of this, in January of 1963, the DOD directed the start of the Nike-X program to develop an advanced ABM system incorporating these various devices. Two months later, Martin Marietta was issued the contract for this new missile under the title Sprint. A year later, the Nike-X system absorbed the earlier Nike Zeus system, creating the two layer defense pattern that would later be used by the Sentinel and Safeguard ABM systems.

Sprint ABM

Flight testing of Sprint components began at White Sands Missile Range in early 1964. The first R&D missile was then delivered in November of 1965; the first guided launch occurred the same month. Construction of the prototype Missile Site Radar (MSR) then began in June of 1966 at Meck Isle in the Kwajalein Missile Range; the MSR would not begin operating until September of 1968 and would not successfully track an ICBM until December of 1969. Following the completion of this radar site in the summer of 1970, full scale system testing could begin, and on 23 December 1970, a Sprint missile successfully intercepted its first ICBM RV. The first dual Sprint launch/intercept was completed on 17 March 1971 with the first intercept of a Polaris missile two months later on 7 May. This test series was completed in the fall of 1971 (16 flights in all: 12 successful, two partial, and two failures).

An additional test series was established from mid-1971 to December of 1973. Twenty-nine of the 32 flights in this series were successful.

While the Sprint was being developed, in September of 1967 the Nike-X system was dropped in favor of a smaller defense system based on the Nike-X. Called Sentinel, the purpose of this thin ABM system (17 sites) was to defend urban/industrial areas against an ICBM attack from Red China. Two years later, however, in March of 1969, President Richard Nixon directed that the program be reoriented to defend the Nation's ICBM force. Now called Safeguard, and even thinner than before (12 sites), construction of the first site began at Grand Forks, North Dakota, in March of 1970 and construction of the second site at Maelstrom began in May.

Though these changes had drastically reduced the scope of the planned ABM system, with the signing of the SALT I agreement, on 26 May 1972, the system was cut down even further to a token force of two ABM missile sites (near Washington, DC and in North Dakota). Two years later, in July of 1974, an addendum to this agreement was signed, limiting the United States and the Soviet Union to only one defense site around either nation's capital city or an ICBM base.

With the signing of the SALT I agreement, in May of 1972, construction was suspended at the Montana Safeguard site. Now the Nation's only ABM site installation of the first missiles at the Grand Forks began in the summer of 1974. An Initial Operational Capability of 28 Sprint and eight Spartan missile was achieved in April of 1975, and on 1 October 1975 the site became fully operational with a total force of 70 Sprints and 30 Spartans. The 30 Spartans and 12 of the Sprints were at the MSR site while the remaining Sprints were at an isolated site called Well Field. The very next day, however, Congress, claiming that the site's radars were too vulnerable to a nuclear attack, ordered the site shut down, the missiles sold and the radars dismantled. Four months later, the MSR was turned off forever.[1]

Though it was deployed for only a few months, the Sprint is one of the most amazing missiles ever deployed. Its actual speed is still classified, but it is known that the Sprint had a forward acceleration of over 3200 ft/sec^2 and that in flight, air friction produced temperatures up to 6200°F on its skin.[2] Along with this great speed, the missile was able to withstand mechanical shock of up to 25,000 Gs—the effect of a nearby nuclear explosion—and had a radio communication link that could penetrate its motor exhaust plume, the cloud of ablative products and the ionized plasma sheath that surrounded the missile in flight. As of last report, no missile has been able to match these capabilities.

The cancellation of Safeguard may have ended the Sprint's deployment, but not the Army's interest in the missile. Back in 1971, the Army began development of a hard site defense system with a smaller, harder, radar system and an improved version of the Sprint called Sprint II. This basing system would evolve into the

Low Altitude Defense, or LOAD, system in 1979 and then into the Sentry system in June of 1982. Research into an improved Sprint missile, however, ended in 1983 when research began into conventional Anti-Ballistic Missile systems.

[1] Following the deactivation, the Sprint missiles were put up for sale to research facilities as component test vehicles.
[2] The missile's heat shield could withstand heating rates up to 850 BTU/ft/sec.

Spartan (LIM-49A)

SPECIFICATIONS
Length: 55 ft 2 in   Span: 9 ft 9.6 in
Diameter: 3 ft 7.1 in   Weight: 29,000 lb

PERFORMANCE
Speed: supersonic   Ceiling: 350 mi
Range: 460 mi

PROPULSION First stage Thiokol TX-500 solid fuel rocket motor—Max thrust: 450,000 lb
Second stage Thiokol TX-454 solid fuel motor
Third stage Thiokol TX-239 solid fuel motor (same third stage as the Nike Zeus B)
Firing temperature limits: 70° to 90° F

GUIDANCE Radio command

WARHEAD Single W-71 thermonuclear warhead of 5 mt yield (the kill was achieved by a high energy burst of X-rays)

CONTRACTOR Western Electric and McDonnell Douglas

Spartan ABM

The Spartan is the fourth and last nuclear tipped ABM the United States has developed. It was the result of continued development and enhancement of the Nike Zeus B missile.

Following the first Nike Zeus ICBM intercepts, Western Electric and McDonnell Douglas began research into an improved, longer range missile called the Extended Range Nike Zeus. This new missile, coupled with the long tracking range of the planned Missile Site Radar MSR, was intended to increase the area defended by the planned Nike-X missile site, and thus allow the DOD to reduce the number of these sites it had to construct. The production contract for this missile was issued in the summer of 1965, with development beginning in October of that year. Two years later, in September of 1967, the DOD cancelled the Nike-X system in favor of a thin defense called Sentinel. That same month the Nike Zeus EX was given the new name of Spartan.

The first Spartan R&D missile was delivered in March of 1968. That same month, on the 30th, it was successfully launched from a concrete cell at Kwajalein Atoll. By April of 1970, development testing had been completed; there was a total of 11 successful flights, two partial, and two failures. Following completion of the Kwajalein Prototype Missile Site Radar in mid-1970, full system testing then began, with the first Spartan intercept of a Minuteman RV occurring on 28 August 1970. Five months later, on 11 January 1971, the first dual Spartan launch occurred with one missile intercepting an ICBM RV, the other intercepting a fixed point in space (an anti-satellite test).

While the Spartan was being tested, President Richard Nixon took certain political steps that would eventually limit the number of these missiles that would be deployed. First, in March of 1969, President Richard Nixon replaced the Sentinel system with an even thinner system called Safeguard around the nation's ICBM sites. Eight months later, he would start negotiating the first Strategic Arms Limitation agreement (SALT I) which — when it was signed on 26 May 1972 — limited the United States and the Soviet Union to two 100 missile ABM sites apiece. An addition to this agreement signed on 3 July 1974 further limited each nation to one site of 100 missiles around either that nation's capital or an ICBM base. As a result of these changes, no more than 30 Spartan missiles would ever be deployed.[1]

With the limitations imposed by the SALT I agreement, the first missiles were installed at the one Safeguard site at Grand Forks, North Dakota, in late 1974. An Initial Operational Capability of eight Spartan and 28 Sprint missiles was achieved in April of 1975 with the system becoming fully operational with 30 Spartan and 70 Sprint missiles on 1 October 1975. The next day, however, Congress ordered the site shut down on the grounds that the protection this single site gave was insufficient to warrant continued operation, and that the radars were too vulnerable to a nuclear strike. As this order required, in February of 1976 the MSR was permanently switched off.

The deactivation of the Grand Forks Safeguard site was not the end for the Spartan missile. In the years that followed, its design was kept on the shelf as a hedge against a Soviet violation of the SALT I agreement (the original warheads were kept in storage until 1986). The Spartan, in fact, almost made a comeback in June of 1982 when the Ballistic Missile Defense Office dusted off the design in order to give the Sentry missile system a long range space interceptor. With the cancellation of the Sentry system in 1983, however, the Spartan has finally been dropped in favor of conventional space interceptors.

[1] This doesn't include any Spartan missiles at either Kwajalein or White Sands on test launchers.

Nike Hercules (MIN-14B)

SPECIFICATIONS

Length: Missile — 26 ft 10.5 in   Span: Missile 7 ft 6 in
        Booster — 14 ft 2.85 in   Booster — 11 ft 6.2 in
Diameter: Missile — 1 ft 9.2 in   Weight: Missile — 5531 lb
          Booster — 2 ft 7.5 in   Booster — 5180 lb

PERFORMANCE

Speed: 4000 mph   Ceiling: 150,000 ft
Range: 88 mi

POWERPLANT Sustainer — one solid fuel (internal burning star) rocket engine. Max thrust: 10,000 lb Booster — four solid fuel rod and tube charge rocket engines. Firing temperature limits: 20°F to 125°F

GUIDANCE Radio command by Western Electric

WARHEAD One W-31 fission nuclear warhead of 20 kt yield

CONTRACTOR Western Electric

NUMBER OF MISSILES Over 25,000 produced
863 deployed US, 186 in Europe

Spartan ABM

The Nike Hercules is the most powerful surface-to-air missile ever deployed by the US Army. For over 20 years, this missile gave the US Army the ability to intercept both high altitude enemy aircraft or tactical missiles.

Even before the first Nike Ajax missiles (then called Nike) became operational, in the spring of 1952, US Army Ordnance issued a request to Bell Telephone Labs of Western Electric Company for a feasibility study of an improved, possibly nuclear, missile that could be launched from the operational Nike Ajax launchers. Bell began this study in May of that year; in December, the Department of the Army gave official approval for the project. The design and development contract was issued to Western Electric in June of 1953; in April of 1955, the initial production contract was issued. The following year, on 15 November 1956, the program was 'Nike Hercules'.[1]

The first production Nike Hercules missile was delivered to the Army in December of 1957. Final testing was completed that same month and, in January of 1958, the first Hercules missiles became operational. By June, Hercules was in service at Nike sites around New York; Washington, DC and Chicago. By 1960, all 73 continental Nike Ajax Battalions had finished conversion to Hercules, giving the United States a total of 365 operational Nike Hercules batteries (each Nike Hercules Battalion had five batteries — one HQ and four fire).

The deployment of the Nike Hercules marked a major increase in the capability of the nation's surface-to-air missile system. Because of its longer range — three times that of the earlier Ajax missile — the Nike Hercules increased the area a Nike site could defend from 2000 square miles to 24,000 square miles (11 times larger than before). Additionally, since the missile could fly higher than any operational enemy aircraft, it was impossible for an enemy

bomber to fly above the defense. Finally, the addition of a nuclear warhead made it impossible for any enemy aircraft to avoid the Hercules through extensive maneuvering (in testing or training a successful intercept occurred when a Nike Hercules came within 25 to 50 feet of its target). These last two capabilities also gave the Nike sites a limited anti-ballistic missile capability against medium or intermediate range ballistic missiles (these types of missiles were slower than ICBMs making them easier targets).[2]

On 4 November 1962, a Nike Hercules missile carrying a live nuclear warhead was launched. Known as shot Tightrope of test series Dominic I, the Nike Hercules delivered its W-31 warhead to an altitude of 15 miles, where it was detonated. This is the only known launch of a Nike Hercules with an armed nuclear warhead.

Despite these enhanced capabilities, the Nike Hercules missile was still using the earlier Nike Ajax mechanical radar systems. Even with a Western Electric upgrade, these radars were slow in operation and limited in the number of targets they could effectively track. Furthermore, these radars and their control systems were large and cumbersome, taking 20 vehicles just to move the long range acquisition radar system. This all changed in early 1960, however, with the development of the General Electric High Power Acquisition Radar or HIPAR. This new, more compact radar required only three vehicles to move it, increasing the mobility of the whole Nike Hercules system. This new radar system also improved the missile's capabilities against high speed targets, allowing the Hercules to intercept a Corporal SRBM in mid-1960, and then another Nike Hercules in September. By 1961, HIPAR-equipped semi-mobile Nike units were being deployed in Western Europe and Asia.[3]

The reason the Nike Hercules units deployed in Western Europe and Asia were designated 'semi-mobile' had to do with their large size. Though the development of HIPAR made mobility practical, the Nike batteries were still extremely large units, making movement a major operation. Setting a battery up was just as hard, requiring nearly a week to get everything properly assembled and the electronics calibrated. Consequently, most of the units deployed to Europe or Asia were set up like prefabricated houses, with the trailers placed on fixed supports and their wheels permanently removed.

In 1963, US Army Nike Hercules deployment in Europe reached its peak of 134 batteries (26 combat battalions and one training). By that same year, 644 Hercules launchers were in service with the armed forces of Belgium, Denmark, West Germany, Greece, Italy, the Netherlands, Norway, Turkey, Japan, South Korea and Taiwan.[4] Production of the nuclear capable Nike Hercules terminated in March of 1964 in preparation for the deployment of the SAM-D missile. As of last report, Japan continues to manufacture a conventional Nike Hercules under contract with McDonnell Douglas.

A few years after Nike Hercules production was ended, the United States Congress came to the conclusion that since the Soviet Union did not have a true long range strategic bomber force, it was unnecessary to continue operating the continental air defense system. As a result of this, SAM-D, the next generation continental defense missile, was reduced to a low cost research effort and, in 1968, a gradual phaseout of the Nike Hercules missiles began. By 1975, the only Nike Hercules units still in operation in United States territory were four semi-mobile training batteries — two in Florida and two in Alaska, which were used to train Army battalions deployed in Europe.

Where the US Congress in 1968 no longer saw a need for the Nike Hercules missiles, in Western Europe the view was quite different. These nations, so much closer to the Soviet Bloc and their medium and light bomber aircraft, needed the Hercules to maintain a high altitude defense of their national territory. Since the US units in Europe were in a similar situation, the Army also

Nike Hercules SAM

continued to operate three semi-mobile battalions (not counting the training battalion in the US). In addition, to maintain the system's effectiveness until SAM-D was deployed, in the late 1960s the Army equipped the European units with the new Tracking Only Radar (TOR), to enhance the ability to see through enemy ECM systems and thus maintain the missile lock.

The wait for SAM-D, now called Patriot, would last throughout the 1970s and into the early 1980s. To keep the Nike Hercules functional, the original analog computer system was replaced by a high speed, high reliability, digital computer system in the early 1980s. Regardless of this last modification, however, time and technological developments had made the Nike Hercules hopelessly outdated. With an airframe that was designed in the 1950s, the majority of its electronics from the vacuum tube era, and mechanical radars that limited each battery to the engaging of one target at a time, Hercules was a dinosaur in a world of micro-computers, solid state electronics and phased-array radar systems.

With the deployment of the first Patriot units in December of 1984, the US Army withdrew its last Nike Hercules missiles from Europe. In the near future, as the Patriot becomes available to those nations that still operate the Nike Hercules, the remaining Nike Hercules missiles will also be retired from service. At this time, it is unclear whether the nuclear warheads for these remaining Nike Hercules missiles are still in existence.

[1] Originally called Nike B
[2] During the Cuban missile crisis, several Nike units were installed in southern states, possibly to intercept Cuban missiles.
[3] In 1958, prior to the development of HIPAR, a battalion of Nikes was sent to Taiwan.
[4] US troops stationed in these countries maintained control of the nuclear warheads for these missiles.

SM-2 (RIM-66B)

SPECIFICATIONS
Length: 27 ft (Extended Range)   14 ft 8.4 in (Medium Range)
Diameter: Missile 1 ft 1 in
          Booster 1 ft 6 in
Span: Missile 3 ft 6 in
          Booster 5 ft 3.5 in
Weight: 2920 lb (Extended Range)   1350 lb (Medium Range)

PERFORMANCE
Speed: Mach 2.5 (Extended Range)   Mach 2 + (Medium Range)
Range: 75 mi (Extended Range)   35 mi (Medium Range)
Ceiling: 65,000 ft

PROPULSION Sustainer — Aerojet and Hercules Mk-56 solid
              fuel rocket motor
           Booster — Atlantic Research solid fuel rocket
              motor, no booster on medium range version

GUIDANCE Inertial reference system with command control to
            target area
         Semi-active radar homing in terminal phase

WARHEAD At present only a high explosive warhead (Mk-70
           or Mk-90 fragmentation type)
         Under development is the W-81
           one kt fusion warhead

Nike Hercules SAMs

CONTRACTOR General Dynamics

NUMBER OF MISSILES 4000 already in service, 350 are to
be retrofitted with the W-81 warhead

The SM-2, or Standard Missile 2, is the newest long-range surface-to-air missile in the US Navy's arsenal. It is intended to replace the earlier Terrier, Tartar and SM-1 missiles in use by the fleet.

The Standard series of missiles is the result of an early 1960 Navy proposal for a modern family of missiles to replace the earlier Tartar and Terrier missiles. Though these missiles are externally similar to the earlier Homing Terrier, allowing them to use the same launchers and handling equipment, internally they are completely modern weapons. In place of the earlier vacuum tube electronics, solid state circuitry is used to improve the reliability of the system and to reduce warm-up time. In addition to this, the earlier heavy hydraulic control system and its auxiliary power unit were replaced with an all-electric system powered by a one shot dry cell battery. The first of these new all-electric missiles, called SM-1, became operational in 1969.

Even before the SM-2 was deployed, the Navy had revised its air defense requirements to take into account recent developments in anti-ship cruise missiles. Thus in the early 1970s, the Navy began development of the Aegis phased-array radar system. To meet the new operating requirements of this system, General Dynamics began work on a modified version of the SM-1 called the SM-2.

The SM-2 differs from the SM-1 in its use of a monopulse radar homing receiver, a digital guidance computer and an inertial reference system with command links. Though the other changes are significant, the IRS is the major enhancement because it allows the missile to guide itself to the target area, freeing the ship's fire control system to target other aircraft and missiles, and doubling its range by making its flight profile more energy-efficient. If the target changes course during this phase of flight, or if the guidance system has to be corrected, the IRS can be quickly updated via its command link to the launching ship. Once at the target area, the missile switches to semi-active radar homing, locks on to the target and destroys it. The first flight of this missile took place in November of 1972.

Regardless of all these improvements, the US Navy knew that an SM-2 equipped ship could still be overwhelmed by a massive wave of enemy missiles: it was this fact that forced the Navy to retain the obsolete Terrier BT-3A/N. As a result of this, and the need to replace the long-since outmoded Terrier BT-3A/N, development began in 1975 on a nuclear warhead for use by the SM-2. Called the W-81, this modified version of the B-61 warhead is significantly safer than the Terrier's W-45, through the use of modern security systems and PBX-9502 insensitive high explosives. This new warhead is also one point safe, which means that if a detonation occurs at any point in the high explosive system, the probability of achieving a nuclear yield greater than four kt of TNT shall not exceed one in one million.

Originally, the SM-2/N (N for Nuclear) was to be deployed in 1985. Funding for production was deleted that year, however, and in 1986, Congress deferred production of the nuclear warhead for a period as yet undetermined. It is uncertain at this point whether a nuclear armed SM-2 will ever be operationally deployed.

SM-2 SAM

SM-2 SAM

Land and Naval Munitions

280mm Atomic Cannon (T131)

SPECIFICATIONS (Gun Carriage)
    Length: emplaced, 38 ft 5 in   Weight: emplaced, 94,000 lb
          in transit, 84 ft 2 in   with transporters, 166,638 lb

PERFORMANCE OF GUN
  Range: (HE) 31,400 yd (17.84 mi)
           (Nuc) Mk-9: 26,300 yd (15 mi)
           (Nuc) Mk-19: 32,700 yd (18.6 mi)
           Muzzle Velocity: 2500 ft/sec

WARHEAD Either a conventional or a Mk-9 or Mk-19 nuclear
        projectile of 15 kt yield

NUMBER DEPLOYED 20 guns were manufactured, one battalion formed

The 280mm Atomic Cannon was the first nuclear capable artillery piece in the world. Not only was this cannon the largest mobile field piece the US Army ever deployed, it was also the most powerful, capable of firing the largest nuclear projectile ever developed for the Army.

Following their creation by the US Air Force, on 18 September 1947, the US Army began looking at guided missiles as an alternative method of delivering nuclear warheads to Air Force and Navy aircraft. Though this action makes it seem that the Army believed in these missiles, this decision was made because the available nuclear warheads were too big to be carried by anything other than large aircraft or missiles (Congress had forbidden the development of small nuclear warheads on the grounds that nuclear weapons were too powerful for the battlefield). Following the detonation of the Soviet Union's first nuclear device in August of 1949, this situation changed. Congress gave permission for the development of small aerial nuclear bombs like the Mk-8 and the Mk-7. As a result of this, the Army began looking at artillery as a means of delivering a nuclear warhead in late 1949. The 240mm Cannon was of particular interest.

The 240mm (9.5 inch) Mobile Cannon had been under development by the Army since November of 1944. An enormous weapon weighing over 80 tons, it was intended for use against hardened point targets, communications centers, and long range artillery (the American answer to the German railroad guns). For all its great size, it was an extremely mobile weapon capable of speeds of up to 40 mph on paved roads. With this mobility, the cannon was also extremely easy to set up compared to other artillery pieces, with a number of systems hydraulically powered for operation ease. The most important feature was its ability to deliver a projectile to its target over several miles, day or night and in any weather, with pinpoint accuracy (this was something fighter bombers of the period could not do).

Regardless of all these capabilities the 240mm cannon had one problem — for all its great size it was still too small to handle the smallest nuclear warhead in development. As a result of this, and the Army's desire to have an operational nuclear weapon as soon as possible, in the spring of 1950, the order was given to have the cannon's barrels rebored to a new diameter of 280mm (11 inches). At this larger size, not only could it handle a nuclear warhead, but its range would be even greater.[1]

Development of the 280mm cannon was accelerated by the start of the Korean War on 25 June 1950. The first of the new guns was ready in the spring of 1952. Testing began soon afterwards, at Fort Sill in Oklahoma, with both conventional rounds and dummy nuclear projectiles being successfully fired by the spring of 1953. Then, to inaugurate the entrance of the gun into service, on 25 May 1953, a 280mm atomic cannon fired the world's first live nuclear round at Frenchman's Flat, Nevada. Called the Grable shot of Operation Upshot-Knothole, the round, a Mk-9, traveled a distance of seven miles and then exploded 524 feet in the air with a yield of 15 kilotons.

Deployment of the 280mm to Europe began soon after the Grable shot, only one battalion was ever deployed. Initially, these guns were armed with Mk-9 nuclear shells which limited their engagement range to about 15 miles compared to their conventional range of over 17. In mid-1955 the Army began replacing the Mk-9 with the lighter Mk-19 round, which had a longer range than the conventional rounds. Deployment of this round was completed in 1957.

While deployment of the Mk-19 was underway, in 1956, the Army began deploying the first Mk-33 nuclear rounds for the 8 inch Howitzer. Now nuclear capable, this smaller, more mobile howitzer was a much more effective and survivable weapon system compared to the 280mm. Thus as more of these new shells became available, the Army began phasing out the 280mm cannon from the US arsenal. The last cannon was retired from service in 1963.

280mm atomic projectile

280mm cannon

The Grable nuclear test

A total of three 280mm atomic cannons are still in existence at the following museums: Aberdeen Proving Grounds, the National Atomic Museum and Fort Sill, Oklahoma. The one at Fort Sill is of special significance, since it is 'Atomic Annie,' the cannon that fired the Mk-9 round for shot Grable.

[1] The accuracy life of the 280mm barrels was only 300 rounds.

MK-23 16 inch Naval Shell

SPECIFICATIONS
Length of Projectile: 5.3 ft   Diameter of Projectile: 16 in
Weight of Projectile: 1900 lb

PERFORMANCE
Range of Gun: 23 mi with   Yield: 15 to 20 kt
      a 2700 lb shell

DEPLOYMENT Approx 50 made for use by the MK-7 Naval guns, carried by the *Iowa* class battleships

The Mk-23 nuclear shell (called KATIE) was designed for use by the Navy's *Iowa* class battleships in the attacking of enemy coastal military targets. Though it doesn't seem to have been operationally deployed, it was the largest nuclear projectile ever developed by the United States.

Mk-23 16 inch nuclear projectile

Though no exact information is available, by the time the Army live-fired the 280mm atomic cannon in shot Grable, the Navy was considering the practicality of deploying a nuclear projectile for its 16 inch naval guns. Though such a projectile would be shorter in range than available Navy aircraft or missiles, it had the virtues of having an all-weather strike capability, something the Navy fighters of the period lacked, and of having a higher accuracy than operational missiles. Development of the Mk-23 projectile began in September of 1953, four months after the Mk-9 projectile was successfully live-fired. Three years later, in December of 1956, it was placed in the Navy stockpile.

By the time the Mk-23 was deployed, however, the Navy had begun mothballing its *Iowa* class battleships. The first one to be decommissioned was the battleship *Missouri* on 26 February 1955. The *New Jersey* was then deactivated on 21 August 1957, followed by the *Iowa* on 24 February 1958. The last ship, the *Wisconsin*, was subsequently decommissioned on 8 March 1958,[1] leaving the Mk-23 with no operational firing platform. (Though three of these ships were in service following the introduction of the round, there is no information revealing whether the Mk-23 was ever carried at sea on any of these ships).

Regardless of its lack of a firing platform the Mk-23 remained in the US stockpile until October of 1962.

[1] For several months prior to this the *Wisconsin* was undergoing bow reconstruction following a collision with an escort destroyer.

M422 8 inch Nuclear Projectile

SPECIFICATIONS
Length: 37 in approx   Weight: 243 lb
Diameter: 8 in

WARHEAD A W-33 fission device of 1 to 2 kt yield

PERFORMANCE Range: 8.76 mi

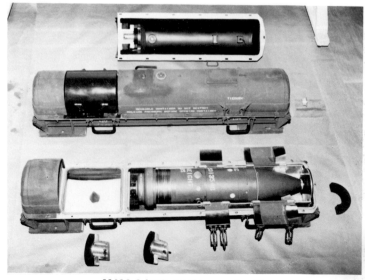

M422 8 inch nuclear projectile

The M422 8 inch projectile is the oldest nuclear artillery round in the US arsenal. It was intended for use against large units of enemy armor and infantry.

Even before the 280mm Atomic Cannon had been deployed, by 1951 the Army was aware that this weapon system would have several limitations. Because of its large size and weight, the 280mm was slow to deploy and could only be transported over major roads and bridges. Furthermore, because only 20 of these guns were ever built, the possibility existed that a potential enemy could neutralize the system by simply hunting down and destroying the guns. As a result of these problems, in April of 1952, the US Army began lobbying for a smaller nuclear shell capable of being fired from standard eight inch howitzers.

Development of the M422 shell was authorized in June of 1953, with funding being issued in February of 1954. Two months later, the program was put on a crash basis, and in February of 1955, emergency production of the round was started. Stockpiling of the M422 then began in 1957.

With the deployment of the first M422s, the Army now had a highly mobile nuclear system that was incapable of being completely neutralized by enemy fire; it was also more reliable than the 280mm, since the eight inch guns were, on the whole, always available. With these new capabilities, however, the round had a major limitation in that it was not ballistically similar to the operational conventional rounds and thus could not use the same gun settings as these rounds. To rectify this, a special high explosive spotting round (M424) was also deployed to be fired first against the planned target. Only through the use of the spotting round is it possible to achieve a reasonable accuracy with this round. The need to fire this spotting round, however, plus the fact that the M422 is assembled in the field, makes this weapon system very slow to respond to a fire order.

An improved model of the M422, the M422A1, was deployed in 1964; like the earlier model, this model also lacked the ballistic similarity necessary for high accuracy. Thus, in June of 1971, the Army began development of a new nuclear projectile using a W-75 warhead. Though this round was cancelled in June of 1973, in January of 1975, development began on a second nuclear round called the M753. Production of this round began in 1980, and in mid-1981, the M753 began replacing the M422 on a one for one basis.

Because of a Congressional mandate, in August of 1986, production of the M753 was ended before the last M422 was removed from the stockpile. As a result of this, in mid-1987, about 900 M422 and M422A1 projectiles were still in service with US forces. As of last report, work is underway to refurbish the remaining M422s in the stockpile to keep them functional.

Davy Crockett

SPECIFICATIONS

M-29 155mm recoiless	M-28 120mm recoiless
Length: 8 ft 2 in	5 ft 1 in
Weight: 371 lb	116 lb

PERFORMANCE
Range:

Min 1000 ft	1000 ft
Max 2.5 mi	1.24 mi

WARHEAD Either a conventional or a W-54 variable yield fission device (from 20 to 250 tons)

NUMBER DEPLOYED 6247 guns known funded; only 400 nuclear-tipped XM388 projectiles produced

The Davy Crockett was the third nuclear artillery piece the US Army ever deployed. With this weapon, Army squads were able to destroy large units of enemy tanks or infantry.

The Davy Crockett was developed to give Army infantry units an effective weapon against large units of Soviet armor. The weapon system, first deployed in late 1961, consisted of a standard projectile (the XM388) and two gun types, the heavy 155mm M-29 and the light 120mm M-28. The M-29 was transported by either a M-113 armored personnel carrier or a large truck, but fired on the ground. The M-28 was generally carried and fired on a Army jeep, though it could also be carried for a short distances by a three man team. Both guns, however, used the same XM388 279mm projectile.

Loading or assembling a Davy Crockett was totally different than loading a howitzer. First a powder charge, with its own mechanical firing mechanism, was inserted into the Crockett gun tube. Then the XM388 projectile was attached to a long bar, or 'spigot,' which was then slid tail-first into the barrel of the Crockett (the XM388 was not inserted down into the gun barrel of the Crockett but stayed on the end of the spigot). Once this was done, all that remained was for the Crockett to be aimed at the planned target and the firing mechanism to be triggered. The powder charge would then detonate, hurling the spigot and the attached nuclear projectile a great distance (some of the explosion was directed out the back of the tube to counteract recoil).

During its time in service, the Davy Crockett warhead was live fired two times. The first time was a weapon effects test on 7 July 1962, code named Little Feller I. The second time, Little Feller II on 17 July, was a complete test of the Davy Crockett system as part of the Ivy Flats military exercise. Unlike the previous test, in which the round was manually emplaced, in Little Feller I, the round was fired from a Davy Crockett launcher a distance of 1.77 miles, where it exploded slightly above ground. Twenty-six minutes later, a company of men from the 4th Infantry Division and a platoon of tanks entered the shot zone to complete the maneuvers.

Prior to the Little Feller tests, on 9 June 1962, the Davy Crockett became operational with 7th Army units in West Ger-

Davy Crockett nuclear gun

many. Following this deployment, however, the US government became concerned about the fact that this weapon, when fielded, was controlled by an Army sergeant, and was thus subject to relatively unrestricted use. Production of the Crockett was thereafter ended in February of 1965, with the first weapons being withdrawn in July of 1967. The last Davy Crockett was removed in early 1971.

ASROC (RUR-5A)

SPECIFICATIONS
Length: 15 ft   Span: 2 ft 9.25 in
Diameter: 1 ft 0.5 in   Weight: 1000 lb

PERFORMANCE
Speed: Mach 1   Range: 9 mi

PROPULSION Navy solid fuel rocket motor
                 Max thrust: 11,000 lb

GUIDANCE Technically unguided; has a timer system for
                 thrust cutoff and payload separation

WARHEAD Either a conventionally armed torpedo or a W-44
                 nuclear depth bomb of low kt yield

CONTRACTOR Honeywell Inc

NUMBER OF MISSILES Over 1000 rockets produced,
                 approximately 500 nuclear warheads
                 in stockpile

The ASROC is the first, and only, nuclear capable Anti-Submarine system to be deployed on US Navy destroyers and cruisers. With this weapon these ships have the capability to destroy any operational enemy submarine no matter how fast, or how deep, it can travel.

Back in the early 1950s, the US Navy began development of a rocket launched homing torpedo to give its destroyers, cruisers and frigates a standoff attack capability against enemy submarines. Called the RAT (Rocket Assisted Torpedo), this little rocket soon proved to be extremely limited in both range and payload, and was so poor in accuracy that the torpedos missed their targets. Regardless of this setback, however, the Navy still wanted a standoff antisubmarine weapon, and in 1955 began development on a longer range, more powerful rocket called the RAT C. Later that same year, this program was combined with another Navy project to develop a rocket-boosted nuclear depth charge with the resulting weapon system named ASROC (Anti-Submarine Rocket).

Development of the ASROC officially began in mid-1956, with the June issuing of the development contract to Honeywell. Though development of the nuclear depth charge was delayed until late 1960, development of the rest of the weapon system was very swift, allowing the Navy to begin shipboard evaluation in 1960 on the USS *Norfolk*. Initial operational capability was then achieved on four destroyers in 1961.

The ASROC is one of the simplest weapons systems in service with the US Navy. Once a hostile submarine is detected, an ASROC is programmed and the ship's launcher, either an eight shot Mk-112 or a Terrier Mk-10, is rotated towards the target and elevated to the proper angle for maximum range. Once launched, the weapon's range is controlled by the Ignition and Separation Assembly (ISA), which detonates explosive blocks to shut off the rocket's motor once a specified amount of time has elapsed. Once the rocket motor has been shut off, the ASROC begins to descend, completing a ballistic flight path to the target area. The ISA then separates the payload which, if it is a depth charge, plunges into the water. If it is a torpedo, a parachute lowers it into the water.

Following the deployment of the ASROC system, at 1 pm on 11 May 1962, 425 miles south-southwest of San Diego, California, the Destroyer USS *Algerholm* fired a nuclear armed ASROC. This successful test, named Swordfish, was conducted to both proof-fire the weapon, and to determine what effect the detonation of the warhead would have on the launching ship and its sonar system.

The ASROC has changed little in the two decades since it was first deployed in 1961. In 1965, the original torpedo (the Mk-44) was replaced by the lightweight Mk-46, but other than this and a new separation mode, the weapon has remained essentially the same. At this time, however, because of the development of vertical launch systems, the Navy has begun development of a new missile called Vertical Launched ASROC. These new missiles should begin replacing the present ASROC in the early 1990s, so that the earlier system will be fully withdrawn by the year 2000. These new weapons will be conventionally armed due to a 1985 Navy decision that an unconventional warhead was not required for

ASROC

the VL ASROC. Therefore, when these missiles are deployed, Navy surface warships will lose their present nuclear anti-submarine capability.

At this time, the ASROC is operationally deployed on ships of the following nations: the United States, West Germany, Spain, Italy, Greece, Japan, Taiwan, South Korea, Canada, Brazil and Pakistan.

SUBROC (UUM-44A)

SPECIFICATIONS
Length: 21 ft   Weight: 4000 lb
Diameter: 21 ft

PERFORMANCE
Speed: Supersonic   Range: 28.5 mi

PROPULSION Single Thiokol TE-260G composite solid fuel rocket motor. Max thrust: 36,500 lb

GUIDANCE Inertial guidance system by Kearfott

WARHEAD Single W-55 fission warhead

CONTRACTOR Goodyear Aerospace

NUMBER OF MISSILES At least 300 produced; each attack submarine carries from four to six missiles

The SUBROC is the only standoff anti-submarine weapon in use by US Navy submarines. With this weapon, a Navy attack submarine can engage one or more enemy submarines while remaining out of range of their torpedos.

Studies into a submarine launched anti-submarine missile began in 1953 as part of the Navy Aliex Study. Two years later, the commander of the Navy's Regulus missile force proposed a solid fueled, torpedo tube launched, nuclear bombardment missile for use by Navy submarines against both subsurface and land targets. Though such a weapon would have given all the Navy's submarines a surface strike capability, the idea was eventually scaled down to an anti-submarine missile with only a secondary airburst capability. A feasibility study was then begun on 19 September 1957, and in June of 1958, development of the SUBROC began at the US Naval Ordnance Laboratory at White Oak, Maryland. The first test launch occurred on 3 August 1959.

The SUBROC system was much harder to develop than its surface ship counterpart, the ASROC. Where that rocket system could use the sonar systems in service on operational ships, the SUBROC required a new long-range sonar system to detect enemy submarines over a distance of 35 to 40 miles, and a special fire control system which could use the sonar data to both program and prime the missile for its flight. This incompatibility would eventually require the Navy to have the *Permit* class of attack submarines, authorized in 1958 and 1959, specifically designed to use this new missile system.

Along with the sonar and fire control problems, the SUBROC system was also delayed by problems with the missile. Development of the solid fuel rocket motor took several years because of problems with water pressure, chilling of the solid fuel by the water and the formation of large air bubbles in the motor cavity (this last problem either snuffed out the igniter or interfered with the control system). Other problems that took years to solve involved shock and vibrations due to the missile leaving the ocean for the air; maintaining guidance control after rocket motor separation; and the impact forces on the depth charge during re-entry into the ocean. It

SUBROC

would take several years to solve these problems, preventing the SUBROCs from coming into service until mid-1965.

Regardless of the development problems, however, once they were deployed, the SUBROCs would quickly show that they were worth waiting for. Equipped with these missiles, Navy attack submarines could now engage enemy submarines at distances far beyond that of the enemy submarine's torpedos. Also, because the SUBROC travels primarily through the air, the target submarine can not detect the approach of the missile with its sonar and thus take any kind of evasive action. In addition to this, since the SUBROC travels at supersonic speeds through the air, the time it takes for the missile to reach its target is extremely short compared to torpedos, adding to its effectiveness. As a result, production of the SUBROC did not end until the year 1972.

In the mid to late 1970s an improvement program was proposed for the SUBROC, in which the missile's analogue guidance system would be replaced with a new digital system, and the solid fuel motor would be regrained to retard the effects of time (solid fuel motors deteriorate over time). In 1979, however, Congress decided against this upgrading in favor of a new missile: the Anti-Submarine Warfare/Standoff Weapon (ASW/SOW). Development of this missile, now called Sea Lance, has been extensively delayed, however, forcing the Navy in 1983 to begin the earlier SUBROC enhancement program. As of last report, these improvements have been completed.

In mid-1986, the Navy dropped the nuclear depth charge for the Sea Lance missile in favor of the Mk-50 lightweight torpedo. When this missile begins replacing the SUBROCs in the early 1990s, US Navy Attack submarines will no longer have a nuclear anti-submarine capability.

MARK 45 Torpedo (ASTOR)

SPECIFICATIONS
Length: 18 ft 9 in   Weight: 2680.26 lb
Diameter: 19 in

PERFORMANCE
Speed: 40 knots   Depth: 6.5 to 49 ft
Range: 10 mi

PROPULSION Electrically powered (battery), 9 minute life span

GUIDANCE Command control via wire system

WARHEAD Either a conventional warhead or a W-34 fission device

CONTRACTOR Westinghouse

NUMBER OF MISSILES: At least a thousand produced, approximately 600 nuclear armed

The ASTOR is the only nuclear capable torpedo the US Navy has ever deployed. It was intended to destroy hostile deep diving submarines.

In 1955 intelligence information indicated that the Soviet Union was in the process of building a massive submarine fleet which, according to CIA estimates, by 1956 would pose a serious threat to the Allied sea routes. To counter this threat, in December of 1956 the Navy began considering the possibility of arming the developmental Mark 45 torpedo, called ASTOR, or Anti-Submarine Torpedo, with a nuclear warhead. Development of the warhead was then requested in mid-1957, and by the summer of 1960, the W-34 warhead, already proven in the Lulu depth bomb, was released for use by the Astor. Production of the Astor torpedo began in 1961 and the first deliveries took place in 1963.

By the time the Astor was deployed, however, it was already obsolete. Because this torpedo was guided to its target by commands transmitted to it through a wire connection, the range of this weapon was restricted to the amount of wire it carried. (The wire uncoiled from a spool in the rear of the torpedo).[1] An additional problem caused by this wire guidance system was that the launching submarine had to use active sonar to track the target, giving away its own position to the enemy submarine. These problems quickly overshadowed the Mark 45's high accuracy and its great destructive power.

On 21 May 1968 the Navy attack submarine USS *Scorpion* (SSN-589) went down with all hands approximately 400 miles SW of the Azores. Recent information (declassified in 1984) suggests that one of the Mk-45 torpedos carried by this submarine exploded, causing the accident.

Regardless of the problems with the Mark 45, it wasn't until the deployment of the first Mark 48 homing torpedos in 1972 that the Navy could begin withdrawing the Astor without causing a major

ASTOR

ASTOR

reduction in anti-submarine capabilities. Retirement was slow, however. The last Astor was removed from the stockpile in 1977. Following withdrawal, the bulk of these torpedos have been converted into conventionally armed, homing 'Freedom' torpedos for use by Allied forces.

[1] This restricted range gave the torpedo the reputation for a dual kill capability: the target and the launching sub.

M454 155mm Nuclear Projectile

SPECIFICATIONS
Length: approx 2 ft 10 in   Weight: 119.5 lb
Diameter: 155mm

WARHEAD A W-48 fission device of 1 to 2 kt yield

PERFORMANCE Range: 8.75 mi

NUMBER DEPLOYED Approx 1060

The M454 is the smallest nuclear artillery round the US Army has ever deployed. Like the eight inch and Crocket nuclear systems, it was intended for use against large units of enemy armor and infantry.

Even as development of the M422 eight inch nuclear projectile was beginning in April of 1954, the Army began lobbying for an even smaller, low yield, nuclear device for use by the 155mm Howitzers used by US Army Airborne units and the US Marine Corps. The Department of Defense called for a feasibility study in April of 1955, and on 20 September 1956 the AEC was requested to concentrate its Nuclear Projectile work on the 155mm shell project. Development of the M454 projectile began in mid-July of 1957.

M454 155mm nuclear projectile

Development of the M454 was slow compared to the earlier M422 eight inch projectile. Part of the problem was the need to determine the launch forces to which a 155mm round was subjected, but the primary reason was that the M454 projectile was not a high priority project. Production engineering didn't begin until January of 1961, and the shell's design was not released for production until January 1963. Production finally did start in October of 1963, and by March of 1968, 1060 M454 Mod-0s had been produced.

The M454 Mod-0 was not a very well designed round; it had no ballistic similarity to operational conventional shells, no spotting round to check the correctness of the gun settings, and it had to be assembled in the field. Retirement of this round began in January of 1965, and with the deployment of the improved M454 Mod-1 in 1969, the last M454 Mod-0 was withdrawn. Since that time, additional improvements have been made, and as of last report an M454A5 round has been fielded.

Even with these improvements, the M454 round has no ballistic similarity to operational conventional rounds, is shorter-ranged and is not compatible with the Self Propelled/Field Howitzer 70 series guns used by NATO. Development of a new round to correct these problems has been a slow, halting process, and with the 1986 Congressional mandate limiting the number of new nuclear rounds that will be produced, only half of the 900 M454 Mod-1 rounds in stockpile will be replaced. As a result of this, the M454 may still be in the US nuclear stockpile in the year 2000.

M753 8 inch Nuclear Projectile

SPECIFICATIONS
Length: 43 in   Weight: 215 lb
Diameter: 8 in

WARHEAD Either a W-79-0 fission device with a variable yield from 1 to 10 kt, or a W-79-1 fission warhead with three yields, ranging from subkiloton to 2 kt

PERFORMANCE Range: 18 mi

The M753 eight inch projectile is the newest nuclear artillery round to be deployed by the US Army. It is intended to replace the M422 in the engaging of large units of enemy armor and infantry.

In the years following the deployment of the M422 eight inch projectile, the population of Europe increased to such an extent that the possibility existed of a friendly unit or civilians being hit if this rather inaccurate round was fired. In addition to this, by the early 1970s improvements in the aerodynamic design of conventional rounds and the development of solid fuel boosters made it possible for US artillery to conventionally engage enemy armor at twice the range that they could using the M422 nuclear projectile. As a result of this, following the start of work on a new 155mm shell, in June of 1971 development began on a new eight inch nuclear projectile.

Two years after development of a new round began, in June of 1973, the project was cancelled by Congress on the grounds of rising costs and the lack of an Enhanced Radiation (neutron) capability. The Army was then forced to start work on a neutron shell, and in January of 1975 development began on the M753 round. Stockpiling of this weapon was approved in January of 1977, with tooling for production beginning in October of 1978. Operational testing of dummy rounds then began in October of 1979, and in July of 1981 the first rounds were operationally deployed.

The deployment of the M753 has resulted in a 50 percent increase in the destructive power of US Army eight inch Howitzer units. At the same time, due to the ballistic similarity between this round and the M650 conventional round, the nuclear engagement range of the Howitzers has been doubled and the accuracy has been increased to such an extent that the possibility of injuring civilians or friendly troops (collateral damage) has been reduced by 80 percent. The speed at which the round can be deployed, though increased by the ballistic similarity, has also been improved by having the M753 fielded in one piece with only the insertion of the fuse being required: to insure against the round falling into the hands of terrorists, a special shipping container is used with modern electronic locks and a command disable system that will render the round useless.

In FY1985, Congress ordered that all new production nuclear projectiles be built without the Enhanced Radiation capability. As a result of this, production of the W-79-0 neutron warhead was ended in favor of the non-neutron W-79-1 warhead: the warhead can be converted into a neutron device through the addition of ER components. Production of the M753 was then ended at 550 rounds in August of 1986, following the issuing of a Congressional order limiting the number of modern nuclear rounds to 925 examples: by that time, 325 Enhanced Radiation and 225 non-ER M753s had been produced, for a total of 550. As of 1988, the Army was still lobbying Congress for removal of the ceiling on production of new nuclear projectiles. As of 1987, about 340 M753 rounds were still in the US stockpile.

M-110 8 inch Howitzer

XM785 115mm nuclear projectile

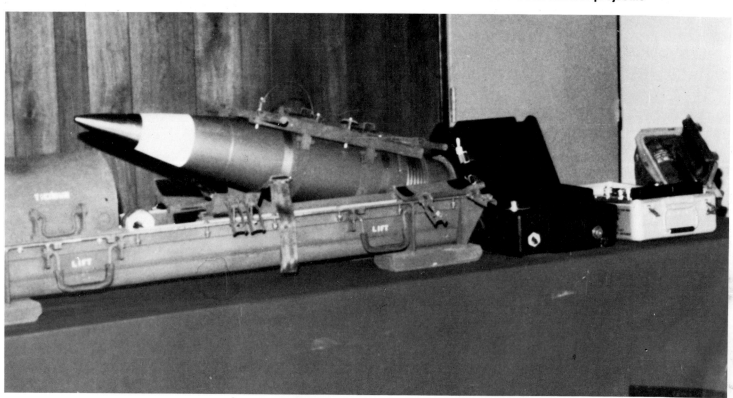

M753 8 inch nuclear projectile

XM-785 155mm Nuclear Projectile

SPECIFICATIONS
Length: 2 ft 10.3 in   Weight: approx 95 lb
Diameter: 155mm (6.1 in)

WARHEAD A W-82-1 fission device of 1 to 2 kt yield

PERFORMANCE Range: 18.5 mi with rocket assist

The XM-785 155mm projectile will be the next nuclear artillery round to be deployed by the United States. In 1969 the US Army issued a request for a new nuclear projectile to replace the earlier M454 round. Development of this round began the following year, but, in 1973, Congress cancelled the program on the grounds of rising costs and a belief that a neutron capability was necessary. Congress then barred the Army from restarting research into such a shell until, in 1977, a Congressional analysis stated that a new 155mm projectile was necessary for force modernization. Work on the XM-785 then began in September of 1977, with the requirement that the W-82 warhead have a neutron capability.

Development of the XM-785 has been slow, compared to other weapons, because of politics. In 1979 Secretary of Defense Harold Brown cut development funding for the round by 67 percent in the Fiscal Year 1981 budget. (He zero-funded the round in FY 1982.) Though development funding was restored by the Reagan administration, production was continually delayed by Congress and, in FY 1985, Congress ordered that all new production nuclear projectiles be non-neutron. To meet this requirement, development

of the W-82-0 warhead was ended in favor of the W-82-1 warhead in 1986. As of last report, production of the XM-785 should not begin until 1989: production will be limited to around 500 rounds due to a Congressional ceiling of 925 new nuclear rounds.

Regardless of these delays, when the XM-785 is deployed, it will be a major improvement over the deployed M454. Not only will it be more accurate and have a higher yield: this new round will also have, like the M454, a shipping container with modern safety and control systems to prevent the weapon from falling into the hands of terrorists in a functional mode.

Atomic Demolition Munitions (ADMs)

Various versions:

(Name)	(Warhead)	(Deployment Period)
Unknown	Mk-7	1954 to late 1950s
Unknown	W-31	1958-1965
XM-113	W-30	1961-1967
MADM	W-45	1965-1987
SADM	W-54	1964-present

The Atomic Demolition Munitions are the only nuclear weapons that could be used against enemy forces and not cause any casualties. Their purpose is to deny enemy forces the use of various routes and facilities during an invasion.

M-109A2/A3 155mm Howitzer

Atomic Demolitions Munitions, or ADMs, are the worst documented of all the nuclear weapons ever deployed by the United States. With a few exceptions, most of the information in this chapter is unsubstantiated: even the table at the top of this section is in dispute.[1] It is because of this problem that the author decided to create this section to give a general briefing on the purpose of the ADM force.

Atomic Demolition Munitions are intended for use by Army engineers to instantly destroy bridges, railways, highways, mountain tunnels and buildings prior to their occupancy by an enemy force. Against buildings, this capability would prevent enemy forces from capturing intact special underground bunkers, communications facilities, or supply centers. As for their use against railways, bridges, tunnels and highways — by destroying these transportation routes the ADMs would allow NATO commanders to block the advance of enemy units along those routes,[2] forcing them to detour or even backtrack. This, in turn, would slow down the overall enemy advance and, if the ADMs were used properly, would allow NATO to channel the invasion along specific routes that accord with NATO battle plans.

The ADMs have several distinct advantages compared to other US nuclear weapons. First, because the ADMs would be deployed primarily by retreating NATO forces, (note: see SADM) they are strictly defensive in nature and of no threat to neighboring nations. Another advantage is that they are to be emplaced deep within a structure, or underground, and do not produce a massive fireball, and the fallout would be localized. (The amount of fallout is massive, hence the ADMs are designated 'dirty bombs.') Finally, because the ADMs can be detonated by radio command or timer, the device could be set off after NATO forces had evacuated the area, but prior to the enemy occupying it.

With these pluses, however, the ADMs have a distinct disadvantage: one could call it a fatal flaw. Because of the problem of maintaining security around emplaced ADMs, none of them could be installed at its prescribed point: the danger of terrorists stealing them for their own nefarious uses is just too great. This, coupled with the extensive time necessary to install one, would probably make the ADMs of little use in a real invasion.

Because of the problem of emplacement security, the US Army worked for a time on a special earth penetrator warhead for use on the Pershing II missile. Recent information states that work on this warhead was shelved in 1980, when the Pershing II program was changed from a tactical weapon program to a long range strategic missile program. Three years later NATO issued the Montebello Decision, which called for the removal of all ADMS from Europe. This order was completed in 1985, ending almost 30 years of ADM stockpiling by NATO.

ADM (W-7)

SPECIFICATIONS

Length: Packing Crate —
    2 ft 5.87 in
Height: Packing Crate —
    3 ft 3.38 in

Width: Packing Crate —
    2 ft 5.87 in
Weight: Packing Crate —
    1527 lb

YIELD Since it was the W-7 warhead, it was probably around 20 kt

This was the first ADM ever deployed by the United States. Like all the ADMs that followed, its purpose was to allow Army commanders the ability to destroy bridges, roadways and tunnels ahead of advancing enemy columns.

Considering the period when it was developed, it is not unlikely that this ADM was nothing more than the warhead used by the Mk-7 bomb, the Corporal SRBM and the Honest John rocket. Regardless of its rather extensive use, the W-7 was a very large device, requiring a team of engineers to emplace and arm it. This, plus its high yield, probably made it more trouble than it was worth to military commanders of the period. It was retired in the late 1950s.

ADM (Mk-31)

SPECIFICATIONS

Length: Packing Crate —
    2 ft 5.87 in
Height: Packing Crate —
    3 ft 3.38 in

Width: Packing Crate —
    2 ft 5.87 in
Weight: Packing Crate —
    1113 lb

YIELD Since it was the W-31 warhead, it was probably around 20 kt

This ADM was the second such weapon to be deployed by the United States. Since it was also carried by the Honest John rocket, it is quite possible it had the same dimensions (and the shipping crate) of the earlier ADM (W-7): hence, the use of the ADM (W-7) dimensions in this section. It is known, however, that this bomb was lighter in weight than the earlier W-7.

Even with its lighter weight, this bomb was still very hard to emplace or deploy, especially in a short period of time. As a result of this, following the deployment of the far lighter XM-113, this weapon was gradually withdrawn from the stockpile. None were in service by 1965.

XM-113

SPECIFICATIONS

Length: 5 ft 4 in
Diameter: 2 ft 11 in

Weight: 840 lb

YIELD Kiloton class (W-30 warhead)

The XM-113, commonly called the 'Sewer Pipe,' was the third ADM to be deployed by the United States. With its deployment in 1961, combat engineers now had a reasonable chance of emplacing the weapon during an invasion of Europe.

XM-113 ADM

Because it was lighter in weight than the previous ADM (Mk-7), the XM-113 was significantly easier to handle and emplace at its planned site: again, like all the other ADMs, the XM-113 was never emplaced throughout its service life. In addition to this, the XM-113 could be emplaced underwater, allowing it to be used in the destroying of canals, dams and other water-related installations. This capability could also have been used by Navy Seals to destroy enemy naval facilities.

Following the deployment of the MADM and the SADM, the XM-113 was gradually withdrawn from the stockpile. By 1967 none were in service.

Medium Atomic Demolition Munition (MADM)

SPECIFICATIONS

Length: Shipping Container –
3 ft 6.5 in

Width: Shipping Container –
2 ft .5 in

Height: Shipping Container –
2 ft 4 in

Weight: Shipping Container –
391 lb

Nonspecific information on MADM: Diameter no greater than 1 ft .5 in — the diameter of the Little John warhead section, which also carried the W-45 warhead

YIELD 1-15 kt (W-45) fission warhead

Like the other ADMs, the MADM was developed to give US Army and Marine Corps commanders the ability to channel the advance of enemy forces. Development began in 1956, and in 1965 it entered the US stockpile. Deployment in Europe probably occurred the same year.

In the years that followed its deployment to Europe, the MADM sat in secure, possibly underground, nuclear bunkers at US Army facilities. Then, following the October 1983 Montebello Decision, the last MADM was withdrawn to the United States in 1985. Withdrawal from the arsenal began about the same time, and in late 1987 the last MADM was removed from stockpile.

Special Atomic Demolition Munition (SADM)

SPECIFICATIONS

Length: Shipping Container –
35 in

Width: Shipping Container –
26.2 in

Height: Shipping Container –
26.6 in

Weight: Shipping Container –
163 lb

Nonspecific data on SADM: Weight of the warhead is less than 79 lb. Length approx 20 inches, diameter less than 11 in

YIELD Varied yields listed for the W-4 warhead; for 1 to 0.1 kt, not adjustable in the field

The Special Atomic Demolition Munition is the only ADM still in service with US armed forces. It is also the only ADM the US ever deployed that could be used offensively.

The SADM was developed to improve the capability and effectiveness of the NATO ADM force. The smallest nuclear device the US ever deployed, this ADM can easily be carried to its target by helicopter, truck, jeep or in the backpack of a single US soldier: the SADM has since been labeled the 'suit case bomb.' As a result of this ease with which it can be moved, the SADM can be deployed faster than any other US ADM.

The ability to attack targets in an enemy's rear, when in the hands of Navy Seals and Special Forces, has made it possible for the SADM to be used in the attacking of industrial and military facilities deep inside the national territory of hostile nations.

As per the October 1983 Montebello Decision, by 1985 all SADMs had been removed from Europe. This device is still in the US stockpile, however, and should remain there for several years to come due to its tactical versatility.

[1] One source lists a total six ADMs deployed by the US.
[2] This tactic is called Area Denial.

MADM

MADM

Glossary

AAM Air-to-Air Missile

AASM Advanced Air-to-Surface Missile

ACM Advanced Cruise Missile

AD Area Denial

ADC Air Defense Command (US Air Force)

ADMs Atomic Demolition Munitions

ADS Aerospace Defense Squadron (US Air Force)

AEC Atomic Energy Commission

AFB Air Force Base

AGM Air-to-Ground Missile

AIM Air Intercept Missile

AIR Air Intercept Rocket

ALBM Air-Launched Ballistic Missile

ALCC Airborne Launch Control Center

ALCM Air-Launched Cruise Missile

AMSA Advanced Manned Strategic Aircraft

ASALM Advanced Strategic Air-Launched Missile

ASAT Anti-Satellite weapon, or capability

ASM Air-to-Surface Missile

ATA Advanced Tactical Aircraft

ATACMS Advanced Tactical Missile System

ATB Advanced Technology Bomber

ATF Advanced Technology Fighter

BMD Ballistic Missile Division (US Air Force)

BOAR Bureau of Ordnance Atomic Rocket (alternately, Bombardment Aircraft Rocket)

BW Bombardment Wing

CEP Circular Error Probable — the probable target radius within which one out of every two warheads from a given vehicle type will impact

CSRL Common Strategic Rotary Launcher

DASO Demonstration and Shakedown Operation

ERCS Emergency Rocket Communication Satellites

ER/DL Extended Range/Data Link guidance system

DX A missile project rating signifying 'highest national priority'

ERV Extended Range Vehicle

EX External-mount dropshape — a bomb configured for external aircraft mounting

EXPO Extended Range Poseidon missile

FBM Fleet Ballistic Missile, an appellation given to US Navy ballistic missiles

FSD Full Scale Development

GAM Ground Attack Missile

GLCM Ground-Launched Cruise Missile

GOR General Operation Requirement

HML Hard Mobile Launcher, or 'Armadillo' — a mobile launch system which is designed to withstand nuclear attack

ICBM Intercontinental Ballistic Missile

IN Internal-mount dropshape — a bomb configured for internal aircraft mounting

IOC Initial Operating Capability

IRBM Intermediate Range Ballistic Missile

IRS Inertial Reference Sphere, part of the guidance system for an ICBM or other intercontinental strategic missile

JATO Jet-Assisted Take-Off

JPL Jet Propulsion Laboratory

Kt Kiloton

LABS Low Altitude Bombing System

LCC Launch Control Capsule — an operational unit containing 10 missiles; a flight of missiles

LCT Launch Control Trailer

LGM Silo launched, surface-to-surface missile

LOAD Low Altitude Defense

LOX Liquid Oxygen (LO$_2$)

MADM Medium Atomic Demolition Munition

MIRV Multiple Independently Targeted Re-entry Vehicle

Mk Mark, a vehicle class designation, usually accompanied with a number, as in 'Mk-12A.'

MLRS Multi-Launch Rocket System

MPS Multiple Protective Shelters

MX Missile, Experimental (frequently used today to refer to the LGM-118A Peacekeeper)

NAGPAW North American General Purpose Attack Weapon

NASA National Aeronautics & Space Administration

NATO North Atlantic Treaty Organization

NORAD North American Defense Command

NSC National Security Council

OAS Offensive Avionics System

OT Operational Tests

PACAF Pacific Air Forces (US Air Force)

PSI Pounds Per Square Inch, a measure of atmospheric pressure which is relevant to conditions caused by powerful, especially nuclear, explosions

QOR Qualitative Operational Requirement

RAF Royal Air Force (Great Britain)

RATO Rocket Assisted Take-Off

RE Retarded-External dropshape, a bomb configured for external aircraft mounting and parachute retardation

R&D Research and Development

RFP Request For Proposal, one of the initial steps in military technological development procedures

ROC Required Operating Capability

RP-1 Rocket Propellant, 1

RV A re-entry vehicle, such as a warhead

SAC Strategic Air Command (US Air Force)

SAM Surface-to-Air Missile

SADM Special Atomic Demolition Munition

SARH Semi-Active Radar Homing

SALT Strategic Arms Limitations Talks

SCAD Subsonic Cruise Aircraft Decoy

SICBM Small Intercontinental Ballistic Missile

SLBM Submarine-Launched Ballistic Missile

SLCM Sea-Launched Cruise Missile

SM Strategic Missile

SMS Strategic Missile Squadron (US Air Force)

SMW Strategic Missile Wing (US Air Force)

SRAM Short Range Attack Missile

SRBM Short Range Ballistic Missile

SSBN SLBM-launch capable submarine

SSM Surface-to-Surface Missile

SSN Nuclear-powered attack submarine

SSR System Ready Requirement, a designation given to proposed missile types in the early developmental stage

TAC Tactical Air Command

TERCOM A guidance system used on advanced cruise missile designs

TF Turbofan, a kind of jet engine, or a device within a jet engine

UGM Underwater Guided Missile

B-61 bomb

Spartan missile launch

Index

Jupiter IRBM

F-105 Thunderchief